MW00488850

Leisure, Health, and Wellness:
Making the Connections

Leisure, Health, and Wellness:
Making the Connections

edited by

Laura Payne

Associate Professor and Extension Specialist
Office of Recreation and Park Resources
Department of Recreation, Sport and Tourism
University of Illinois at Urbana-Champaign

~

Barbara Ainsworth

Professor
Exercise and Wellness Program
Healthy Lifestyles Research Center
College of Nursing and Health Innovation
Arizona State University

~

Geoffrey Godbey

Professor Emeritus
Department of Recreation, Park and Tourism Management
The Pennsylvania State University

Venture Publishing, Inc.
State College, Pennsylvania

Production Manager: Richard Yocum
Manuscript Editing: George Lauer, Richard Yocum

Library of Congress Catalogue Card Number 2010935430
ISBN-10: 1-892132-89-3
ISBN-13: 978-1-892132-89-5

Table of Contents

Preface

As our understanding of the basis of good health changes, it is apparent that leisure and its use are an important issue in both achieving and maintaining good health. This book represents a collection of ideas brought together by scholars willing to venture outside of the safe confines of their own disciplines to write transdisciplinary chapters with colleagues from numerous fields related to health or leisure. Many of these authors did not know their co-authors before this writing experience.

The scholars and practitioners who have contributed to this book have played a significant role in building bridges and advancing the knowledge base related to leisure, health, and wellness and their interconnections. They have attempted to do so in ways that relate to everyday life. Our deepest gratitude and appreciation goes to all who have generously volunteered their time, energy, and expertise to bring this book from an idea to a finished product.

The pioneers of the parks and recreation movement who had the foresight to understand that recreation and leisure experiences can be a positive force for physical, mental, intellectual, social, and spiritual health deserve much of the credit for the understanding which produced this book. In the midst of profound change during the American Industrial Revolution, they identified the need to bring tranquility, solitude, and wonder into the city to help people adjust, "recreate," and restore their bodies, minds, hearts, and souls. People such as Joseph Lee (grandfather of the playground movement) and Luther Gulick (a physician and physical educator; founder of Campfire Girls; author of many books including the 1910 book *The Healthful Art of Dance*) did much to advance the study and management of parks, recreation, and leisure studies. Landscape architects such as Frederick Law Olmsted and colleagues who designed many major city parks systems across the United States also deserve credit for creating inviting and interesting natural landscapes for people to enjoy. Jane Addams championed the settlement house movement, where use of leisure was a central concern. Dorothy Enderis lighted the Milwaukee schools for community use of leisure after the school day was over.

Later, scholars and educators such as Charles K. Brightbill and Allen V. Sapora (respectively) wrote the *Challenge of Leisure* among other important philosophical and more applied texts. In the area of disability, Dr. Timothy Nugent is credited with pioneering educational and recreation opportunities for people with disabilities. Evidence of his passion for improving the quality of life for people with disabilities is now seen all over the world: curb cuts, wheelchair ramps on buses, world-class athletic programs, and so on.

This, then, is the story of how parks, recreation, and leisure studies contribute to the health and well-being of individuals, families, communities, and societies. This is also the story, however, of how public health contributes to parks, recreation and leisure studies; the intersections and connections between and among these fields, concepts, and professional practices. Public health pioneers similarly discovered that what happened during leisure within a community critically shaped health and wellness. The ancient Greeks realized that physical activity was important for promoting health and well-being for youth and adults and instituted sports and exercise programs for all citizens. Appropriately, the U.S. Department of Health and Human Services recently released the first ever national Physical Activity Guidelines and Physical Activity Plan as a recognition of the importance between leisure-time physical activity and health for persons of all ages.

The idea for this book emerged, in part, from ideas generated from a 2004 two-day intensive Summit on Leisure and Health, cosponsored by the University of Illinois' College of Applied Health Sciences and the National Recreation and Park Association. Although the chapters span across many disciplines and topics, by no means is this book meant to be comprehensive and all-inclusive. Rather, it represents a variety of ideas contributed by many scholars and practitioners working in these areas. There is a noticeable emphasis in many chapters on physical activity, symbolic of the times we live in and the obesity epidemic that plagues North America.

Kathy Spangler deserves special thanks for aggressively moving the health agenda forward within community parks and recreation during her 20 years at NRPA. She has been an excellent leader, ambassador, and servant to the field of parks and recreation and was instrumental in getting our field on the radar screen in public health. In the 1990s, the U.S. Centers for Disease Control and Prevention recognized the importance of physical activity as a public health priority by establishing the Physical Activity and Health Branch within the National Center for Chronic Disease Prevention and Health Promotion. Under the Branch leadership of David Buchner and Michael Pratt, transdisciplinary activities have been created to promote physical activity for all persons and within diverse settings.

More than ever, we believe leisure and recreation experiences are central to our health and well-being. Americans today struggle with more mental health issues due to the stressors of everyday life and the pressure to accomplish more things each day. Our society is aging, with increased chronic conditions, even as the Baby Boomers search for ways to stay healthy and well. The number of centenarians (i.e., people who live to 100 years) continues to increase rapidly as does the population of people 85 and over. In 1958, Eleanor Roosevelt said it best in her syndicated column called *My Day* when she commented on the proliferation of television. She stated,

> If the use of leisure time is confined to looking at TV for a few extra hours every day, we will deteriorate as a people. Actually, the preparation for the use of leisure time should begin with our schoolchildren...These (art, music drama, hobbies, etc.) are all things that can give us joy and many of us will find that we are capable of acquiring a certain amount of skill we never dreamed we had....But these things must be taught, and in the age now developing about us they are important things (Roosevelt, 1958, p. 265).

Leisure is not only the final test of a civilization; it is a shaper of health and wellness. In this book we seek to understand this relation and why it has become more critical to our well-being—and yours. Join us!

Chapter 1
Leisure—An Overview
Garry Chick

Introduction

Leisure is a human universal. While it may differ in form cross-culturally, there is no evidence to suggest that leisure has not been part of the lives of people in all places and at all times in human history.[1] It exists, in one form or another, in societies at all levels of cultural complexity, from technologically simple food collectors to the sophisticates of the information age. Precisely defining leisure, however, even as it occurs in Western civilization, has been a traditional problem for researchers. Historically, the word "leisure" descends from the Latin *licere*, also the root of "license," and means "to be allowed or permitted." While this is of etymological interest, it has limited value for the study of leisure and its effects in the lives of individuals and groups. Definitions of concepts can be derived in several ways.

The Problem of Definition

Ordinary language philosophers such as Ludwig Wittgenstein hold that the meaning of words depends on how they are used in everyday discourse. Most English speakers would probably regard leisure, for example, as residual, nonproductive time remaining after obligatory activities, such as paid work, household chores, and personal maintenance, have been completed. Leisure researchers have attempted to remove ambiguity from ordinary language practice by claiming that leisure must have characteristics such as freedom of choice and intrinsic motivation, a practice more in line with analytic philosophy as practiced by Bertrand Russell, for example. Words can also be compared and contrasted with similar or related terms. (Leisure is commonly distinguished from *recreation* with the former being regarded as release from situations that are normally mandatory or life sustaining, while the latter implies some form of activity that is mentally and/or physically refreshing, simulating, or relaxing.)

An ordinary language approach to the meaning of leisure might be termed "bottom-up" as it is ethnographic in nature. It is the determination of the meaning of the concept to those who use it in everyday life. An analytic approach, in contrast, is "top-down" in that presumed experts determine the meaning of leisure.

Conditions For Leisure

Leisure researchers generally think of leisure as incorporating three characteristics, each of which is necessary but none of which are generally regarded as sufficient. First, leisure occurs in free or otherwise unobligated time and where freedom of choice is both important and possible. Second, certain activities or kinds of activities are usually associated with leisure. These include play, games, sport, reading, watching television, many outdoor activities, resting, festivals, and numerous other forms of both individual and social entertainment. Moreover, activities that may appear to be work-like for many can be leisure for others. Volunteering or deliberately risky or dangerous activities, such as mountain climbing, are examples. Finally, leisure may be thought of as an existential condition or state of mind wherein neither time not activity type is as critical as the meaning that an individual attributes to his or her activities. If it feels like leisure, it is. Individually, each of these definitional types has merit but also serious drawbacks. Taken together, however, they may inform us about aspects of leisure that should be considered in the relationship of leisure to health and well-being.

Leisure as Time. Few leisure scholars regard leisure as nothing more than free time, to be used at an individual's discretion, although it is often operationalized as such in the context of research. While free time seems to be a relatively objective way to think of leisure and can be measured with reasonable precision, it suffers from major conceptual problems. For example, prisoners in solitary confinement, those who are hospitalized, or the institutionalized aged appear to have abundant free time but it is unlikely that they or external observers would regard it as leisure. Moreover, even among individuals living in more typical settings, free time filled with boredom seems different from free time filled with happiness or pleasure.

The amount of free time available to people seems to differ both cross-culturally and based on the environment and ecology where they live. Early theorizing by anthropologists such as Franz Boas (1) held that leisure, conceptualized as free time, was instrumental in cultural evolution. As humans shifted from food collection via hunting and gathering to sedentary agriculture, Boas reasoned that their allegedly more dependable food supply provided more free time. They then used this free time to think and invent, including new ways to save time and labor. So, as "surplus" leisure increased, so did the development of technology that then provided even more leisure.

This "surplus theory" soon collided with evidence. In the 1950s, studies of the *San* peoples (previously known as Bushmen) of the Kalahari Desert in southwest Africa showed that they spend relatively little time in their food quest, usually about three to four hours per day. Moreover, while the types of food they acquired changed during the yearly cycle, it was generally highly dependable. So, in 1980, anthropologist Peter Just (2) theorized that as cultures became more technologically complex, the amount of free time available to their members generally decreased, rather than increased.

In an article in 1986, I hypothesized that the relationship between cultural complexity and free time availability is curvilinear as earlier theorizing involved only groups of very low or very high cultural complexity (3). Anecdotal evidence suggested that societies of midrange complexity have relatively less free time than those either at the lower or higher ends of the complexity continuum. In a 1992 paper, using secondary data, I compared 42 societies across this range and found some support for my hypothesis (4). In a more recent study, Sharon Xiangyou Shen and I (5) got similar results using highly detailed time allocation data for 13 societies that range from hunter-gatherers to complex agriculturalists.

Even if the amount of free time available initially decreased with technological evolution and then increased, what about its availability in recent years? This has been a matter of some contention. Schor (6), for example, claimed that the average workweek for Americans increased from 39.8 hours in 1969 to 40.7 hours in 1987. On the other hand, the U.S. Bureau of Labor Statistics (7) indicated that the average U.S. worker put in about 37 hours of paid work per week in 1970 but only 33.9 hours in 2009 (7). Similarly, time diary data compiled by Robinson and Godbey (8) show that Americans have more free time than they had 30 years ago, again in contrast to Schor's claims. The differences appear to be due to the way raw data on work and leisure time was initially gathered and then processed. In a recent discussion, Nazareth (9) essentially sidesteps the issue of whether free time has increased or decreased over the last 30 years or so with the claim that many of us attempt to pack so much into what discretionary time we do have that it seems like the time available for ourselves is decreasing.

Regardless, other than for some societal subgroups, such as prisoners or slaves, there is no evidence that members of any present or past society had no free or discretionary time. So, having time that permits some measure of freedom of choice with respect to its use seems to be a necessary, if not sufficient, component of leisure.

Leisure as Activity. Leisure is often described in terms of certain activities or kinds of activities. These are generally nonproductive in an economic sense and are chosen by participants. In addition to games, play, sport, and other forms of entertainment, mentioned above, we should include expressive activities such as the production of music and art by amateurs, certain religious activities, and travel and tourism. At least some of these activity types appear to be human universals. Brown (10) claimed that aesthetics (including various forms of art), dance, music, myths and other narratives, play, toys and playthings, and visiting are common to all humans. Earlier, Murdock (11) listed some 70 "common denominators of culture" including games, music and dance, sports, and visiting/socializing.

Games have probably been studied more from a cross-cultural comparative perspective than other activities generally thought of as leisure-related. Some games and forms of game play, such as the ancient Mesoamerican rubber ball game and lacrosse among some Native American tribes, do have ritual aspects but it is likely that these were often played for fun, as well (12). In a classic 1959 article, Roberts, Arth, and Bush (13) proposed that games model important aspects of social reality such as hunting, warfare, interaction with others, and interaction with the supernatural. Subsequent cross-cultural and intracultural studies have supported their contentions. Whether other leisure activities model facets of reality or everyday life does not appear to have been a focus of leisure research to date.

Leisure as a State of Mind. While free time and activity type are thought of as objective measures of leisure, it is also often regarded, more subjectively, as a state of mind or existential condition. The philosopher Josef Pieper (14), for example, wrote of leisure as similar to contemplation, something that permits individuals to step outside the everyday world, and even as the basis of culture. Some scholars suggest that time and activity are irrelevant when leisure is thought of only in terms of its meaning to those experiencing it (e.g., 15). This position suggests that the subjective experience is both necessary *and* sufficient for the existence of leisure, unlike free time and activity type. It does seem, however, that people will experience this subjective condition more frequently during free time and when engaged in a freely chosen, intrinsically motivated, and enjoyable activity.

Freedom of choice, intrinsic motivation, and enjoyment appear to be generally accepted by leisure researchers as conditions for the leisure experience. But freedom of choice is relative. Social activities almost always involve some obligation and sometimes even coercion, as when your boss asks you to join her for a round of golf. Similarly, some activities are obviously more enjoyable than others and even the same ones can be experienced differently under different conditions. Finally, while leisure researchers have tended to unquestioningly accept the concept of intrinsic motivation—the notion that people do some things simply because they want to and in the absence of any obvious external reward—even it is not uncontroversial. Moreover, intrinsic motivation is often touted, explicitly or implicitly, as superior to extrinsic motivation—that is, motivation based on a reward. In support, researchers commonly cite canonical work by Deci and Ryan (e.g., 16, 17) and Lepper and colleagues (e.g., 18, 19) that indicates that intrinsic motivation is undermined by external rewards. On the other hand, Reiss (20) rejects the concepts of extrinsic and intrinsic motivation on both logical and empirical grounds. In their place, he proposes 16 basic desires that guide meaningful behavior. These include desires for power, curiosity, independence, status, social contact, romance, and acceptance, for example. Regardless of whether one accepts his particular list, Reiss claims that motivational desires cannot be reduced into just two categories. (Leisure researchers should keep in mind that concepts such as perceived freedom, enjoyment, and intrinsic motivation can vary depending on circumstances, may themselves be multivariate, and may not be universally accepted.)

A subjective conceptualization of leisure also has kinship to Csikszentmihalyi's (21) familiar notion of "flow," a condition of total concentration and absorption that can occur in overtly work-like as well as leisure-like activities and contexts. Flow is achieved when the skill of an individual matches the challenge afforded by a task. When activities are either too difficult or too easy for individuals, stress and anxiety or boredom occur, rather than flow. Csikszentmihalyi's work on flow is consistent with the recent and growing field of positive psychology. Concerned over the field of psychology's fixation on mental illness, Martin Seligman (22) made positive psychology—basically the study of happiness, fulfillment, and optimal human functioning—the theme of his term as president of the American Psychological Association in 1998. Research in the new field has expanded rapidly since then. Frederickson et al. (23), for example, found that positive emotions help reduce stress back to baseline conditions for individuals. They hypothesized that positive emotions, as experienced in the context of leisure, help reduce physiological conditions such as increased heart rate, elevated blood sugar levels, and immune system suppression that result from stress. In turn, positive emotions may reduce mortality and morbidity resulting from coronary heart disease and other stress-related conditions.

Leisure and Adaptation

The stress reduction aspects of leisure are relatively well known (e.g., 24) but considerably less is known and understood about leisure as an agent of *adaptation*, the degree to which an organism is suited to its environment. Natural selection is the general process by which adaptation occurs. What about leisure? Given its ubiquity among humans, is it merely a byproduct or is it something that gives humans an adaptive advantage, a special means of dealing with our habitats? Humans are among the most adaptable of living things. We live in the rain forests of the tropics, in deserts, in mountains at very high altitudes, and in the arctic. Recently, we have even managed long-term survival in space. All of these adaptations are the result of our prowess with technology, something that we have to a far greater extent than any other animal.

But where does leisure fit? Other animals have free time, something obvious to anyone who has a cat or a dog. Some other animals may even engage in leisure-like activities. The playfulness of cats and dogs comes to mind, but also activities such as grooming among monkeys and apes, appears leisurely. Knowing the state of mind of other people is difficult enough and we know little about the minds of animals other than that those that play seem to enjoy it. As noted earlier, some 20th century anthropologists felt that free time was adaptive in terms of technological evolution but this was largely dismissed after the 1950s. However, a team of anthropologists did find evidence that leisure, defined as activity taking place during free time, had adaptive consequences for four native tribes of the Amazon basin. Rubin, Flowers, and Gross (25) showed that while adults in all four tribes spent approximately the same amount of time in both work and leisure, significantly more of the leisure of members of two of the tribes who lived in relatively degraded environments was spent passively with the members of the two tribes living in relatively richer environments engaged in more active pursuits. The authors interpreted this as using leisure as a means of adapting to their environments. Acquiring the required caloric intake to engage in active leisure would have required members of the two tribes living in degraded environments to work both harder and longer. Instead, they chose to adapt by reducing their needs through passive leisure.

Similarly, if leisure activities such as games model other culturally relevant real-world activities, they may serve as buffered learning contexts. That is, knowledge of common human problems such as marriage, food acquisition, and warfare is critical but acquisition of such knowledge from the activities themselves is difficult and often dangerous. However, if such knowledge can be gained through participation in models, available in leisure activities such as games, its acquisition becomes far more benign. Hence, an important feature of leisure, as engrossing activity engaged in largely during discretionary time, may be that it affords not only positive emotions that may lead to stress reduction and associated health benefits but also adaptation to one's environment in a broader sense.

Summary

Leisure, in all of its guises, appears to be a universal part of human cultures and may help people adapt to their environments wherever they may be. Being environmentally well-adapted would seem to be a prerequisite for health and healthy living. However, there has been very little research on leisure as a means or process for adaptation so the suggestions and implications above must remain just that for the moment.

Footnote

[1] It is difficult to say exactly how old "human history" is or when it began. Humans who were morphologically identical to us existed at least 200,000 years ago by some estimates (e.g., 26). We now have physical evidence of possible human ancestors (i.e., *Sahelanthropus tchadensis*) that date to approximately 7 million years ago (27).

References

1. Boas F. *Race, language and culture*. Macmillan: New York, 1940.
2. Just P. Time and leisure in the elaboration of culture. *J Anthropol Res* 1980:**36**:105–115.
3. Chick G. Leisure, labor, and the complexity of culture. *J Leis Res* 1986;**19**:154–168.
4. Chick G. Leisure and the evolution of culture: Cross-cultural tests of several hypotheses. In Jonson P, Veal T (eds). *Leisure and Tourism: Social and Environmental Change*. Sydney: Centre for Leisure and Tourism Studies, University of Technology, Sydney, 1993, pp. 293–300.
5. Chick G, Shen X. Time allocation and cultural complexity: Leisure time use across twelve cultures. In LeBlanc C, Vogt C (eds). *Proceedings of the 2007 Northeastern Recreation Research Symposium*. Bolton Landing, NY: Gen. Tech. Rep. NRS-P-23. Newtown Square, PA, U.S. Department of Agriculture, Forest Service, Northern Research Station, 2008, pp. 25–31.
6. Schor JB. *The Overworked American: The Unexpected Decline of Leisure*. Basic Books: New York, 1992.
7. U.S. Bureau of Labor Statistics. *Average hours and earnings of production and nonsupervisory workers on private nonfarm payrolls by major industry sector, 1964 to date*. ftp://ftp.bls.gov/pub/suppl/empsit.ceseeb2.txt. Accessed February 21, 2010.
8. Robinson JP, Godbey G. *Time for Life: The Surprising Ways Americans Use their Time*. The Pennsylvania State University Press: State College, PA, 1997.
9. Nazareth L. *The Leisure Economy*. John Wiley & Sons Canada, Ltd: Mississauga, ON, 2007.
10. Brown DE. *Human Universals*. McGraw-Hill: New York, 1991.
11. Murdock GP. The common denominator of cultures. In Linton R (ed). *The Science of Man in the World Crisis*. New York: Columbia University Press, 1945, pp. 123–142.
12. Blanchard K. *The Anthropology of Sport: An Introduction*. Bergin & Garvey: Westport, CT, 1995.

13. Roberts JM, Arth MC, Bush, RR. Games in culture. *Am Anthropol* 1959;**59**:597–605.
14. Pieper J. *Leisure: The Basis of Culture*. New American Library: New York, 1963.
15. Kelly JR, Freysinger VJ. *21ˢᵗ Century Leisure: Current Issues*. Allyn and Bacon: Boston, 2000.
16. Deci EL, Ryan RM. *Intrinsic Motivation and Self-Determination in Human Behavior*. Plenum: New York, 1985.
17. Ryan RM, Deci EL. Self-determination theory and the facilitation of intrinsic motivation, social development, and well-being. *Am Psychol* 2000;**55**:68–78.
18. Lepper MR, Greene D, Nisbett RE. Undermining children's intrinsic interest with an extrinsic reward: A test of the "overjustification" hypothesis. *J Pers Soc Psychol* 1973;**28**:129–137.
19. Lepper MR, Greene D. Turning play into work: Effects of adult surveillance and extrinsic rewards on children's intrinsic motivation. *J Pers Soc Psychol* 1975;**31**:479–486.
20. Reiss S. Multifaceted nature of intrinsic motivation: The theory of 16 basic desires. *Rev Gen Psychol* 2004;**8**:179–193.
21. Csikszentmihalyi M. *Beyond Boredom and Anxiety: Experiencing Flow in Work and Play*. Jossey-Bass: San Francisco, 1975.
22. Seligman MEP. *Authentic Happiness: Using the New Positive Psychology to Realize Your Potential for Lasting Fulfillment*. Simon & Schuster: New York, 2002.
23. Fredrickson BL, Mancuso RA, Branigan C, Tugade MM. The undoing effect of positive emotions. *Motiv Emot* 2000;**24**:237–258.
24. Iwasaki Y, Mactavish JM, MacKay K. Building on strengths and resilience: Leisure as a stress survival strategy. *Br J Guid Counc* 2005;**33**:81–100.
25. Rubin J, Flowers NM, Gross DR. The adaptive dimensions of leisure. *Am Ethnol* 1986;**13**:524–536.
26. The Smithsonian Institution: Human Origins Program. *Homo sapiens*. http://anthropology.si.edu/humanorigins/ha/sap.htm. Accessed February 18, 2010.
27. Lebatard AE, Bourles DL, Duringer P, Jolivet M, Braucher R, Carcaillet J, et al. Cosmogenic nuclide dating of *Sahelanthropus tchadensis* and *Australoithecus bhareghazli*: Mio-Pliocene hominids from Chad. *Proc Natl Acad Sci U S A* 2008;**105**:3226–3231.

Chapter 2
Health, Wellness, and Quality of Life—Accent the Positive

Diane L. Gill
Leandra A. Bedini

Health, wellness, and quality of life are all commonly used and commonly understood terms. However, despite the common usage, precise definitions are elusive and common understandings vary a great deal. Often the terms are used interchangeably, but some sources make distinctions among them. It is clear that, health, wellness, and quality of life are overlapping constructs, if not synonymous, and the key feature is the accent on the positive. That is, health, wellness, and quality of life all refer to positive health.

Health. Virtually all texts and resources on health, wellness, and quality of life start with reference to the World Health Organization (WHO) definition, "Health is a state of complete physical, mental, and social well-being, and not merely the absence of disease or infirmity," which is found in the preamble to the 1946 constitution of the WHO (1) and easily accessed at websites of WHO and many other health organizations. That definition clearly accents the positive and moves away from the traditional medical model that focuses on treatment of major diseases such as cardiovascular disease, cancer, and diabetes. Nearly all health programs and agencies have moved closer to the positive health model in recent years.

That trend toward accenting the positive extends to many research and professional areas, including physical activity, leisure and recreation, as well as psychology and traditional health-related fields. For example, Martin Seligman, the key leader in the positive psychology movement recently proposed a new field: positive health (2). Citing the WHO definition and drawing on the positive psychology focus on mental health (positive emotion, engagement, purpose) rather than mental illness, Seligman suggested that positive health reflects a combination of excellent status on biological, subjective, and functional measures.

In *Healthy People 2010* (3), the widely cited statement of national health objectives, the first goal is to help individuals of all ages increase life expectancy *and* improve their quality of life. For the field of leisure and recreation, and indeed in most health-related fields, the focus is clearly on promotion of positive health and well-being. That shift toward positive health is one reason that the terms 'wellness' and 'quality of life' are often used in health-related programs and resources.

Wellness. The term *wellness*, which is newer and less common than *health*, has a more limited and explicit focus on positive health. Wellness as positive health stands in contrast to illness (negative health). Many texts and resources used in health and wellness courses (e.g., Corbin et al. (4)) refer to wellness as the positive component of health or as optimal health. Jensen and Allen (5) distinguished between the two by stating that health is "stability, balance, and integrity of function" while wellness is "the subjective experience of health" (p. 361).

Jane Myers has developed models and measures of wellness and used those in her counseling research on issues related to counseling and wellness (see website for further information: http://www.uncg.edu/~jemyers/wellness/docs/wellness.htm). According to Myers, wellness refers to a holistic approach in which mind, body, and spirit are integrated. More specifically, "We define *wellness* as a way of life oriented toward optimal health and well-being in which body, mind, and spirit are integrated by the individual to live more fully within the human and natural community." (p. 252) (6).

The National Wellness Institute, established in 1977, offers the following definition: "Wellness is an active process through which people become aware of, and make choices toward, a more successful existence" (7). They further note that the many different definitions and interpretations of wellness share the following features:

- Wellness is a conscious, self-directed, and evolving process of achieving full potential
- Wellness is a multidimensional and holistic, encompassing lifestyle, mental and spiritual well-being, and the environment
- Wellness is positive and affirming

Quality of life. Many of the health and wellness resources have been using quality of life to refer to, or in place of, positive health and wellness. Indeed, quality of life is targeted in governmental health-related programs and funding agencies, as well as in a rapidly expanding body of research and scholarly publications. Both health professionals and the general public consider quality of life the marker of positive health. Quality of life is widely cited and understood, but definitions are elusive. Moreover, some scholars have distinguished the terms 'quality of life' (QoL) and 'health-related quality of life' (HRQoL).

Rejeski, Brawley, and Shumaker (8) who authored a seminal review of physical activity and health-related quality of life (HRQoL), defined QoL as a subjective, multidimensional construct and suggested that HRQoL refers to those aspects of QoL related to health. Since the Rejeski et al.

review, the distinction between HRQoL and QoL has blurred. Current work in physical activity and health, which overlaps leisure and health, typically refers to quality of life, but offers no precise definitions. Rejeski and Mihalko (9) identified lack of precision in the definition of QoL as a barrier to consensus about the relationship between physical activity and QoL, and McAuley and Elavsky (10) argued that we cannot determine whether physical activity enhances QoL unless we can accurately operationalize and reliably measure this construct.

O'Connor (11) (p. 9) cites a number of definitions of QoL and HRQoL, all of which are similar, and his summary description, patients' subjective experience of their overall health state, reflects the typical approach to QoL. O'Connor also considers QoL a *multidimensional* concept and refers to the WHO definition of health, which serves as the basis for most QoL definitions and measures. The WHO has developed measures of QoL, and the introduction to the WHO QoL measures defines Quality of Life as an individual's perception of their position in life in the context of the culture and value systems in which they live and in relation to their goals, expectations, standards and concerns. It is a broad-ranging concept affected in a complex way by the person's physical health, psychological state, personal beliefs, social relationships and their relationship to salient features of their environment (12). Like O'Connor, the WHO defines QoL as an individual perception (subjective) and as multidimensional, specifically citing physical, psychological, social, and environmental factors. The definition also implies that QoL is integrative, in that perceptions are influenced by multiple factors and integrated within the individual's personal and cultural context. In light of the literature on physical activity and QoL, and in line with the WHO definition, the first author of this chapter has elsewhere (13) defined QoL as a broad, integrative construct, comprising the person's perceived physical, social, and psychological well-being.

Positive health, wellness, and quality of life. All definitions and discussions of the terminology share common features. Whether the term of choice is health, wellness, or quality of life (QoL), the key feature is the accent on the positive. *Positive* health is an optimal state, not merely the absence of illness. As well as the focus on positive or optimal states, health, wellness, and quality of life are defined as subjective or personal self-evaluations; persons with chronic disease or disabilities can have high quality of life, and, although the environment clearly affects health, those in difficult circumstances can have positive health. Virtually all definitions and discussions describe health, wellness, and QoL as multidimensional, including psychological and social as well as physical domains. Also, the most relevant definitions and models, as discussed in the next section, refer to an integrative or holistic construct. Thus, *positive* health (i.e., wellness, quality of life) is subjective, multidimensional, integrative optimal well-being.

Models of Health, Wellness, and Quality of Life (QoL)

Theoretical frameworks and conceptual models of health, wellness, and quality of life (QoL) are even rarer than definitions. However, several models related to the definitions provide the elements of a conceptual framework for operational measures and research on positive health and leisure. The most relevant and useful models are multidimensional and in line with the key features of the positive health definitions discussed in the previous section. Although scholars do not offer common definitions or components, physical, social, emotional, and mental health domains are consistently cited, with spiritual health often included. All those domains are relevant for leisure and health promotion, and are included in the most relevant models. For example, in their early work, Rejeski et al. (8) conceptualized health-related quality of life along six dimensions, including global HRQoL and sub-domains of physical function, physical symptoms/ states, emotional function, social function, and cognitive function. The WHO definition of QoL, cited earlier, reflects a multidimensional model with physical, psychological, social, and environmental dimensions.

The first author and colleagues (e.g., Gill (13, 14)) have developed a working conceptual model for QoL as a broad, integrative construct reflecting positive health. That model, shown in Figure 2.1, is multidimensional, including physical, social, spiritual, emotional, and cognitive well-being. The model is also *hierarchical*, with those sub-domains contributing to an integrative subjective QoL.

Along with their definition of wellness, the National Wellness Institute (NWI) (7) offers a six-dimensional model of wellness. That model, developed by Dr. Bill Hettler, cofounder and president of the NWI, is an interdependent model with the following six dimensions: occupational, spiritual, physical, intellectual, emotional and social. The model is not hierarchical, and does not include a separate integrative wellness component. However,

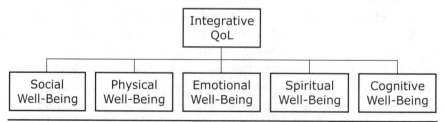

Figure 2.1 A Conceptual Model for Sub-domains of Quality of Life (QoL)

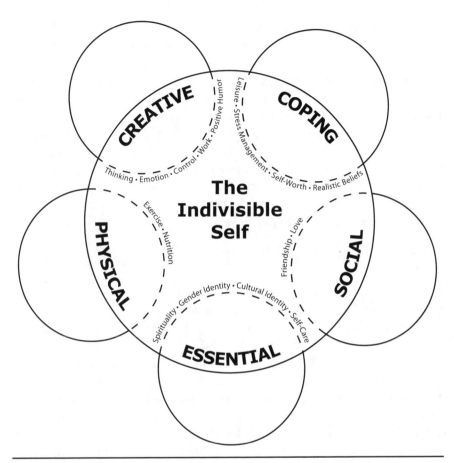

Figure 2.2 The Indivisible Self Model of Wellness

all six dimensions are interrelated, and thus together make up overall or integrative wellness.

The Indivisible Self Model (ISM) by Myers and Sweeney (15) is an evidence-based wellness model that views wellness holistically across the life span. Based on the Wheel of Wellness (6), the ISM addresses wellness as well as prevention over the life span. The model presents one "higher order wellness factor" that is composed of five second-order factors (Essential Self, Social Self, Creative Self, Physical Self, and Coping Self) and 17 separate wellness dimensions (thinking, emotions, control, work, positive humor, leisure, stress management, self-worth, realistic beliefs, exercise, nutrition, spirituality, gender identity, cultural identity, self-care, friendship, and love). Like the wellness model, the ISM, shown in Figure 2.2, depicts the five factors as interrelated, together making up the indivisible self.

Carruthers and Hood (16) recently proposed a strengths-based service model, the Leisure and Well-Being Model (LWM), that is based on the concept that contexts central to well-being must be facilitated through positive emotion and the development of relevant resources and capacities. Grounded in theories of psychology, leisure, and human developmental, the LWM focuses on "the centrality of positive emotion in creating a life of meaning..." (p. 299) (17). The first component of the LWM, Enhancing Leisure Experience, includes five ways of cultivating and enhancing leisure experiences: (a) savoring leisure, (b) authentic leisure, (c) leisure gratifications, (d) mindful leisure, and (e) virtuous leisure. A second component, Developing Resources, addresses the development of one's psychological, social, cognitive, physical, and environmental resources. Together these components contribute to well-being, positive experience, and expression of one's full potential (see Figure 2.3).

Measures of Health, Wellness, and Quality of Life

As several sources (e.g., Rejeski (8, 9)) and other chapters in this text suggest, leisure and physical activities are consistently related to quality of life and positive health. However, that research and related implications for professional practice are limited by the lack of measures that match the definitions and models of positive health. Nearly every study uses a different measure, and few are based on guiding theoretical frameworks. Measures range from overall subjective well-being or life satisfaction to aggregate measures of separate components such as physical function, social, cognitive, and spiritual well-being.

The most widely used measure in health-related research, the SF-36 (18), is part of the larger QoL measures used in the Medical Outcomes Study. The SF-36 is simple, has adequate psychometric properties and is readily available, but the SF-36 was designed for clinical purposes, and the items emphasize physical function rather than positive health.

The Centers for Disease Control and Prevention (CDC) has a Healthy Days measure of QoL that is valuable for gathering epidemiological data, but the measure was not developed within a conceptual framework or theory-based research on health promotion. Like the SF-36 and most commonly-used measures of health-related QoL, however, the CDC measure focuses on limitations and symptoms, and fails to capture multidimensional positive health and well-being.

Based on the ISM and wellness models, Myers and colleagues have developed The Wellness Evaluation of Lifestyle (WEL) Inventory (19), which is a 131-item clinically-oriented tool designed to facilitate individuals' choices toward a healthy lifestyle. Their more recent Five Factor Wellness Inventory (5F-Wel) (13) is a shorter evidence-based version of the WEL based on the Indivisible Self Model (ISM). It is applicable for children,

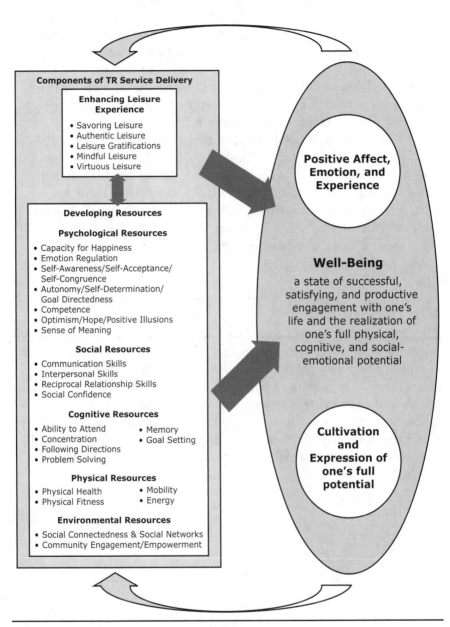

Figure 2.3 The Leisure and Well-being Model of Wellness

adolescents, as well as adults (available at: http://www.mindgarden.com/products/5fwels.htm).

The Perceived Wellness Scale (PWS) by Adams, Bezner, and Steinhardt (20) is a measure of wellness perceptions in each of six separate subscales. The PWS identifies individuals who score high on perceived wellness as: (a) more physically healthy, (b) have a greater sense of meaning and purpose in life, (c) expect that positive things will occur in their life no matter what the circumstances, (d) be more connected with family or friends, (e) be more secure and happy with who they are, and (f) be intellectually vibrant. Research has found this measure to be successful with various populations including survivors of traumatic brain injury, survivors of breast cancer, as well as high school students.

The WHO has developed two instruments for measuring quality of life (the WHOQOL-100 and the WHOQOL-BREF) in line with their definitions of health and quality of life. Information on the development of the measures, as well as the manual and related research is available at the WHO website (http://www.who.int/mental_health/resources/evidence_research/en/index.html). The WHO measures, and several other measures, reflect the common understanding of positive health as a subjective, integrative, multidimensional construct.

Summary

This chapter is not comprehensive (an impossible task), but it is representative of the dominant models and approaches to health and wellness across a range of disciplines and professional areas, including public health, kinesiology and counseling. We have drawn from and presented constructs, models, and measures to represent that literature, and also to be relevant to leisure studies. Common themes link all these constructs, models, and measures to converge and accent *positive* health. Positive health is a subjective, integrative, multidimensional construct that reflects optimal well-being.

References

1. World Health Organization (WHO). Preamble to the Constitution. 1946. http://www.who.int/governance/eb/constitution/en/index.html. Accessed May 10, 2009.
2. Seligman MEP. Positive health. *Appl Psychol-Int Rev* 2008;**57**:3–18.
3. U.S. Department of Health and Human Services. *Healthy people 2010.* Washington, DC: DHHS, 2000.
4. Corbin CB, Welk GJ, Corbin WR, Welk KA. *Concepts of fitness and wellness* (7th ed.). McGraw Hill: Boston, 2008.
5. Jensen LA, Allen MN. A synthesis of qualitative research on wellness-illness. *Qualitative Health Research* 1994;**4**:349–369.
6. Myers JE, Sweeney TJ, Witmer JM. The Wheel of Wellness for counseling wellness: A holistic model for treatment planning. *J Counsel Dev* 2000;**78**:251–266.
7. National Wellness Institute. http://www.nationalwellness.org. Accessed May 10, 2009.
8. Rejeski WJ, Brawley LR, Shumaker SA. Physical activity and health-related quality of life. *Exerc Sport Sci Rev* 1996;**24**:71–108.
9. Rejeski WJ, Mihalko SL. Physical activity and quality of life in older adults. *J Gerontol A Biol Sci Med Sci* 2001;**56A** (Special Issue No 2):23–35.
10. McAuley E, Elavsky S. Physical activity, aging, and quality of life: Implications for measurement. In Zhu W (ed), *Measurement Issues and Challenges in Aging and Physical Activity Research.* Champaign, IL: Human Kinetics, 2005, pp. 57–68.
11. O'Connor R. *Measuring quality of life in health.* Elsevier Limited: London, 2004.
12. World Health Organization (WHO). Quality of Life Users Manual. (retrieved 5/28/09 from: http://www.who.int/mental_health/evidence/who_qol_user_manual_98.pdf)
13. Gill DL, Williams L. *Psychological dynamics of sport and exercise* (3rd ed.). Human Kinetics: Champaign, IL, 2008.
14. Gill DL, Chang YK, Murphy KJ, Holder KM. Quality of life assessment in physical activity and health promotion. *Med Sci Sports Exerc* 2006; **38** (5, Supp):S370–S371.
15. Myers JE, Sweeney TJ. The Indivisible Self: An Evidence-Based Model of Wellness. *J Indiv Psychol* 2004;**60**:234–245.
16. Carruthers C, Hood CD. Building a life of meaning through therapeutic recreation: The Leisure and Well-being model, Part I. *Therapeutic Recreation Journal* 2007;**41**:276–297.

17. Hood CD, Carruthers C. Enhancing leisure experience and developing resources: The Leisure and Well-being model, Part II. *Therapeutic Recreation Journal* 2007;**41**:298–325.
18. Ware JE, Sherbourne CD. The MOS 36-item short-form health survey (SF-36). I. Conceptual framework and item selection. *Med Care* 1992;**30**:473–483.
19. Wellness Evaluation of Lifestyle. http://www.mindgarden.com/products/wells.htm. Accessed May 10, 2009.
20. Adams T, Bezner J, Steinhardt M. The conceptualization and measurement of perceived wellness: Integrating balance across and within dimensions. *Am J Health Promot* 1997;**11**:208–18.

Chapter 3
Relations Between Leisure, Health, and Wellness

Laura Payne
Elizabeth Orsega-Smith

Introduction

If you were born in 1900, statistically, how long would you be expected to live? The answer might surprise you. In 1900, Americans' life expectancy at birth was only 47 years old. Today, Americans are living much longer lives. Females born today are expected to live for 80 years and males to age 75 (1). The dramatic increase in life expectancy is explained by improvements in water quality, food production/security, medical technology, modern vaccines, and other major medical and sanitation advances. Although these advances deserve much credit, another major influence on health is our own behaviors.

With the increasing prevalence and incidence of many behavioral related diseases, there was a shift in public health efforts. In the late 1800s the public health emphasis was on contagious diseases and infections. However, when the epidemics began to involve behavioral-related diseases such as heart disease and lung cancer, the public health emphasis switched to the areas of disease prevention and health promotion. In 1976, the Office of Disease Prevention and Health Promotion was established in the United States within the Centers for Disease Control and Prevention. Through the 1980s much of focus in medicine was on the treatment of disease and chronic conditions, rather than a focus on prevention and wellness (2).

Currently, a higher proportion than ever of youth and adults must deal with the ongoing issues (e.g., management, treatment, prevention of secondary conditions) associated with having one or more chronic conditions. In the U.S., the leading chronic diseases are heart disease, cancer, diabetes, and arthritis (3). Now, rather than dying from infectious disease, our biggest concern is to learn how to live with and successfully manage a host of ongoing health conditions. Recognition of the influence of lifestyle factors (e.g., nutrition, physical activity, smoking, second-hand smoke) has led to a movement that emphasizes prevention of disease and promotion of wellness, rather than the costly (both economic and quality of life costs) reactive philosophy of the medical treatment model of health. Let's take a closer look at what we mean by health promotion and disease prevention.

Defining Health Promotion and Disease Prevention

The definitions of health promotion and disease prevention can sometimes be confusing. However, there are several definitions that may help in delineating the two concepts. "Health Promotion is the art and science of helping people to discover the synergies between their core passions and optimal health, and become motivated to strive for optimal health. Optimal health is a dynamic balance of physical, emotional, social, spiritual, and intellectual health. Lifestyle change can be facilitated through a combination of learning experiences that enhance awareness, increase motivation, build skills, and most importantly, through creating supportive environments that provide opportunities for positive health practices."(4). However, disease prevention covers measures not only to prevent the occurrence of disease, such as risk factor reduction (e.g., reduce cigarette smoking, increase physical activity), but also to limit disease progress and reduce its consequences (i.e., death, disability) once established.

Optimal health can include multiple dimensions including social, emotional, spiritual, physical, mental, and environmental health. The U.S. government has put forth efforts to assist individuals to achieve optimal health by establishing health indicators through the Healthy People program (Healthy People 2000, Healthy People 2010, Healthy People 2020). The overall goal of this program is to increase the quality and years of healthy life along with eliminating health disparities. The leading health indicators for 2020 include physical activity, obesity, tobacco use, substance abuse, responsible sexual behavior, mental health, environmental health, and access to health care.

The Role of Behavior Change in Health Promotion/ Disease Prevention

Most of the leading health indicators are impacted by making some type of behavior change. Behavior change involves other factors (i.e., personal, social, environmental, community) besides the health behavior. For example, an increase in one's physical activity may also involve physical and social environmental factors such as the availability of sidewalks or recreational facilities, opportunities for recreational sport participation among youth, or having a family atmosphere that encourages play and physical activity. Motivation is another factor that affects behavior. Someone who dislikes running, but does it solely to lose weight, is extrinsically motivated, whereas a college student who takes up Ultimate Frisbee for the love of the sport is intrinsically motivated. People who find something they enjoy doing and find meaningful are far more likely to continue doing the activity, than someone who does it as a means to an end (e.g., to lose weight, to please my spouse) (5, 6). Continuing participation despite the limitations of chronic disease is also an important strategy to maintain health and well-being. To use arthritis as an example, Betty, an older woman, developed osteoarthritis in her hands, which prevents her from her knitting, her favorite lifelong activity. For a while she stopped knitting completely, but found she felt down and lacked a sense of purpose. After participating in a focus group with other older adults with arthritis, she learned a way to adapt her knitting needles to continue participating. She taped a thin layer of foam around each needle, which made it more comfortable to grip the needles, and required less fine motor skills. This relatively simple adaptation enabled Betty to return to this activity she finds rewarding and enjoyable.

The social environment often impacts behavior. Many of the behavior change theories (i.e., social cognitive theory, theory of reasoned action and planned behavior) incorporate the social environment as part of the behavior change process. Peers, coworkers, and family members may influence one's behavior. For example, an older adult may perceive higher comfort levels in a tai chi class led by someone in his/her age bracket. The peer leader may provide both encouragement and be a role model. In turn, he/she may continue to come on a regular basis for both the social interaction and feeling of success. On the contrary, if an older adult is one of a few seniors who attends a tai chi class led by a college student, he/she may feel intimidated and dropout after only a few sessions.

Some aspects of the physical environment that affect health are outside of our immediate control. For example, numerous rural communities lack the infrastructure for sidewalks which make it safer and easier to walk. Rural communities often lack parks, playgrounds, and recreation facilities. However, several national initiatives have laid the framework for promoting active, walkable communities (i.e., The Robert Wood Johnson Foundation's Active Living by Design and Active Living Research Programs). In some cases, communities have attempted to create mixed use neighborhoods that have connectivity and easy access to schools, playgrounds, and open spaces (7). Moreover, there is a lack of available healthcare facilities (e.g., hospitals, clinics, critical access hospitals) in rural areas compared to their urban counterparts (8, 9). In contrast, African Americans and Latinos who are more likely to live in poor urban areas are often exposed to toxic chemicals, have landfills located in their neighborhoods, and have abandoned industrial sites in close proximity to their homes (10, 11). Exposure to toxic chemicals increases their risk of getting cancer, lung disease, and other life threatening diseases. These are just a few examples of how environmental factors can work against community health and well-being. Despite these alarming issues, communities are organizing themselves and working with local governments, nonprofit organizations, and other advocacy groups to reduce or eliminate these harmful substances. Likewise, rural communities are collaborating with parks and recreation agencies, schools, healthcare organizations, and other local groups to improve facilities, programs, and services that promote healthy living.

These individual, social, and physical environmental factors shape peoples' behaviors and decisions about how their time is used. Also, the study of health promotion and disease prevention spans across a variety of disciplines and fields of practice. For example, in order to achieve some of the Healthy People 2020 goals, coalitions have been developed and many of these involve the organizations within the field of leisure and recreation. For example, the American Alliance for Health, Physical Education, Recreation and Dance (AAPHERD) and the National Recreation and Park Association (NRPA) have been active public health partners for a number of years. While national organizations have played an instrumental role in moving recreation and parks into the health arena, many local park and recreation agencies have led grassroots efforts that embrace their role in health. Leisure and recreation can play a vital role in targeting a number of the health indicators. Next we explain how parks and recreation contributes to public health and we present several examples of how recreation, parks and leisure organizations have collaborated with public health organizations to address society's most pressing public health issues.

The Role of Leisure and Recreation in Health Promotion and Disease Prevention

There are a number of reasons why community parks and recreation agencies are involved in health promotion. Historically, parks and recreation was founded on the principle that non-work activity could improve the health, education, social adjustment and life chances of poor people, children, the elderly, "handicapped," and others who had few resources to help them replace the recreation patterns of agriculture-based peasant life (12). On an individual level, free time or non-obligated time is the life context where people have the most choice and freedom to pursue what they want to do. Therefore, people have more opportunity to engage in healthy or unhealthy behaviors during free time. At an organizational level, community parks and recreation agencies have access to people, programs, and facilities. These are all important factors in shaping peoples' behavior during their free-time. The role of leisure and recreation in health has evolved over time and several key partnerships help us understand how parks and recreation has become an important player in the promotion of health/wellness. Let's take a look at a few key initiatives that have helped highlight parks and recreation's increasing involvement in public health.

In the late 1990s the National Heart, Lung, and Blood Institute (NHLBI) collaborated with NRPA to create a national, community-based program, Hearts N' Parks. Since health and wellness issue are important core concepts to the organization, NRPA was a natural partner for the program. The overall goals of this program were to increase the percentage of children and adults engaging in healthy nutrition and physical activity and increase both knowledge and attitudes towards healthy nutrition and activity. In this program, additional community partners such as local chapters of the American Heart Association, University Extension (i.e., outreach) organizations, and local hospitals and universities aided in the implementation of these community programs to help residents aim for a healthy weight, engage in healthy eating, and become physically active.

Hearts N' Parks was launched in July 1999 as the Arlington County Department of Parks and Recreation and Community Resources was the first community to offer the program. Various themes were implemented each year within the communities (e.g., community sports and health). In 1999, Hearts N' Parks was initiated in approximately 12 North Carolina communities and reached over 2,000 individuals. In 2001, Hearts N' Parks was further expanded to include 50 communities in 11 states. These programs were initiated in various settings included summer camps, afterschool programs, senior center programs, city employee programs, and general park and recreation programs.

The overall results of the pre-post test evaluation demonstrated improvement in children's knowledge and behavioral intention of heart-healthy eating and physical activity while adults showed increases in their knowledge and attitudes of nutrition and physical activity (13). This initiative showed the strength of developing a partnership between a government agency and the National Park and Recreation Association and involving community partners to carry out a public health initiative. After the Hearts N' Parks initiative, NRPA established a memorandum of understanding with the CDC in 2002 to coordinate the promotion of good nutrition and increase physical activity among Americans. One of the major initiatives that grew from this strategic partnership is the *Step Up to Health Community Mobilization Initiative*. In this program, community parks and recreation agencies serve as grassroots catalysts for cross-disciplinary cooperation to improve physical activity and nutrition in local communities. The model also utilized the Hearts N' Parks principles of the six "Ps" (people, programs, places and spaces, public visibility, partnerships, policies and practices, and performance measures). In the winter and spring of 2004, NRPA staff traveled the country hosting Step Up to Health Summits where participants learned about the initiative and how to implement activities and programs to launch their local Step Up to Health program. Thousands of agencies nationwide joined the initiative and made significant positive changes in their communities. For example, San Diego Parks and Recreation led an initiative to change the vending machine contents in their facilities so they were consistent with the California Public School's policy. In the end, all San Diego Parks and Recreation and California State Parks vending machines' contents had to include at least 50 percent healthy snack choices. This program served as a model for numerous other communities across the state.

The collaboration between parks and recreation and public health has continued to grow with the 2008 launch of the CDC's ACHIEVE (Action Communities for Health, Innovation, and Environmental Change) program. The purpose of this five-year national initiative is to facilitate collaboration among local governments, non-profits, county public health, parks and recreation agencies, schools, business, and other local agencies to make numerous program, policy, and environmental improvements to health. Public health issues of interest in this program are 1) physical activity, 2) smoking cessation, 3) nutrition, and the 4) prevention and management of chronic conditions (i.e., heart disease, stroke, cancer, diabetes, arthritis, obesity). Five key national organizations have been funded for ACHIEVE and include the 1) National Association of Chronic Disease Directors, 2) National Association of County and City Health Officials, 3) National Recreation and Park Association, 4) Society for Public Health Education, and 5) YMCA of the USA. Part of the funding will be used to design and implement online training programs accessible by community park and recreation agencies. A large portion of the funding is being used to organize a competitive grants program to which local organizations applied. A total of 53 organizations have been funded thus far and the first ten grantees in 2008 have already demonstrated positive changes in their communities. For example, Salamanca, New York successfully passed an ordinance that bans smoking in all city parks and playgrounds. Signs that say "Young Lungs at Play" have been posted throughout the parks to deter smoking. The grantee in Black Hawk, Iowa implemented the "Stairwell Campaign" using point of choice signs to encourage people to take the stairs instead of the elevator. Some examples of the signs include "In one minute, a 150 pound person burns about 10 calories walking the stairs, and only 1.5 calories taking the elevator." Another sign exclaims "Small steps make big differences." All signs are anchored at the bottom with a logo of a person walking stairs that says "take the stairs."

While NRPA was instrumental in building a movement that mobilized many national and local organizations, numerous local park and recreation agencies had been engaged in health promotion for many years. Be Active Bitterroot is a local example of community health partnership in which residents of the Bitterroot Valley (Montana and Idaho) have the opportunity to participation in numerous outdoor and volunteer activities centering around active lifestyle. Local partnerships including chiropractic and physical therapy service, physical offices, police departments, hospitals, schools, history society, Audubon Society, local parks, gyms, and universities were able to offer a variety of program (i.e., river clean ups, walks, bike rides, educational forums, screenings and health fairs) to residents. This is a year-long program in which participants may pick and choose their activities from a menu listing. This is a local example of a successful health partnership focusing on prevention. In another example, for many years, the Morton Grove Park District has partnered with a local hospital to implement a phase four cardiac rehabilitation program at the agency's recreation and fitness center. In this environment, patients are exposed to numerous programs, facilities, and resources that they can utilize after their structured rehabilitation program ends.

As evidenced by these local and national initiatives, park and recreation community partnerships are important contributors in promoting overall health (14, 15). Partnerships often involve multiple organizations collaborating to reach a common goal. For example, Active Options is a community based program in which the Foothills Park and Recreation district (near Denver, Colorado) partnered with numerous community agencies to deliver a health initiative. Partners included insurance companies (Kaiser-Permante), physician offices, local public health agencies, and not-for profits (i.e., American Heart Association, American Cancer Society, Susan G. Komen Foundation). Sharing of resources (i.e., personnel, facilities, information, finances), increasing credibility, and providing opportunities for the community are vital to a successful partnership (16). Health partnerships involving parks and recreation also include a wide variety of disciplines such as urban planning, law, public health agencies, local health care organizations, and specialists. Such partnerships may help to push the health agenda to the forefront while promoting park and recreation as a leader in health.

The foundation has been established for community partnerships to be developed and sustained to impact leading health indicators and increase quality of life. Most communities have park and recreation programs that a large portion of the residents can access. However, many park and recreation agencies have relied on traditional programming for youth and adults emphasizing sports and exercise. Parks and recreation can have a bigger impact through health-related partnerships that may lead to programs extending beyond the traditional ones that address important health issues and culturally specific needs.

For parks and recreation to have a greater impact in the future on health-related issues there may be several research and practice issues to pursue:

- Improved access to parks, recreation, and wellness facilities in both urban and rural areas.
- Access to develop usable green space in urban and rural areas.
- Equitable distribution of parks, playgrounds, and recreation centers in urban areas.
- Access to high quality locally grown foods (e.g., fruits and vegetables).
- Increased opportunities for physical activity (via recreation and sports) among individuals with disabilities (both physical and intellectual).
- Implementation of culturally specific programming in parks and recreation facilities.
- More grass-roots and public policy level advocacy efforts to increase funding for prevention and chronic disease management services via evidence-based health and wellness programs for youth, adults and older adults.
- A better understanding of the long term effectiveness of community health fairs and other special events. What impact do they have on behavior change, if any?

References

1. Arias E. United States life tables 2004. *National Vital Statistics Reports* 2007;**56/9**:30–34.
2. Longino CF. Beyond the body: An emerging medical paradigm. *American Demographics* 2007;**19/12**:15–17.
3. Centers for Disease Control and Prevention. The power to prevent: The call to control. http://www.cdc.gov/nccdphp/publications/AAG/chronic.htm. Accessed June 21, 2010.
4. O'Donnell M. Definition of health promotion: Part III: Expanding the definition. *Am J Health Promot* 1989;**3/3**:5.
5. Csikzentmihayli M. *Flow: The Psychology of Optimal Experience.* Harper and Row: New York, 1990.
6. Godbey G, Caldwell L, Floyd M, Payne L. Implications from Leisure Studies and Recreation and Park Management Research for Active Living. *Am J Prev Med* 2005;**28**(2S2):150–158.
7. Heath G, Brownson RC, Kruger J, Miles R, Powell KE, Ramsey LT, et al. The effectiveness of urban design and land use and transportation policies and practices to increase physical activity: A systematic review. *J Phys Activ Health* 2006;**3**(3S):S55–S76.
8. Collins BK, Borders TF. Utilization of hospital services among rural older persons: A comparison of critical access hospitals and community hospitals. *J Health Hum Serv Adm* 2005;**28/1**:135–152.
9. Green-Hernandez C. Transportation challenges in rural healthcare. *Nurse Pract* 2006;**31/12**:10.
10. Lee C. Environmental justice: Building a unified vision of health and the environment. *Environ Health Perspect* 2002;**110/2**:141–144.
11. Morello-Frosch R, Jesdale BM. Separate and unequal: Residential segregation and cancer risk associated with ambient air toxics in U.S. Metropolitan areas. *Environ Health Perspect* 2006;**114/3**:386–393.
12. Cross G. *A social history of leisure since 1600*. Venture Publishing, Inc.: State College, PA 2000.
13. National Recreation & Park Association. Hearts N' Parks: Year 2. *Parks & Recreation Magazine* 2003;**38/7**:46–48.
14. Henderson K, Bialeschki MD. Leisure and active lifestyles: Research reflections. *Leisure Sciences* 2005;**27/5**:355–365.
15. Spangler K, Caldwell L. Implications of public policy related to parks, recreation, and public health. *J Phys Act Health* 2007;**4/1**:64–71.
16. Mowen A, Payne L, Orsega-Smith E, Godbey, G. Assessing the health partnerships practices of park and recreation agencies: Findings and implications from a national study. *Journal of Park and Recreation Administration* 2009;**27/3**:116–131.

Chapter 4
What Constitutes "Good" Health and Wellness?

Ann Sebren
Jack Chisum

If beauty is in the eye of the beholder, so too must be "good" health and wellness. Determining what qualifies as "good" health and wellness varies widely depending upon historical, cultural, demographic, socioeconomic, and professional standpoints. The attempt to define health, much less define "good" health, is complicated by the need to take into account both lay and professional definitions that themselves involve multiple points of view. For example, the definitions of health and wellness that have been described, developed, and assessed by health professionals range from multidimensional models of well-being (1) to leading a life of purpose with quality connections to others (2) to the functional state that makes the achievement of life's goals and activities possible (3). From the lived perspective of individuals; how someone defines health, views its purposes, engages in behaviors that impact health, and identifies obstacles to health and behavior vary widely depending upon a great many factors such as culture, age, gender, socioeconomic status, and level of education. The complexities inherent in approaching the question of "good" health calls, perhaps, more for an exploration of questions than for a definitive answer.

Is "Good" Health Not Having "Bad" Health?

Surely the simplest and most common way that "good" health is conceptualized is as the absence of "bad" health. The conceptualization of health and wellness as either poor health or positive health is clearly conveyed by the concept of the health-illness continuum. The idea of the continuum, which has symptoms, illness, and disability progressing toward premature death on one pole and a progression of average to good to optimal health on the other pole, suggests that one cannot be ill and healthy at the same time. In medicine, for example, health has typically been conceptualized as the absence of symptoms or disease. Bowling (4) points out that many measures of health continue to assess the negative side of this continuum rather than the positive side because it is easier to measure the departure from health than it is to determine indications of health. From this perspective, clinical outcomes can become the yardstick of "good" health. Objective measures of risk factors that fall within established norms; such as those related to blood pressure, lipids, glucose, and even BMI, become analogous to good health as indications of the absence of symptoms or risk. The message that normative clinical screenings equals good health has been adopted by both health professionals and lay populations alike.

Evidence indicates that individuals frequently adopt the orientation that they are healthy when they do not have pain or symptoms, are not sick, have normal function in their body, have no physical constraints, do not need to see a doctor, or when there is nothing wrong in their medical checkups (5–9). This is perhaps not surprising given Leder's (10) suggestion that the healthy body is experienced as an 'absent presence' in everyday life and only becomes a subject of conscious awareness when illness or dysfunction occur. How individuals perceive good health may well depend upon the degree to which they experience the physical body as the predominant constituent of health. Although studies have indicated that individuals often perceive themselves to be in good health if they do not have symptoms or diagnosis of illness, most people have a definition of "good" health that also includes the presence of positive characteristics as well (5–6). Indeed, many of these positive characteristics reflect a view of "good" health that includes many domains of life beyond just the physical.

Is "Good" Health One Thing or Many Things?

In 1947, the World Health Organization (WHO) defined health as a state of complete physical, mental, and social well-being, not merely the absence of disease and infirmity (1), thus setting the stage for the contemporary emphasis on health as a positive and holistic concept. Health and wellness have come to be conceptualized, both professionally and popularly, as being a function of the multidimensional components of physical, mental, social, and spiritual health. Physical health refers to the biological integrity of the individual, ability to perform daily tasks without undue fatigue, and ability to recover from illness and injury. Mental health includes both intellectual function as well as emotional well-being. Social health involves having a strong social support network, meaningful and satisfying relationships, and the ability to interact well with others in the environment. Finally, spiritual health, a component that has since been added to the WHO definition, reflects the understanding that one's value systems, sense of meaning and purpose in life, and connectedness with self, others, and the larger community impacts overall health. Many health and wellness models convey these multiple domains as being interrelated with one another such that enhancement or diminishment in one domain affects all of the others in an overall movement toward or away from greater health and wellness.

This conceptualization of health and wellness typically expressed in textbooks and among health professionals is reflective of the way most individuals define health for themselves. Indeed, evidence indicates that most people evaluate themselves in relation to domains of life that they consider to be relevant and important and, thus, conceive of health as including multiple dimensions (4). Studies in which individuals were asked to describe their own conceptions of good health indicate that their responses include such multidimensional factors as being energetic, having vitality, feeling fit, and having resistance to illness (4–9); having a mind capable of clear thinking, having a positive outlook, being happy, being able to cope with stress, and emotional equilibrium (4–9); having a good marriage, having strong social support and positive, meaningful social relationships (4–6), and having a good life, being satisfied with life, and having joy in living (4, 6, 7). Not only do people describe their own health as having multiple dimensions, they experience these multiple dimensions as a whole rather than segmenting their lives into component parts. Additionally, they experience the multiple dimensions of health as inextricably intertwined with the range of goals and activities in their daily life, including those related to leisure (12). For example, feelings of strength, energy, and vitality may be related to engagement in a variety of daily and leisure activities that can contribute to outlook and function, ability to cope with stress, and social relationships.

Although research indicates that a variety of domains of health are included in the way people perceive and conceptualize "good" health, it is also critical to note that there is tremendous individual variation in which domains are perceived as more relevant, important, and valuable for good health. Which domains are more valued is likely influenced by demographic, cultural, and socioeconomic factors and appears to change over the life course. Physical health as the absence of disease, for example, is often seen as less critical to one's experience of "good" health in older adults. In a context in which symptoms of illness are seen as the norm, then "good" health may need to be defined in different ways, such as the ability to cope or to remain socially active and engaged regardless of the presence of illness (5). Similarly, women appear to be more likely than men to identify positive, meaningful relationships with others, family, and children as a characteristic of "good" health (5). Cultural and acculturation factors also play a role in which domains of health are perceived as essential to "good" health.

That health is experienced as multidimensional appears to be consistent with how individuals perceive leisure, that is, as occurring within a variety of domains of life (13). In many ways, how individuals have described the characteristics of the various dimensions of health are a corollary to the way leisure has been defined and described. Leisure as activity, a counter-balance to stress, opportunity for cultural and family stability and interaction, and pleasure, fun, and enjoyment (13) are reflective of "good" health conceptualized as energy and vitality, positive outlook, ability to cope, positive social relationships, and joy in living (4–9). It is possible that the way individuals perceive "good" health may influence both perceptions of leisure as well as leisure activities.

Is "Good" Health Work or Freedom?

Beyond the perception that "good" health involves multiple dimensions of life, behavior also appears to play a central role in how individuals view health and wellness. Studies have indicated that individuals also conceptualize "good" health as a life filled with healthy behaviors, such as eating the right things, getting exercise, sleeping well, and getting regular exams (5–7, 9). The way individuals experience the relationship between "good" health and behavior is likely to be influenced by their personal constructions of "good" health as well as a range of factors that influence perceptions of health, behavior, and leisure.

Crawford's (14) ethnographic study of adults' views of health provides one way of considering how individuals experience the relationship between their ideas of "good" health and behavior and how this relation-ship may have implications for leisure. When "good" health is primarily experienced as an expression of self-control, health becomes a goal to be achieved that is dependent upon adopting appropriate, disciplined, health-promoting activities. The goal of "good" health thus requires a reordering of priorities and comes to compete with other life goals, often resulting in the view that "leisure or 'down time' must be converted to the 'up time' of health promotion" (p. 69). From this perspective, the achievement of "good" health is experienced as the equivalent of hard work.

On the other hand, Crawford (14) also found that an equally strong orientation toward "good" health involved the experience of health as plea-sure seeking, enjoyment, contentment, and well-being. The perception of restraint and renunciation as the means to achieve good health is replaced in this orientation with an attitude that health is the outcome of enjoyment of life accomplished through not worrying and not adopting a load of self-denying constraints. For those who expressed this orientation, it was criti-cal that leisure time not be invaded by a sense of continued discipline and work. "Good" health incorporated a view of leisure as a time of freedom to do what one wanted without the imposition of controls.

The tension between how behavior is placed within these two orienta-tions of "good" health is perhaps echoed in contemporary conceptualiza-tions of wellness. Many approaches to wellness define it as an active, conscious process of self-directed choice to engage in behaviors that lead to improved health and well-being (15). This definition is clearly reflective of the idea that good health is equivalent of the ability to adopt appropriate, disciplined, health-enhancing behaviors. Wellness has also been defined as a positive state exemplified by quality of life and sense of well-being and available to everyone regardless of their limitations and conditions, involving the integration and balance of the multiple dimensions of health through the adoption of health-enhancing conditions and behaviors rather than through attempts to minimize illness (16–17). This approach to wellness adopts the idea that wellness is a state of being characterized by the capacity to enjoy life and withstand challenges (17). Corbin and Pangrazi (17) emphasize that, in their view, wellness is the outcome of behavior and that healthy behavior per se does not constitute wellness.

The distinction between health as a goal to be achieved or as freedom from constraint that leads to enjoyment and satisfaction with life is a critical factor in how both behavior and leisure are perceived and experienced. O'Donnell (18) recently suggested that optimal health is the "striving" for balance among the multiple dimensions of health and the alignment of the dimensions of health with one's passions in life. In his model of wellness, there is a distinction between engaging in health behaviors motivated by a striving for personal growth and aspirations and engaging in behaviors primarily motivated by compliance with directions for risk reduction. Good health as something to be achieved through the self-discipline to comply with health-promoting prescriptions and proscriptions is a quite different orientation than a view of health as the enjoyment and satisfaction with life that emerges as a result of behaviors that reflect personal goals, interests, passions, and aspirations. This distinction appears to have a strong corollary in the way leisure is often approached and experienced. If leisure is characterized by a sense of freedom and an internal motivation to participate in self-selected activities that primarily take place in non-work and non-employment time, it is likely then that individuals do not experience leisure if they perceive that participation in an activity is compulsory either directly as a requirement or indirectly as an expectation (19–20). It may well be that a view of good health as hard work in which health-promoting behaviors are perceived as being constraints in conflict with opportunities for leisure may reduce motivation to engage in those behaviors. In Laffrey's (20) study on health conceptions and health behavior, for example, those who viewed "good" health as being more eudaimonistic, or an expression of exuberant well-being, tended to engage in more health-promoting behaviors than those who viewed health primarily as the absence of disease and were motivated primarily by the goals of risk reduction.

Whether good health is viewed as work or freedom is often linked to the idea of good health as a means to an end or an end in itself. The ways individuals conceptualize "good" health as the absence of illness or a positive state, as having dimensionality, and as linked to behavior appear to be influenced by a variety of sociocultural factors, particularly socioeconomic status. Differences in participation in healthy lifestyle behaviors across levels of socioeconomic status have consistently been reported in literature. Research seems to suggest that while healthy lifestyle behaviors occur across many demographics, including class, the extent and quality of participation in healthy lifestyle behaviors is less the lower one's socioeconomic status (21). Some evidence suggests that these differences may be influenced by how individuals of different socioeconomic status conceptualize "good" health.

Those of higher socioeconomic status have been found to view "good" health as a personal value to be cultivated for one's own benefit; inclusive of a broad range of multidimensional elements such as fitness and activity, eating a balanced diet, being happy, and being able to cope with life, in order to experience greater vitality and enjoyment (6–7). In contrast, individuals of lower socioeconomic status have been found to take a more unidimensional, utilitarian view of health in which "good" health is the means through which they are able to fulfill their social roles and tasks, such as being able to get through the day, continue to work, and care for their home and family (6–7). Health behaviors are thus viewed primarily through the lens of preventative actions that will enable them to avoid illness or infirmity and discharge their responsibilities rather than as actions that promote more optimal states of health for greater life satisfaction and well-being.

While care must be taken not to oversimplify these types of constructions, given the role that race, ethnicity, culture, education, age, and gender must play in any interpretation of socioeconomic differences in views of health, these differences may still point to several concepts that have implications for leisure. Critical factors that have been identified as having an impact on the experience of leisure include the contingencies of time, number of options available, and expense (22), factors similar to those that have been identified as playing a role in socioeconomic health disparity. Available time, choices, and financial resources likely influence individuals' sense of freedom, a condition that has been discussed as a necessary prerequisite for intrinsic motivation to engage in self-directed behaviors (23). This appears to be a critical intersection between how good health and leisure is experienced and the motivations and perceptions that underlie participation in health and leisure behavior.

Can "Good" Health and Wellness be Defined and Why Does It Matter?

It would have been easier, perhaps, to simply answer the question "What is 'Good' Health and Wellness?" with "It depends" or more appropriately, "You decide." The idea of defining "good" health and wellness must inherently be contingent upon the myriad contextual factors that influence both professional and lay perspectives alike. This attempt at an exploration of the idea of "good" health was meant in many ways to serve as a springboard for further discussion and exploration. How "good" health is conceptualized has consequences for both individual behavior and social policy. "Good" health is the backdrop against which individuals assess themselves and make health- and leisure-related behavioral choices. More broadly, however, health promotion and leisure promotion policies rest to some degree upon the sociocultural and ideological tensions involved in views of freedom and work, life satisfaction and function, and perhaps even mind and body. Understanding how ideas of "good" health are constructed, viewed, and experienced may be an important additive to an interpretation of the junctures between "good" health and "good" leisure.

References

1. World Health Organization. Constitution. 1947.
2. Ryff C, Singer B. The contours of positive human health. *Psych Inquiry* 1998;**9/1**:1–28.
3. Hanlon JJ. *Public Health*. Mosby: St. Louis, MO, 1974.
4. Bowling A. *Measuring health: A review of quality of life measurement scales* (3ʳᵈ ed.). Open University Press, New York, 2005.
5. Blaxter M. *Health and lifestyles*. Tavistock, New York, 1990.
6. Calnan M. *Health and illness: The lay perspective*. Tavistock, New York, 1987.
7. d'Houtaud A, Field M. The image of health: Variations in perception by social class in a French population. *Sociology of Health & Illness* 1984;**6**:30–59.
8. Herlizch C. *Health and illness: A social psychological analysis*. Academic Press: New York, 1973.
9. Lau RR. Cognitive representations of health and illness. In Gochman D (ed), *Handbook of Health Behavior Research I: Personal and Social Determinants*. New York: Plenum Press, 2007, pp. 51–69.
10. Leder D. *The Absent Body*. Aldine: Chicago, 1990.
11. Hendry F, McVittie C. Is quality of life a healthy concept?: Measuring and understanding life experiences of older people. *Qual Health Res* 2004;**14/7**:961–975.
12. Parr MG, Lashua BD. What is leisure? The perceptions of recreation practitioners and others. *Leisure Sciences* 2004;**26**:1–17.
13. Crawford R. A Cultural Account of "Health": Control, Release, and the Social Body. In McKinlay JB (ed), *Issues in the political economy of health care*. New York: Tavistock, 1984, pp. 60–103.
14. National Wellness Institute. http://www.nationalwellness.org/. Accessed June 21, 2010.
15. Report of the 2000 Joint Committee on Health Education and Health Promotion Terminology. *J Health Educ* 2001;**32/2**:89–103.
16. Corbin C, Pangrazi, R. Toward a uniform definition of wellness: A commentary. *President's Council on Physical Fitness and Sports Research Digest* 2001;**3/15**:1–8.
17. O'Donnell MP. The face of wellness: Aspirational vision of health, renewing health behavior change process and balanced portfolio approach to planning change strategies. *American Journal of Health Promotion* 2008;**23/2** (Supp):1–12.
18. Iso-Ahola SE. *The social psychology of leisure and recreation*. Thomas: Springfield, IL, 1980.

19. Tinsley H, Tinsley D. A theory of attributes, benefits, and causes of leisure experiences. *Leisure Sciences* 1986;**8/1**:1–45.
20. Laffrey SC. Health behavior choice as related to self-actualization and health conceptions. *West J Nurs Res* 1985;**7/3**:279–300.
21. Cockerham W. Lifestyles, social class, demographic characteristics, and health behavior. In Gochman D (ed), *Handbook of health behavior research I: Personal and social determinants*. New York: Plenum Press, 1997, pp. 253–265
22. Mundy J. *Leisure education: Theory and practice* (2nd ed.). Sagamore: Champaign, IL, 1998.
23. Iso-Ahola SE. Motivational foundations of leisure. In Jackson E, Burton T (eds), *Leisure studies: Prospects for the twenty-first century.* State College, PA: Venture Publishing, Inc., 1999, pp. 35–51.

Chapter 5
What is Good Leisure from the Perspective of Health?

Geoffrey Godbey

Can the question be answered? Perhaps. "Health" is a multi-faceted concept that varies among cultures and within them. Since individuals are unique in their stunningly complex genetic endowments and in the environments in which they exist, starting in the womb, "health" must ultimately be defined in terms of the individual, even if there are some generalizations which may be made (e.g., smoking is bad for your health). In so many cases, however, the huge number of individual behaviors is so complex that simple generalizations, while true, don't tell us enough about consequences (e.g., one may quit smoking but gain thirty pounds and drink more alcohol). The point here is that the health effects of individual acts are stunningly complex. (Since lung cancer is the leading form of cancer among both men and women, and smokers lose, on average, five to seven years of life, quit smoking.)

Epigenetics, while in its infancy as a science, already informs us that our vast genetic endowment is characterized, in effect, by the shutting and opening of genes on a daily basis. A fetus whose mother eats a junk food diet, for example, may have a genetic reaction in which it is programmed to enter what is assumed to be a nutrition-scarce world, since the junk food eaten by the mother is so low in nutrition. Thus, the fetus is programmed to eat a lot and the resulting child may be predisposed to become obese. To some extent, then, good health must ideally be understood in terms of the individual's genetic predispositions. Some people need to drink more water than others. Some people need more or less sleep than others. What makes one person happy may not make another happy, such as high stress levels or strenuous exercise. Optimal arousal is much higher for one child than another (which is why playground equipment needs to provide different levels of arousal). Thus, what constitutes good health is more complex than might be assumed—and identifying "healthy" leisure even more complex! While our own personal habits play an important role in determining how long we live, our unique genetic endowment is critical.

This is not to argue that good health cannot be generalized about, only that such generalizations are almost always started with the unspoken assumption: "All things being equal . . ." They are, however, not equal and the more we know about the individual, both genetically and environmentally, the more good health and healthy leisure can be understood. Our genes shape our behavior—our behavior shapes our genes. There is much we don't know.

Is Healthy Leisure the Same for Everyone?

No! What constitutes healthy leisure for one person may constitute very unhealthy leisure for another. A few glasses of red wine while watching the sunset may be wonderfully healthy for one person but for a person with a drinking problem, it is an invitation to trouble. Resting in front of a TV after work may serve as necessary recovery for a coal miner, but not for a teenager who does so all day. Tennis may produce physical fitness for one person and skin cancer for another. What interests, stimulates, fascinates, and satisfies individuals varies and, in leisure, these differences mean healthy leisure differs for different people.

It does seem evident, however, that use of one's human capacities during leisure is healthy. That is: "Use it or lose it." A baby's brain generates roughly double the number of nerve cells it needs to function; with those cells that receive both chemical and electrical stimuli surviving, and the remaining cells dying. It appears that if a cell is not appropriately stimulated by other cells, it self-destructs (1).

It is not only the brain, however, that declines with lack of "use." So, too, does our forearm strength, our imagination, our ability to laugh, and our ability to play the guitar accompaniment to "Dust in the Wind." Thus, we may generalize that healthy leisure involves using our human capacities, although this may be done in an endless variety of ways.

In leisure, the ideal situation is that one uses their capacities, such as leg strength, not in order to maintain or increase leg strength, such as by riding an exercise bicycle, but by doing an enjoyable activity, such as riding a bicycle down a country lane or through a park, because one wants to do it. Leisure does not have "purposes" related to health. It is impossible to do a leisure activity "in order to." The beauty of riding the bicycle down the country lane is that improved leg strength occurs as serendipity, an unintended beneficial consequence. The reason for riding the bike was that it was worthwhile, pleasurable, and meaningful.

Thus, we see a first warning. Planning leisure activities based only on the basis of health is not a good idea. Leisure is always done for its own sake—because one loves to do it. While people may have to do some personal maintenance in order to be healthy, such as walking on a treadmill, the ideal is to find activities that are intrinsically worth doing which just happen to be healthy.

Is Healthy Leisure the Same in Every Culture?

No. The forms healthy leisure will take differs in different countries and cultures. In this respect, healthy leisure is not too different from healthy eating. As observed by Michael Pollan (2), healthy eating must be understood within a cultural context, not as ingesting a given kind of nutrients in isolation from shared meanings and pleasures of food. So it is with leisure.

It may be argued that, as one's life chances improve, motivation for leisure can move from the desire for rest and relaxation to the desire to find pleasure to the desire to find meaning (3). In some cultures, particularly those where people do hard physical work, healthy leisure may center around resting, word games, chatting with friends, or traditional card or table games. Such activity provides a kind of connectedness needed to maintain the culture and the individual's place in it. Pleasure seeking is done only in ways approved by the community. Where societies are highly collective, participating in forms of leisure which are traditional provides meaning. In societies that are highly individualistic, such as North American society, the search for meaning in leisure is often done at an individual level. Healthy leisure differs dramatically by culture. This is one of the reasons that many Japanese and other Asian immigrants suffer from depression at higher rates once in the U.S. The comfort of their former collective culture is largely missing. In its place there is only "free time," a kind of empty container which one fills up as they choose.

What Does "Health" Mean from a Leisure Perspective?

For openers, it means more than longevity or efficient functioning or the avoidance of disease or how much oxygen one can take into their body or how efficiently they metabolize food. Healthy leisure cannot be defined in scientific ways, although non-reductionist science may help us understand a bit. Healthy leisure involves celebration—the ability to celebrate the universe and one's life in it (4). Health, from the perspective of leisure, means the ability to love one's life—to celebrate it. If one can do that, their life is worth protecting, their body worth taking care of, their emotions worth feeling, their brain worth using. This condition is more than self-esteem, since the celebration goes beyond the invidious to all of life, from the finite to the infinite. One may celebrate her life even when "ill."

The role leisure plays here is that one must find something, or many things, they "love" to do for their own sake—you can never "love" in order to . . . This love of the specific activity becomes a symbol of the broader meaningfulness of life.

Some Characteristics of Healthy Leisure

The theory of Healthy Pleasures puts leisure at the forefront. This theory assumes that the human desire for enjoyment evolved to enhance our survival. "Doing what feels right and feeling good are beneficial for health and the survival of the species (5)." Pleasure rewards us twice; first in immediate enjoyment and then in improving our health.

The work ethic is not the only cultural barrier to pleasure. A sensory-deprived religious heritage, assuming humans are inherently evil, also contributes (6).

The following is an attempt to identify some characteristics which might make a leisure activity healthy. You are not asked to uncritically accept these principles, only to consider them in terms of your own life and understanding.

Acting. Healthy leisure involves acting rather than being acted upon. All else being equal, it is healthier to play soccer rather than watch it, to paint a picture rather than to watch someone else paint, to make conversation with a friend rather than hear other people talk on television. Turning on the television, of course, is an act but the issue here is more one of whether, in leisure, one diverts their awareness or consciousness or whether they focus it on a behavior they are drawn toward. Healthy leisure is a joyful act of the human will, and the exercise of the will is as important as the exercise of the body. One of the more important sayings in relation to health, mentioned previously, "Use it or lose it," (7) appears to be largely true. That which is not stimulated, strengthened, or reinforced through use begins to disappear. If you don't use your arm, your brain or your emotions, they start to wither. In healthy leisure, one uses what he or she has been given, not from necessity but from choice.

Creating. Leisure activity which involves creativity is healthier than activity which does not, if creativity is understood in a certain way. Creativity must be considered as "...the production of novel responses which have an appropriate impact in a given context (8)." Creativity, therefore, doesn't simply mean doing something novel, it means the effect of that novel approach must advance or improve the activity. Thus, an artist who drops a balloon full of paint on a canvas from a second floor window is not being creative; only novel. Creativity involves advancing the activity in question within the rules or contexts of the situation. In most cases, creativity in leisure comes after a person has learned quite a bit about an activity—a guitar player needs to learn not only chords, time signatures, and different methods of strumming and plucking the strings, but also harmony.

In learning a leisure activity to the point where one becomes creative, it has been argued that if a person is too closely supervised they will produce appropriate responses but not novel ones. If every child learning to serve a volleyball is not allowed to experiment at all, they may learn an appropriate way to serve but no novel ones. If, on the other hand, they are given complete freedom to serve however they want, they will likely develop novel serves but ones which aren't appropriate within the rules of the game. Therefore, the balance of freedom and discipline a person has in learning a leisure skill is critical in how likely it is that they will eventually become creative.

Meaning. The meaning of life, Csikszentmihalyi suggests, is meaning (9). Healthy leisure can't occur in the absence of meaning. If you don't interpret an act or situation as having any significance or meaning, it can't produce healthy leisure. Sometimes, such an interpretation is made primarily because of a shared meaning, perhaps riding bicycles on a trail with three long-time riding companions. Other times, the interpretation may be much more at an individual level; you find making pasta pesto for friends an enjoyable experience but another person, who works in a busy restaurant, finds it simply something that has to be done in order to earn money. Leisure activities have subjective meanings which often must be learned. Boxing may be simply stupid brutality to one person or the "sweet science" to another. Without these meanings, most leisure activities become ridiculous.

Giving. Healthy leisure involves giving oneself to an activity rather than trying to take from it. Such giving is an act of trust or faith. As people develop healthy leisure behaviors, they come to "believe" in them. Have you ever talked with someone who loved camping? They "know" the activity is worthwhile; know it is worth doing. Their decision to go camping is therefore not a calculated list of costs and benefits: What do I give up?—What do I get back? Rather, it is based on belief—This is a good thing to do—It is worthwhile.

Optimism. Healthy people are generally optimistic—and that trait carries into their leisure. They think things will go well. What people believe and expect about their health "may be more important than objective assessments made by your doctor" (10). People who expect bad health are more likely to get it. Research on heart patients reveals more heart attacks and more blockage of the coronary arteries in those who were hostile, irritable, impatient, and self-centered. They tended to hold the anger in and wall themselves off from other people. Being optimistic may be something which can, to some extent, be learned. To be learned, of course, it must be practiced. Leisure which celebrates helps optimism develop and be retained.

Sensuality. Healthy leisure involves the senses. Touch, smell, taste, sound, and vision all connect us with the pleasures of the world. Taste is critical in our appreciation of food. It is also critical to many other animals who will quit eating if their sense of taste is lost. It appears that healthy people take delight in the small pleasures of everyday life which use their senses: this means delighting in what they smell, feel, taste, hear, or see. Sleeping, eating, sexual behavior, and even the elimination of waste can be pleasurable. In a politically correct society, a no-touching epidemic, described a few decades ago in the British Medical Journal, is alive and well in our society (11).

Research with babies, even those born prematurely, has demonstrated the importance of touching and holding. Babies who were frequently touched and held have been shown to be much more likely to survive. (The same holds true for rats.) In spite of such findings, "Many of us are not getting our minimum daily requirement of sensual pleasure" (12).

Another aspect of sensuality is the need for heat. Studies of the use of saunas, hot tubs, or just hot baths seem to have health benefits. A study of people who used sauna baths found that sitting in a sauna for thirty minutes doubled beta-endorphin levels in the blood. Endorphins are internally produced chemicals that relieve pain and may also produce a sense of well-being and euphoria (13).

Humor. It appears that humor is critical in terms of health. Healthy people seem to maintain a vital sense of humor about life, enjoying a hearty laugh, often at their own expense. The ability to laugh, at ourselves, and at life, is positively related to health and longevity. Our reaction to tragedy may be improved by our continuing ability to laugh. People who take themselves with a great seriousness may rarely laugh, failing to see the humor in their own behaviors. Such seriousness, an inability to laugh at oneself, may be unhealthy. There is wisdom in the old saying: "Laugh and the world laughs with you, cry and you cry alone."

Social Relations. One of the best predictors of how long someone lives is the number of friends they have—or think they have. This isolation from others can harm health. You may not die of loneliness, as some songs suggest, but nevertheless be harmed physically by lack of contact with others.

Some Forms of Healthy Leisure

Almost all forms of leisure can be healthy in moderation. Some, however, seem to be healthier than others. While such generalizations are risky, I would suggest the following:

Skill—Challenge Forms of Leisure—Leisure activities which present a challenge and require skill to meet that challenge, from oil painting to shooting pool to writing poetry, allow for the disciplined freedom that produces flow, the development of human complexity and intelligence, achievement, and, very often, a more positive self-concept. Leisure activities which can increase the challenge almost infinitely may have the potential to be most satisfying over a lifetime, allowing for a career as a dancer, a gardener, or a saxophonist.

Contact with Nature—Humans have evolved over eons to be a part of the natural world. We see better in sunlight than florescent light. We have almost universal preferences for viewing landscapes that contain trees, cut grass, and water. Snow, rain, and the sky delight us. Being in the natural world, even if it is not perfectly natural, often reduces stress and helps us regain our ability to focus our attention when we return (14).

Socializing—It sometimes seems a secret to those who plan various forms of recreation and leisure activity, that the meaning of the experience is often social. While the activity may be a walk in the mall, preparing a fancy meal, or visiting an art gallery, often the pleasure of the experience is being with others.

Contemplation—Contemplation, the gentle emptying of the mind in order to apprehend the universe, is not only deeply refreshing but extremely healthy. Temporarily giving up the need to control things, the need to be who you are, and let things happen, is an act of faith. In such letting go, the stress of the day leaves—understanding increases.

Physical Activity—Humans were designed to move their body—it is also our heritage. As work, housework, and personal care require less and less physical movement, leisure has become the arena in which people move. For many people, physical activity is associated with mood elevation and endorphin release. Such physical activity, however, must be undertaken not for the sake of health, but in pursuit of leisure—kicking a ball, swimming in a pool, hiking a trail, marching in a band playing the tuba, or weeding the flower garden.

Helping Others—To voluntarily help others is often a mutually beneficial use of leisure in which both the helper and the person helped benefit. There is evidence that those who volunteer live longer than those who don't. This is particularly true among males (15).

The previous list is made based on judgment. Think of all the exceptions. For an exhausted mother of four kids, plopping down to watch a mindless soap opera may be just what the doctor ordered—down time to clear the mind and rest the body. Getting out of the house and going to a movie may be a wonderful experience for an eighty-year-old woman. A night at the roulette table may bring a thrill to a busy executive. For the most part, however, the forms of leisure listed above appear to constitute healthy leisure.

Promoting Healthy Leisure

In Sao Paulo, Brazil one evening, I was on the roof of a tall apartment building where a small garden had been constructed. The colleague with whom I was talking and having a glass of wine was a leading scholar of leisure studies in Brazil and had worked with a national organization which provided various forms of leisure activity for workers and their families. As we looked down at people on the street, traveling home from work, he told me that, with regard to leisure, people should have opportunities to do what they want but, more importantly, what they can learn to want. Most forms of leisure expression which use our physical, spiritual, emotional, social, creative, and other capacities are learned. Healthy leisure involves human growth and the ability to celebrate it.

References

1. Coulson E. Science Daily. http://www.sciencedaily.com/ releases/2008/02/080207091859.htm. Accessed June 21, 2010
2. Pollan M. *In Defense of Food*. Penguin Press, New York, 2008.
3. Godbey G. *Leisure In Your Life: New Perspectives*. Venture Publishing, Inc.: State College, PA, 2007.
4. Pieper J. *Leisure: The Basis of Culture*. Mentor-Omega: New York, 1952.
5. Ornstein R, Ehrlich P. *New World: New Mind: Moving Toward Conscious Evolution*. Doubleday: New York, 1989, p. 5.
6. Ibid.
7. Diamond M. *Enriching Heredity*. Free Press/Simon & Schuster: New York, 1988.
8. Bishop D, Jeanrenaud C. Creative growth through play and its implications for recreation practice. In Goodale T, Witt P (eds), *Recreation and Leisure: Issues in an Era of Change*. State College, PA: Venture Publishing, Inc., 1982, pp. 81–99.
9. Csikszentmihalyi M. *Flow: The Psychology of Optimal Experience*. Harper and Row: New York, 1990.
10. Ornstein & Sobel, Ibid. p. 28.
11. Heylings P (1973, April 14). The no touching epidemic: An English disease. British Medical Journal, pp. 46–7.
12. Ornstein & Sobel, Ibid. p. 37.
13. Ornstein & Sobel, Ibid.
14. Kaplan S, Kaplan R, Ryan R. *With People in Mind: Design and Management of Everyday Nature*. Island Press: Washington, DC, 1998.
15. Rockefeller-Growald E, Luks A. The immunity of Samaritans: Beyond self. *American Health* 1988; March: pp. 51–55.

Chapter 6
Leisure and Physical Health

Michael J. LaMonte
Hsueh-wen Chow

Introduction

The public's interest in physical activity (PA) has increased substantially over the past 50 years or so, to great extent because of its presumed health benefits. Regular PA improves functional and psychological well-being, delays the onset of major chronic diseases, and extends longevity (1, 2). Ironically, recognition of the critical role that PA has in maintaining health and quality of life has occurred amidst an era of mechanization and automation that has substantially influenced the population's pattern of, and motivation for, PA (3). Reduced occupational PA, disappearance of human locomotion as a major form of transportation, aversion to structured exercise, and free time spent pursuing computer usage and television viewing are key factors contributing to the physical inactivity epidemic. Currently, about half of U.S. adults do not achieve PA levels recommended for health and nearly 1 in 4 lead sedentary lifestyles (2). A major focus of public health efforts to increase population PA levels has been to expand the traditional exercise paradigm from one that focused almost exclusively on structured exercise aimed at enhancing physical fitness to one that includes a broader view of physical activities that promote both health and fitness benefits (1, 2). Greater emphasis has been placed on the health-enhancing effects of physical activities performed during leisure time. Leisure scientists have long seen opportunity to enhance population PA levels through application of leisure concepts to the built environment and to public health and individual decision making regarding PA (4). Only recently has systematic evaluation been used to elucidate the intersection of leisure and public health (4).

In this chapter we briefly summarize the physical health (heretofore *health*) benefits of leisure PA from an epidemiological perspective. Our review is delimited to studies on aerobic PA. Discussion of the health benefits of resistance activities can be found elsewhere (1, 2, 5). We shift then to discussion on physical health from a leisure perspective. We conclude with a summary of key points and recommendations for future research and translational applications.

Leisure and Physical Health:
An Epidemiological View

Epidemiologic study on the health benefits of PA was pioneered in the second half of the 20th century by Professors Jeremy Morris, Henry Taylor, and Ralph Paffenbarger, Jr., each of whom reported that the frequency of developing coronary heart disease (CHD) was about 50% lower in men who had physically active jobs compared with men who had predominantly sedentary jobs (1). As manual labor gave way to a more technological workplace and because occupational PA provides only a limited view of overall activity habits, subsequent epidemiologic studies were expanded to include measures of leisure-time PA. Definitions of leisure-time PA have ranged from simply nonoccupational PA to combinations of specific activity domains including house and family care, recreation, sports, transportation/ commuting, walking, and stair climbing. Table 6.1 provides a broad over-view of results from studies relating leisure-time PA with various health outcomes. These findings will focus the discussion in the next several sections of this chapter. Citations for the original publications pertaining to the following findings are found in references 1, 2, and 5 of this chapter.

Table 6.1 Overview of Results from Studies Relating Leisure-Time Physical Activity with Various Health Outcomes

Health Outcome	Number of Studies†	Strength of Evidence‡
Total mortality	***	↓↓↓
Coronary heart disease	***	↓↓↓
Stroke	**	↓↓
Peripheral artery disease	*	↓
Heart failure	*	↓
Hypertension	***	↓↓
Type 2 diabetes mellitus	***	↓↓↓
Metabolic syndrome	**	↓↓↓
Cancer		
Breast	***	↓↓↓
Colon	***	↓↓↓
Endometrial	**	↓↓
Ovarian	**	↓↓
Lung	**	↓↓
Prostate	***	↓
Rectal	**	↓
Gastrointestinal	*	---
Pancreatic	*	---
Bladder	*	---
Hematopoietic	*	---
Excessive weight gain	**	↓↓
Osteoarthritis	*	↓
Functional Impairment	**	↓↓↓
Falls and osteoporosis fracture	*	↓

Adapted from Blair SN. 1993 C. H. McCloy Research Lecture: Physical activity, physical fitness, and health. Res Q Exerc Sport 1993;64:365-376. Findings shown here are based largely on studies summarized in references 1 and 2 of this chapter.

† Approximate number of published studies:
    * Small number of studies, <10;
    ** Moderate number of studies, 10 to 20;
    *** Large number of studies, >20.

‡ Strength of evidence for inverse association between physical activity and the health outcome:
    --- Insufficient evidence or no association;
    ↓ Some evidence;
    ↓↓ Good (mostly consistent) evidence from reasonably well designed studies that control for potential confounders and for which there exists some evidence of biological plausibility;
    ↓↓↓ Excellent (very consistent) evidence from well designed studies that control for potential confounders and for which there exists strong evidence of biological plausibility.

Mortality

Total mortality is perhaps the single best measure of the force that a given risk factor or disease exerts on population health. In a landmark report by Professor Paffenbarger (1) on 16,936 male Harvard alumni, men who expended ≥2000 kcal/wk in leisure-time PA had significantly delayed mortality compared with men who expended <2000 kcal/wk. The benefit of PA on longevity persisted even after statistically accounting for differences in other characteristics such as age, weight status, and blood pressure. Numerous ensuing studies further provided strong evidence of an inverse association between leisure PA and mortality from all causes, cardiovascular diseases, and all cancers combined (1, 2). These associations generally are seen in women and men and in older and younger individuals, and remain significant after accounting for other factors that predispose to early mortality. Findings also tend to exhibit a dose-response gradient which implies that higher amounts of PA result in even greater benefit. The consistency of a beneficial effect of PA on mortality across different study samples, the independence of this benefit from other factors that contribute to population mortality differences, and evidence for a dose-response relationship together suggests that a cause and effect relationship exists between PA and mortality. That is, low levels of PA are one of the causes underlying premature mortality. Confidence in the findings on mortality risk from studies that used questionnaire-based assessments of leisure PA is enhanced by parallel findings from studies that used more objective measures of recent PA habits, such as cardiorespiratory fitness and doubly labelled water (1, 2).

Mortality Benefit in Individuals with Existing Disease

Higher PA levels delay mortality even in individuals with increased health risks due to the presence of existing disease. Mortality is significantly lower among physically active adults compared with inactive adults who are afflicted with diabetes mellitus, hypertension, metabolic syndrome, cardiovascular disease, breast and colorectal cancers, depression, overweight or obesity, and functional impairment (2, 5). For example, Holmes et al. (5) reported that among breast cancer survivors, higher levels of PA were related with significantly delayed total mortality, breast cancer mortality, and breast cancer recurrence. Church et al. (5) reported that in men with particularly high cardiovascular risk due to the presence of coexisting obesity and diabetes mellitus, cardiovascular mortality was significantly lower in men with moderate/high cardiorespiratory fitness compared with peers who had low fitness.

Nonfatal Cardiovascular Events

Cardiovascular disease continues to be the leading cause of premature death and disability among U.S. adults. To fully evaluate the role of PA in the prevention of cardiovascular disease, it is imperative to quantify associations with nonfatal as well as fatal events. Lovasi et al. (2) reported both strenuous and nonstrenuous leisure-time PA was significantly associated with a lower likelihood of having had a nonfatal myocardial infarction. Sui et al. (5) reported study findings in adults with 2 or more existing cardiovascular risk factors and thus whom would be considered at high-risk for developing some form of cardiovascular disease. The occurrence of nonfatal cardiovascular disease (e.g., heart attack, stroke) in women and men with higher cardiorespiratory fitness was about half that experienced by those who had low fitness.

Type 2 Diabetes Mellitus

One of the most consistently reported benefits of regular PA is protection against developing diabetes mellitus. The association transcends sex and age groups and generally remains significant after accounting for differences in other factors that predispose to diabetes including elevated fasting glucose, high body fat, dietary intake, and family history of diabetes (1, 2). For example, Hsia et al. (5) reported on diabetes occurrence in 86,708 post-menopausal women in the Women's Health Initiative. After statistically accounting for differences in age, race, body size, and dietary intake, women with higher PA levels experienced significantly less diabetes development than their physically inactive peers. When analyses were restricted to only walking PA, the same finding was observed. A study by Hu et al. (2) showed that higher PA levels protected against developing diabetes in Finnish adults who were at high risk for diabetes because of the presence of impaired glucose metabolism ("pre-diabetes") and obesity.

Hypertension

The benefit of PA on hypertension is reasonably well established, though reported data are less consistent than for CHD and diabetes. Parker et al. (2) showed that each standard deviation increment in the average amount of PA reported across 6 assessments was associated with a 15% lower occurrence of hypertension. Barlow et al. (5) reported that among women at high risk for hypertension because of elevated resting blood pressure ("pre-hypertension"), those with moderate and higher cardiorespiratory fitness had about a 30% lower occurrence of hypertension compared with women who had low fitness.

Cancer

Numerous studies have examined the influence of PA on a variety of site-specific cancers (1, 2). Findings are strongest for colorectal and breast cancer. The occurrence of each cancer is 20% to 40% lower among individuals who engage in 180 minutes/wk or more of moderate to vigorous intensity PA compared with their sedentary peers (2). Associations between PA and other types of cancer are more variable, though sufficiently consistent evidence exists in support of protective benefits for endometrial, ovarian, and lung cancers (2).

Functional Impairment

Growth of the 65 years of age and older segment of the population together with recent projections for increased average life expectancy heighten interests in the role of PA in maintaining functional well-being and independence. Studies consistently show that functional impairment is delayed among physically active compared with inactive adults (2). For example, Visser et al. (2) showed that the occurrence of mobility limitations was two-fold higher in older adults who were physically inactive compared with active peers. Findings were similar when analyses were restricted to only weekly leisure walking habits—significantly lower occurrence of mobility limitations in those who reported walking frequently compared with those who reported no walking. Vailyeva et al. (2) showed that nursing home admission was 40% higher in physically inactive compared with active adults ages 45–64 years.

Weight Gain and Weight Maintenance

The interrelationships among PA, nutrient intake, body weight, and fatness are complex (2, 5). Sedentary habits could precede or result from obesity. Aerobic PA alone produces only modest weight loss (e.g., 1–2 kg) compared to that seen with combined PA and diet intervention, but increases in PA with or without overall weight loss have resulted in reductions in abdominal adiposity (2, 5). Prospective studies show that maintaining moderate and higher PA levels during early adulthood attenuates weight gain and the transition from normal weight to overweight or obesity (2, 5). Sternfeld et al. (2) reported that increases in PA during a 3-year interval was associated with a lower likelihood of experiencing a substantial gain in body weight and waist girth in women ages 42–52 at baseline. Similarly, Dipietro et al. (2) showed that in middle-aged adults an increase in cardiorespiratory fitness was associated with a significantly lower occurrence of weight gain during a 5-year interval. The above findings on attenuation of adult weight gain are gleaned from PA levels that are approximately equivalent to those recommended for broad health benefits (e.g., ≈150 min/wk in activities of moderate or higher intensity) (1, 2). However, higher PA levels appear necessary to avert weight regain in formerly overweight or obese adults (2). For example, Schoeller et al. (2) reported that ≈400 min/wk of moderate intensity PA may be required to curtail weight gain in younger women who previously had achieved a targeted weight loss using conventional methods.

Changes in PA and Subsequent Health Risks

The vast majority of epidemiologic studies, including those reviewed above, have related a single assessment of PA with the occurrence of health outcomes. A stronger approach to establish a cause and effect relationship is to examine the association between changes in PA and the subsequent development of disease. Paffenbarger et al. (5) reported that initially sedentary men who took up PA of moderate or higher intensity had a 21% lower occurrence of hypertension and a 23% lower likelihood of death than their peers who were habitually sedentary. Steffen et al. (2) reported that the recurrence of heart attack was 78% lower in initially sedentary patients who took up PA following their initial heart attack compared to those who remained sedentary. Gregg et al. (2) showed that even older adults (≥65 years) who changed from sedentary to active lifestyles had significantly delayed mortality from all causes, cardiovascular disease, and total cancers compared to their continually sedentary peers.

Leisure and Physical Health:
A Leisure and Recreation Perspective

The benefits of leisure and recreation activities can be attributed to many different dimensions such as psychological, physiological, social, cultural, economics and environmental. Leisure researchers and professionals in the field of parks and recreation have traditionally studied the relationships between leisure and recreation and quality of life, psychological health benefits, such as stress reduction, buffer effects during life crisis, improving self-confidence, feelings of self-competence, and positive changes in mood or emotions. However, the focus has recently shifted to the include relationships between leisure and physical health.

Leisure and Health Benefits

Unlike epidemiological studies, which provide a plethora of research demonstrating the relationship of physical activity to specific health effects, only a few empirical studies indicate the benefits of leisure/recreation participation in relation to explicit physical health outcomes. Among the few studies, current research is focused in three major areas: 1) older adults, 2) pet ownership, and 3) natural vs. built environments.

Three studies have showed an association between use of parks and recreation facilities and better health. In 2004, Orsega-Smith et al. (6) studied park use in Cleveland Metroparks among adults ages 50 years and older. They showed that older adults who visited parks frequently and stayed longer in parks had lower systolic blood pressure, experienced a positive interaction between stress effects and body mass index, and perceived themselves to have good physical health as compared with those who did not visit parks. Chow (7) compared leisure-time PA, occupational PA, and household PA as predictors of older adults' health. She showed that leisure-time PA was a strong predictor of health perception, physical functioning, mental health, vitality, pain, social functioning, and obesity. Sin-Ae and colleagues (8) demonstrated that older adults who engaged in gardening activities were active at levels sufficient to meet the national PA guidelines for health-enhancing PA. They also showed that older gardeners developed better hand strength and pinch force, which are important functions for older populations, compared to nongardening peers.

Pet companionship also offers important psychological benefits, such as stress reduction, and it provides a great way to maintain active lifestyles in their leisure time. Between 2003–2005, 2.5% of the U.S. population reported dog walking as a leisure-time PA (9). In California pet owners were 60% more likely to walk than non-pet owners. They also walked 19 min/day more than those who did not own a pet (10). In Perth, Australia, new dog owners increased their recreational walking from 12 to 48 min/day after getting a dog (11). Dog ownership can translate into improved health. In 1992, Anderson and colleagues showed that dog owners walked more than non-owners and that male pet owners had significantly lower systolic blood pressures, plasma triglycerides, and plasma cholesterol levels following a walking program (12). Likewise, Australian children who lived in families with a dog were 50% less likely to be overweight or obese than children who lived in families without a dog (13).

Leisure researchers also study the interaction between the environment, leisure participation, and health. The natural environment nurtures the living things within it and also provides a magnificent effect for people to recover from daily stress and fatigue. Sugiyama and colleagues (14) studied associations between neighborhood greenness and physical and mental health in Australian adults. Those who rated their physical and mental health highest were nearly two times more likely to perceive their neighborhoods as "green" compared to those with lower physical and mental health scores. It is hypothesized that the presence of natural characteristics in recreation settings allows people to have faster rate of restoration of physical energy, mental relaxation, and to have a better immune system than non-natural, built environments. Evidence supporting this hypothesis is provided by Ulrich and colleagues (15) who studied the effect of people's exposure to different natural and urban scenes after the subjects had just watched a stressful movie. Physiological measures of heart rate, skin conductance, muscle tension, and pulse transit time showed that recovery rates following the stressful experience was faster for those exposed to natural scenes rather than urban scenes.

Parks and Recreation as Sites for Health Enhancing PA

There is a growing recognition for the value of parks and leisure activities in promoting health-enhancing PA. Local parks and recreation facilities/programs attract many people performing PA, as they are inexpensive or free, and easily accessible. Parks or recreation facilities that provide opportunities for enjoyable physically active leisure activities have the greatest potential to inspire people to maintain active lifestyles. Walking for pleasure is a popular health enhancing activity performed in parks and recreation facilities for adults as is playing sports and games in parks for younger children. Park settings that offer gardening opportunities is a way for older adults to engage in physical leisure activities (6).

Summary

The physical health benefits of regular PA are extensive and appear to be obtainable by most adults through moderate amounts and intensity of leisure activities. With the adoption of U.S. PA guidelines (2), government health agencies are committed to improving the public's understanding of the health-related needs to lead physically active lifestyles. Augmenting traditional approaches aimed at increasing population PA with concepts derived from leisure studies (4) and recreation and parks management may provide important additional transdisciplinary mechanisms to improve both public health literacy and population behavior change pertaining to PA.

References

1. U.S. Department of Health and Human Services. *Physical activity and health: a report of the Surgeon General*. Atlanta, GA: U.S. Department of Health and Human Services, Centers for Disease Control and Prevention, National Center for Chronic Disease Prevention and Health Promotion, 1996.
2. Physical Activity Guidelines Advisory committee. Physical activity guidelines advisory committee report, 2008. Washington, DC: U.S. Department of Health and Human Services, 2008.
3. Haskell WL. Physical activity, sport, and health: Toward the next century. *Res Q Exerc Sport* 1996;**67** (3 Supl):37–47.
4. Godbey GC, Caldwell LL, Floyd M, Payne LL. Contributions of leisure studies and recreation and park management research to the active living agenda. *Am J Prev Med* 2005;**28** (2S2):150–158.
5. LaMonte MJ, Kozlowski KK, Cerny FJ. Health benefits of exercise and physical fitness. In RJ Maughan (ed), *Olympic Textbook of Science in Sport*. Hoboken, NJ: Wiley-Blackwell Publishing, 2009, pp. 401–416.
6. Orsega-Smith E, Mowen A, Payne L, Godbey G. The interaction of stress and park use on psycho-physiological health in older adults. *Journal Leisure Res* 2004;**26/2**:232–256.
7. Chow HW. *Physically active leisure among older adults: Measurement, comparison and impact*. VDM Verlag Dr. Mueller e.K.: Germany, 2007.
8. Sin-Ae P, Candice S, Mark H. Can older gardeners meet the physical activity recommendation through gardening? *HortTechnology* 2008;**18**:639–643.
9. Tudor-Locke C, Ham SA. Walking behaviors reported in the American Time Use Survey, 2003–2005. *J Phys Act Health* 2008;**5/5**:633–647.
10. Yabroff KR, Troiano RP, Berrigan D. Walking the dog: is pet ownership associated with physical activity in California? *J Phys Act Health* 2008;**5/2**:216–228.
11. Cutt HE, Knuiman MW, Giles-corti B. Does getting a dog increase recreational walking? *Int J Behav Nutr Phys Act* 2008;**27/5**:17.
12. Anderson WP, Reid CM, Jennings GL. Pet ownership and risk factors for cardiovascular disease. *Med J Aust* 1992;**157**:298–301
13. Timperio A, Salmon J, Chu B, Andrianopoulos N. Is dog ownership or dog walking associated with weight status in children and their parents? *Health Promot J Austr* 2008;**19/1**:60–63.
14. Sugiyama T, Leslie E, Giles-corti B, Owen N. Associations of neighbourhood greenness with physical and mental health: do walking, social coherence and local social interaction explain the relationships? *J Epidemiol Community Health* 2008;**62/5**:e9.

15. Ulrich RS, Simons RF, Losito BD, Fiorito E, Miles MA, Zelson M. Stress recovery during exposure to natural and urban environments. *J Environ Psychol* 1991;**11**:231–248.

Chapter 7
Leisure Pathways to Emotional Health—Public Health Perspectives

Elaine C. Wiersma
Diana C. Parry

"There is more hunger for love and appreciation in this world than for bread"
—Mother Theresa

The impetus for this textbook in general and this chapter in particular is the social trend toward more holistic conceptualizations of health. Indeed, there has been a distinct social shift away from traditional conceptualizations of health that are based upon a medical model and narrowly focused on physical well-being. Alternative discourses around health are beginning to take shape and take into account various *dimensions* of health. These multidimensional views of health resist the separation of mind, body, and spirit, but do not necessarily preclude a biomedical perspective. A multidimensional conceptualization redefines health as the ability to live life fully—with vitality and meaning (1). Health is determined by decisions about living one's life, including one's leisure decisions. Insel and Roth (2) identify social, spiritual, intellectual, environmental, physical, and emotional dimensions of health. All of the dimensions of health interact and impact upon overall wellness, but are separated so that they might be explored in-depth and to understand how each contributes to health. In this chapter, we explore the emotional dimension of health from a public health perspective[1]. In so doing, we establish important links between one's emotional health and one's leisure lifestyle. We begin with an overview of emotional health before turning to the links with leisure.

Conceptualizing Emotional Health

Unlike other dimensions of health whose focus is self explanatory, emotional health requires some clarification and definition. Part of the confusion around this dimension is that other terms, such as "mental health" or "psychosocial health" are often utilized interchangeably with emotional health. There is good cause for using these terms interchangeably as there is overlap between all three. Each set of terms, however, means something slightly different and therefore warrants clarification. Emotional health refers "...to the feeling component and to the ability to express emotions when appropriate and to control inappropriate expressions of emotion.

Feelings of self-esteem, self-confidence, self-efficacy, trust, love, and many other emotional reactions and responses are all part of emotional health." (3) Mental health, as defined by the World Health Organization (4) is based upon subjective well-being and includes aspects of self-efficacy, autonomy, competence, and self-actualization of one's intellectual and emotional potential. Mental health, therefore, is a much broader term than emotional health, but there are clear links between positive emotional states and mental health (5). Psychosocial health is the broadest term of the three as it encompasses intellectual, social, spiritual, and emotional dimensions of health (6). This chapter focuses on emotional health, which means it explores emotional states and feelings of self-esteem, self-confidence, and self-efficacy.

Leisure Pathways to Emotional Health

Leisure choices, activities, and experiences have been found to play an important role in the development and maintenance of emotional health. For the purpose of this chapter, we have conceptualized leisure as pursuits that are intrinsically motivated with a level of perceived freedom[2] (7). Leisure is perhaps best conceptualized as a "pathway" to emotional health. We have identified three leisure pathways to emotional health: interventions, the outcomes of leisure, and leisure landscapes. We begin with leisure as an intervention before discussing the other two pathways.

Leisure as Intervention

In this pathway, leisure is specifically and intentionally used as a way to enhance emotional health. Much of the support for this pathway is found in therapeutic recreation wherein professionals deliberately use recreation and leisure pursuits as a way for clients to achieve goals that will enhance their health. From this perspective, leisure is a way to intervene and address negative emotional health states or mental illness. In short, leisure is seen as a coping mechanism whereby experiences, choices, or activities can decrease stress and promote positive emotional states. For example, Shannon and Shaw (8) studied the ways that a breast cancer diagnosis altered a woman's experience of leisure and choice of leisure pursuit. Shannon and Shaw found the women in their study described leisure as an important coping strategy for negative emotions that resulted from a breast cancer diagnosis and/or treatment including anxiety, stress, fear, anger, guilt, and feelings of uselessness. Participants in the study described consciously choosing specific leisure activities as a means of increasing their emotional health. That is, the women became aware of the therapeutic benefits of leisure pursuits such as gardening, journal writing, and walking, which they described as vital to maintaining good emotional health throughout their experience with breast cancer.

Fullagar (9) studied the link between leisure and women dealing with depression. The study was based upon interviews with 48 women recovering from depression, which was defined as "…an intensification of emotional distress that arises from the performance of particular gender norms that regulate women's everyday lives" (10). Participants linked their depression to a "crisis of feminine identity" meaning they struggled with their sense of self worth and personal identity when measuring themselves against ideals of "a good woman." One participant echoed the sentiments of many when she explained how the "superwoman syndrome" (trying to do it all and do it well) made her feel:

> We are more self-critical, guilt ridden, and supposed to be of use to others and always cheerful. I think it's the things put on women to be inauthentic, always to be cheerful, never angry, never frown, always make everyone else feel good…to be in balance to be real and successful, and it builds up and builds up and the sadness and bits of anger you don't show, which boys can show, build up into this huge depression which bowls you over (11).

This quote hints at how leisure was a source of depression for the women in this study as they often felt responsible for caring for others and not entitled to their own leisure. Interestingly, leisure was also a part of the women's recovery from depression. That is, leisure played a pivotal role in the women's recovery as their choices, pursuits, and experiences enabled them to let go of negative self-evaluations and enhance their emotional health. Through their recovery, the women recognized leisure as a source of "emotion play" wherein they experienced lightness, letting go, relax-ation, and enjoyment. Recovery from depression was linked to deliberately seeking a voice and a space for themselves through their leisure pursuits. Leisure, therefore, provided opportunities for women to feel their way through recovery from depression by rethinking the impossible demands placed upon them and identify ways to care about and for themselves, not just others. The findings of these two studies demonstrate how emotional health can be transformed through leisure.

The Outcomes of Leisure

A second way that leisure can be linked to emotional health is through the outcomes of participation. In this pathway, leisure is not specifically utilized by professionals or individuals as a means to an end, that is, as a means to enhance emotional health. Instead, emotional health is an outcome or byproduct of leisure participation. A key factor in this pathway is that leisure is not deliberately used to enhance emotional health, but rather enhanced emotional health is an unexpected outcome of leisure participation. For example, people may initiate physical activity to lose weight or improve their cardiovascular health, but subsequently feel happier, have more energy, feel more relaxed, and decrease their stress. Pondé and Santana's (12) research with women from a low socioeconomic bracket in Brazil serves an example of this pathway. Five-hundred-fifty-two women were surveyed about their occupational history, work conditions, leisure pursuits, and given a psychiatric questionnaire. The women who said they participated in leisure pursuits (about half the group) reported lower levels of anxiety and symptoms of depression. Although the women did not indicate they engaged in leisure to address emotional health, they nonetheless reaped the benefit of enhanced emotional well-being.

Yarnal and colleagues' (13) research with the Red Hat Society (RHS), which is an international organization of women over the age of 50, serves as another example of the outcomes pathway. In this study, participants listed "fun" as the central reason for joining the RHS, yet reported experiencing relief from the ups and downs of daily life as a result of their membership. In addition, the RHS participants also said they felt the support of other members sustained them through difficult times such as periods of stress, depression, emotional problems, personal illness, and the loss of loved ones. Thus, the women joined the RHS for fun, yet found themselves benefiting emotionally through stress relief and social support during difficult life events.

Leisure Landscapes

The final leisure pathway to emotional health is through leisure landscapes, or the spaces and places of leisure. That is, the context, or the places and spaces in which one participates in leisure pursuits can contribute to emotional health. For example, James (14) explored the bedroom as a leisure site for adolescent girls. The girls reported using their bedrooms to hide from the outside world. In their bedrooms, the girls did not worry about being watched by others or being ridiculed. Instead, the girls described their bedrooms as places of physical security and safety wherein their identity was not questioned. In their bedrooms the girls were able to hide from the stress of the outside world, and used words such "haven," "refuge," and "my little world" to describe their bedrooms (15). The bedroom was also the one place that the girls felt they had control over what happened and who had access to their space. Perhaps most importantly, the girls felt they could restrict access to their bedrooms. As a result of the safe and secure environment that the bedroom provided, the girls were able to "be themselves" and express emotions that they would not do so otherwise.

Glover and Parry (16) also studied a leisure context that played a vital role in the emotional health of people living with cancer. Gilda's Club is a place where men, women, teens, and children living with cancer—along with family and friends—can join with others to build physical, social, and emotional support as a supplement to medical care. Gilda's Club welcomes long-term cancer survivors and those who have lost someone to cancer. Free of charge, Gilda's Club offers support and networking groups, lectures, workshops and physical and social activities in a home-like setting. Twenty-six members of Gilda's Club were interviewed about the meaning of Gilda's Club and its contribution to their health. Participants described Gilda's Club as a "home away from home" where they could "get away" or escape from cancer. In this sense, Gilda's Club offered a warm, light-hearted, inviting atmosphere for participants where they felt "free to be themselves, not their disease." From this perspective, Gilda's Club represented a fun place where participants could escape the stress of home, the outside world, and cancer. Yet Gilda's Club also enabled members to meet and discuss cancer with others also living with the disease—to make "cancer friends." Information sharing, emotional support, and "just lending a helping hand" were all mentioned as outcomes of the new friendships they developed. Shared identities brought this group together, but the leisure-like venue, space, or "moments" kept them attending Gilda's. By extending the concept of place into health research, we come to appreciate that the therapeutic merits of a setting are not only associated with its physical characteristics, but also with its meaning to recipients or those in search of "therapy."

Conclusion and Future Directions

This chapter explored three pathways through which leisure contributes to emotional health. Most of the research in this chapter focused on individual level health outcomes and relationships, but broader, structural issues that occur at the *population* level are of utmost concern. Health Canada's (17) framework for health promotion, which was the foundation for the Ottawa Charter for Health Promotion, argued the most important health issues facing Canadians are to reduce inequalities, increase preventive health, and enhance coping strategies. The first challenge, reducing inequities, highlights the strong link between health and income (18).

The second challenge, increasing the prevention effort, recognizes current population health issues are chronic, not acute. The third challenge reflects the need to enhance people's abilities to cope with chronic conditions such as mental health problems. Addressing these challenges in Canadian society requires a multilevel approach. Indeed, the Institute of Medicine (19) has defined the "mission of public health as fulfilling society's interest in assuring conditions in which people can be healthy" (20). Enhancing emotional health through leisure, therefore, also requires a new approach. While there is a recognition of using leisure to enhance emotional health on an individual level (i.e., stress reduction and coping mechanisms) and there is a recognition of the social nature of emotional health (21), more work on the creation of conditions and surroundings related to leisure that are conducive to health warrant emphasis. Thus, a greater sociostructural approach to leisure is vital to the future of emotional health within leisure studies. More specifically, leisure scholars and practitioners need to extend our emphasis beyond the individual psychosocial domain to a more socio-structural domain to fully understand the relationships between leisure and emotional health. The following questions need to be addressed:

- *How do people from various marginalized groups experience leisure and why?* By marginalized groups we mean people that have been relegated to lower social standing. Some examples of marginalized groups include Aboriginal peoples, people of colour, people with low socioeconomic status, frail seniors, and women. Focusing on marginalized groups enables a greater understanding of sociostructural factors that can impact people's leisure.
- *How do social determinants of health constrain or enable people's leisure opportunities?* "Social determinants of health are the economic and social conditions that influence the health of individuals, communities, and jurisdictions as a whole." (22) Eleven social determinants have been identified, including Aboriginal status, early life, education, employment and working conditions, food security, health care services, housing, income and its distribution, social safety net, social exclusion, and unemployment and employment security (23). Research is needed to understand how social determinants of health constrain or enable people's leisure choices, experiences, and decisions.
- *How can leisure be used to fully explore its emancipatory potential?* Because leisure has been conceptualized as a context in which people make free choices and are less constrained than in other aspects of their lives (such as work), it is often said to have emancipatory potential (24). In other words, leisure is a context in

which people are able to break free from social constraints and feel empowered as individuals and/or groups. For example, previous research has demonstrated that women are able to resist traditional gender roles in their leisure and feel empowered. Future research needs to identify the many ways that leisure serves in an emancipatory manner to help people transcend social and/or personal barriers that constrain them.

- *How are issues of power, domination, and marginalization perpetuated through leisure?* The flip side of resistance is reproduction. In this sense, while leisure has the potential to be emancipatory, it simultaneously has the power to reproduce or perpetuate social inequalities. Understanding the roles leisure plays in reproducing or perpetuating social inequalities is vitally important to changing these social inequalities.
- *How can leisure scholars and practitioners advance a social justice agenda?* A social justice agenda seeks equality and equity for all. It is an agenda that intentionally creates conditions in which people can fully recognize their potential and participate as contributing members of a group or community. A social justice agenda intentionally recognizes inequalities and inequities among groups and people and seeks to eliminate these inequalities and inequities. This begs the question, what can leisure scholars and practitioners do to advance such an agenda to change social inequities?

These are but a few questions to ask ourselves as we strive to incorporate leisure into a public health approach and a focus on emotional health.

Footnotes

[1] It is important to note that we are writing about public health from a Canadian perspective. The Public Health Agency of Canada (2004) describes public health as "…a range of efforts to keep people healthy and out of hospital" (21st paragraph), and is considered to cover a broad range of activities, such as immunizations, health promotion activities, infection control measures, lab testing and regulation—essentially, the numerous activities that help to keep Canadians healthy. Public health within Canada is interdisciplinary in its approach to enhancing and maintaining healthy populations, and leisure plays an important role in maintaining healthy populations.

[2] Please see chapter 2 for a more thorough review of the meaning of "leisure."

References

1. Insel PM, Roth WT. *Core Concepts in Health*. McGraw Hill: New York, 2006.
2. Ibid.
3. Donatelle RJ, Davis LG, Munroe AJ, Munroe A. *Health: The basics (Canadian edition)*. Prentice Hall Allyn and Bacon Canada: Scarborough, Canada, 1998, p. 4.
4. World Health Organization. *The world health report 2001—Mental health: New understanding, new hope*. http://www.who.int/whr/2001/chapter1/en/print.html 2001. Accessed December 16, 2008.
5. Passmore A, French D. A model of leisure and mental health in Australian adolescents. *Behav Change* 2000;**17/3**:208–220.
6. Donatelle RJ, Davis LG, Munroe AJ, Munroe A. *Health: The basics (Canadian edition)*. Prentice Hall Allyn and Bacon Canada: Scarborough, Canada, 1998.
7. Mannell RC, Kleiber DA. *A social psychology of leisure*. Venture Publishing, Inc.: State College, PA, 1997.
8. Shannon CS, Shaw SM. "If the dishes don't get done today, they'll get done tomorrow": A breast cancer experience as a catalyst for changes to women's leisure. *J Leisure Res* 2005;**37/2**:195–215.
9. Fullagar S. Leisure practices as counter-depressants: Emotion-work and emotion-play within women's recovery from depression. *Leisure Sci* 2008;**30**:30–52.
10. Ibid, p. 37
11. Ibid, p. 41
12. Pondé MP, Santana VS. Participation in leisure activities: Is it a protective factor for women's mental health? *J Leisure Res* 2000;**32/4**:457–472.

13. Yarnal CM, Chick G, Kerstetter DL. "I did not have time to play growing up...so this is my play time. It's the best thing I have ever done for myself": What is play to older women? *Leisure Sci* 2008;**30**:235–252.
14. James K. "I just gotta have my own space!": The bedroom as a leisure site for adolescent girls. *J Leisure Res* 2001;**33/1**:71–90.
15. Ibid, p. 78.
16. Glover TD, Parry DC. A third place in the everyday lives of people living with cancer: Functions of Gilda's Club of greater Toronto. *Health Place* 2009;**15/1**:97–106.
17. Health Canada. *Achieving health for all: A framework for health promotion.* http://www.hc-sc.gc.ca/hcs-sss/pubs/system-regime/1986-frame-plan-promotion/index-eng.php. Accessed November 11, 2008.
18. Raphael D (ed). *Social determinants of health: Canadian perspectives.* Canadian Scholars' Press: Toronto, ON, 2004.
19. Institute of Medicine. *The Future of Public Health.* National Academy Press: Washington, DC, 1988.
20. Ibid, p. 7.
21. Glover TD, Parry DC. A third place in the everyday lives of people living with cancer: Functions of Gilda's Club of greater Toronto. *Health Place*, 2009, **15**(1), 97–106.
22. Raphael D. Introduction to the social determinants of health. In Raphael D. (Ed.) *Social Determinants of Health: Canadian Perspectives.* Toronto, ON: Canadian Scholars Press, 2004, p. 1.
23. Ibid.
24. Hemingway JL. Emancipating leisure: The recovery of freedom in leisure. *J Leisure Res* 1996;**28/1**:27–43.

Chapter 8
Leisure and Spiritual Health

Paul Heintzman
Kimberly M. Coleman

The central question that we will consider in this chapter is whether leisure enhances or hinders spiritual health. To answer our question, this chapter will summarize empirical research that exists on leisure style and spiritual health, leisure factors that enhance or hinder spiritual health, and leisure-spiritual coping. The chapter will conclude with implications for both leisure and recreation services and public health practitioners. First though, we need to define spiritual health.

Spiritual Health

Based on an extensive review of literature, Hawks (1) identified a number of internal characteristics of people who are spiritually healthy, and also ways in which spiritually healthy individuals express themselves in their external interactions. Internal characteristics include: 1) a sense of life purpose and ultimate meaning; 2) oneness with nature and beauty, and a sense of connectedness with others; 3) deep concern for and commitment to something greater than self; 4) a sense of wholeness in life; 5) strong spiritual beliefs, principles, ethics, and values; and 6) love, joy, peace, hope, and fulfilment. External characteristics include interactions with other people characterized by trust, honesty, integrity, altruism, compassion, and service; and regular communion or a personal relationship with a higher power or larger reality that transcends observable physical reality. Based upon these characteristics, Hawks (1) developed the following comprehensive definition of spiritual health:

> A high level of faith, hope, and commitment in relation to a well-defined worldview or belief system that provides a sense of meaning and purpose to existence in general, and that offers an ethical path to personal fulfilment which includes connectedness with self, others, and a higher power or larger reality. (p. 6)

From a health promotion perspective, as used in public health practice and research, wellness includes six dimensions of health where spiritual health and the other dimensions exist along a continuum as determined by a variety of health indicators (2). Heintzman (3) explained that spiritual health has been conceptualized as both an elementalistic dimension of holistic health where it needs to be kept in balance with other dimensions of health (physical, mental, emotional, social), as well as an integrative dimension of health where optimal wellness is dependent on spiritual health occurring within each of the other health dimensions.

Leisure Style and Spiritual Health

Ragheb (4, 5) was one of the first leisure scholars to examine whether people's leisure was related to spiritual wellness. In a study of 361 adults, Ragheb (4) correlated the respondents' leisure participation, motivation, attitude and satisfaction, and constraint scores with their physical, intellectual, emotional, social, and spiritual well-being scores. Significant relationships were found between all of these leisure dimensions, except constraints on participation and spiritual well-being. Subsequently, Ragheb (5) surveyed 219 people to investigate whether leisure participation and level of leisure satisfaction were related to five components of perceived wellness. Frequency of leisure participation and level of leisure satisfaction were found to be positively associated with overall perceived wellness, including spiritual wellness. Reading had the highest correlations with perceived wellness and all of its components. Higher levels of satisfaction with the relaxational and aesthetic-environmental components of leisure were dominant in their contributions to perceived wellness, including spiritual wellness. A limitation of these studies was the measurement of spiritual well-being with just one or two questionnaire items, making it difficult to capture the complexity of spiritual well-being and assess the reliability of its measurement. Using six items to measure perceived spiritual wellness, Tsai and Wu (6) discovered correlations between leisure participation and perceived spiritual wellness among adults aged 55 to 75 in Taiwan.

Heintzman and Mannell (7) conducted a more specific study of leisure and spiritual well-being with 268 participants that investigated the relationships between four dimensions of leisure style (activity, motivation, setting, time) and spiritual well-being measured by two spiritual well-being scales. Significant positive relationships were found between spiritual well-being and overall *leisure activity participation*, as well as engagement in the leisure activity categories of personal development activities (e.g., reading for personal growth, holistic exercises such as tai chi and yoga), cultural activities, outdoor activities and hobbies. There were negative correlations between spiritual well-being and the specific activities of watching TV and videos, social dancing, and adventure trekking, but a positive relationship between solitary leisure activity participation and spiritual well-being.

Higher levels of *leisure motivation* were associated with spiritual well-being, as was leisure engaged in for intellectual (e.g., discover new things, be creative) and stimulus-avoidance (e.g., slow down, rest) motives. In regards to *leisure settings*, those who pursued leisure in quiet urban recreation areas and their own homes reported higher levels of spiritual health. There were no significant relationships between *time use* and spiritual well-being. Participation in personal development activities was the best predictor of spiritual well-being, followed by stimulus-avoidance motivations and frequency of engaging in leisure in one's own home. In regards to overall *leisure style*, a "mass media" leisure style (low leisure activity participation except for high participation in mass media activities and low leisure motivation) was very clearly associated with low spiritual well-being. Both those who might be characterized as having what might be termed a "personal development" leisure style (high level of participation in personal development activities) and those with an "overall active" leisure style (high level of participation in all leisure activity categories) were associated with higher levels of spiritual well-being.

Despite some differences, the findings of Ragheb (4, 5) and Heintzman and Mannell (7) in most cases are similar. Both found that reading/personal development activities, outdoor activities, and cultural activities were all significantly correlated with spiritual well-being. The correlation of spiritual well-being with the stimulus-avoidance motivation for leisure (i.e., the need to seek solitude, rest, and to unwind) in Heintzman and Mannell's (7) study is consistent with Ragheb's (5) finding of the important contribution of the relaxational component of leisure satisfaction to spiritual wellness.

Leisure Factors that Enhance or Hinder Spiritual Health

Are there leisure factors that enhance or hinder spiritual health? Heintzman (8) suggested that leisure and well-being theories (e.g., personal growth theories) may help explain the variety of ways that leisure influences spiritual health. Subsequently, Heintzman (9) conducted a qualitative study with eight people who had an expressed interest in spirituality to uncover the processes that link leisure with spiritual well-being. Several themes were identified through the data analysis. There was almost unanimous agreement by the participants that they considered the activities or experiences which enhanced their spiritual well-being to be leisure. Also, there was also almost unanimous agreement that their leisure activities and experiences were associated with their spiritual well-being. Participants saw leisure as important for spiritual well-being because leisure provided the *time and space* for spiritual well-being.

The data suggested that the relationship between leisure and spiritual well-being involved more than just time and space. A number of participants saw the relationship between leisure and spiritual well-being to be somewhat complex; there was not a direct relationship between them. Some activities could be leisure, yet not conducive to spiritual well-being. Some things that were conducive to spiritual well-being were not necessarily leisure. A key factor was the *attitude of openness* that participants brought to their activities: an attitude characterized by "being awake to seeing," "discernment," "intentionality," "focus," a "different way of seeing things," "gratefulness," "gratitude," "seeing with new eyes," and "keeping awareness open."

There was overwhelming consensus amongst participants that *busyness* in life detracted from spiritual well-being. The theme that occurred, in contrast to busyness (although there was less consensus on this theme), was that of *balance*. A balance in life of work, personal/family responsibilities and leisure was conducive to spiritual well-being and well-being in general.

Participants were asked whether they associated any settings of their leisure activities with spiritual well-being or growth. All respondents mentioned the outdoors or *nature*. The reasons why natural settings were more conducive to spiritual well-being varied: nature elicited a sense of wonder and awe; nature helped some participants connect with their God; and the richness and diversity of nature was life-giving and rejuvenating. Participants talked about nature in general—whether that be in the backyard gardening or in remote wilderness areas. A few participants did talk specifically about remote wilderness areas and suggested that leisure in these areas had some particular characteristics which were conducive to spiritual well-being. In general, leisure in these settings allowed participants to leave the demands and expectations of the everyday world behind, that is *be away* to a different environment, and thus to focus on the basics of life which were related to one's spiritual well-being. A minor theme, related to leisure settings, was that participants found settings which had a sense of *personal or human history* conducive to spiritual well-being.

Another recurring theme that appeared was that settings characterized by *silence, solitude and quiet* were conducive to spiritual well-being. While participants viewed silence, solitude, and quiet as being important for their spiritual well-being, this theme is not to be confused with isolation as many participants mentioned the importance of *being with people*. While settings of silence, solitude, and quiet were conducive to spiritual well-being, *noisy settings and activities* were most frequently mentioned as that which detracted from spiritual well-being.

While there were some commonalities amongst participants as to which leisure activities improved spiritual well-being, there was quite a diversity of activities mentioned. It seems that the particular activities in and of themselves were not as significant in terms of spiritual well-being as the function of the activities in the participants' lives. Leisure activities that helped people get in touch with themselves, that helped them be *"true to self,"* and that helped them express their personality, were the ones that promoted spiritual well-being. There was not clear consensus on which activities inhibited or detracted from spiritual well-being. Generally, *unauthentic* activities, or activities that introduced an element of incongruence or tension for the participant, were seen as detracting from spiritual well-being.

While the results of Heintzman's (9) qualitative study cannot be generalized, further research by Heintzman (10, 11) on men's wilderness experience and spiritual well-being has discovered some of the same themes such as being in nature and opportunities to be alone as well as with other people. In addition, qualitative and quantitative studies on leisure and spirituality/spiritual experience, although not specifically focused on spiritual health, have supported these findings (e.g., Schmidt & Little) (12). Heintzman (13) recently summarized these other studies and the factors that have been found to contribute to spiritual benefits (see Figure 8.1). Heintzman (14) has also documented numerous studies which illustrate that many of these same factors link nature-based recreation with spirituality.

	Leisure Dimensions	
	1. Motivation	Attitude of Openness
Busyness	*2. Time*	Leisure: Time & Space Balance
Artificial	*3a. Physical Setting*	Natural Being Away Personal/Human History
Noisy Activities & Settings	*3b. Social Setting*	Quiet, Solitude, Silence Being with People
Incongruent	*4. Activity*	"True to Self"
DECREASED	*Spiritual Health*	INCREASED

Figure 8.1 Leisure Dimensions and Factors Associated with Spiritual Health (Adapted from Heintzman (7, 13))

Interestingly, most of these other studies have focused on the leisure factors that enhance rather than detract from spirituality, and thus further support has not been documented for the themes of busyness, artificial settings, noisy settings and activities, and unauthentic activities which Heintzman (9) found to detract from spiritual health.

Although the above leisure factors were discussed separately, often spiritual health is enhanced by combinations of these factors. For example, Heintzman (10) found that the variety of social settings on a wilderness trip, such as being with one or two other people and being in a group, along with times to be alone in solitude, was viewed as important to spiritual well-being. While it may seem contradictory that both group experiences and times of solitude are associated with spirituality, it seems that both these types of experiences may be important factors in spiritual health.

Simplified Model of Leisure and Spiritual Well-Being

Building upon Heintzman's (9) qualitative study and also Heintzman's (15) model of leisure and spiritual well-being, which proposed a variety of processes that linked leisure style (activity, motivation, setting, and time) with spiritual well-being, Heintzman and Mannell (16) developed a scale to examine these processes. This 36-item Leisure Spiritual Processes scale reflected 12 possible functions or ways in which leisure might influence spiritual well-being (grounding, working through, time and space, sacraliza- tion, attitude, busyness, being away, nature, sense of place, fascination, compatibility, repression). Factor analysis, item analysis, and reliability testing suggested that about two-thirds of the items defined three major factors: the process of *sacralization* (leisure sensitizes one to the spiritual); *place* processes (e.g., nature, sense of place, being away); and *repression* processes (leisure represses a person's spiritual tendency). Both the qualita- tive interview data and the quantitative data suggested that leisure could be used to both enhance and detract from spiritual well-being (see Figure 8.2). The Leisure Spiritual Processes scale was subsequently used by Doi (17), who found that the use of leisure spiritual processes to achieve spiritual well-being was significantly higher for college students that preferred out- door activities in comparison to students who preferred playing sports.

Leisure-Spiritual Coping

Leisure may also enhance spiritual health and ultimately holistic health through leisure-spiritual coping. Research by Heintzman and Mannell (18) suggested that the spiritual function of sacralization may serve as a coping strategy to ameliorate the negative influence of time pressure on spiritual

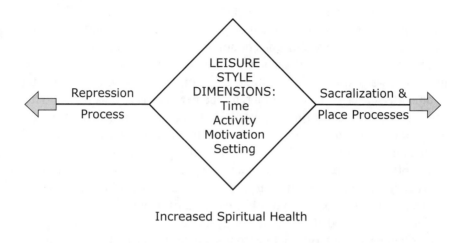

Figure 8.2 Model of Leisure and Spiritual Well-being

well-being. Higher levels of time pressure were associated with greater use of leisure for the spiritual functions of sacralization that in turn were associated with higher levels of spiritual well-being. In their studies on marginal groups, Iwasaki, MacKay, McTavish, Ristock, and Bartlett (19) examined the role of leisure as a contributor to coping with stress. They found that using active leisure to cope with stress included both spiritual activities and spiritual meanings. That is, spiritual activities (e.g., spiritual reading) were pursued in leisure to cope with stress, and active leisure also provided the opportunity to obtain spiritual meaning. For example, Aboriginals were found to engage in culturally relevant leisure to facilitate empowerment and spiritual coping when confronted by racism and other forms of stress.

Building upon the research of Heintzman and Mannell (18) and Iwasaki et al. (19), Heintzman (20) synthesized theory and research findings on leisure, stress, and spiritual coping into a conceptual model of leisure-spiritual coping. Spiritual coping refers to the ways that people receive help from spiritual resources (e.g., higher power, spiritual practices, faith community) during periods of life stress, whereas leisure-spiritual coping is spiritual coping that takes place within the context of an individual's leisure. The model takes into account spiritual appraisals, person factors (e.g., religious orientation), leisure-spiritual coping behaviors (e.g., sacralization, grounding, contemplative leisure, time and space, being away), leisure-spiritual coping resources (e.g., connections with nature, others, and transcendent other), and meaning making (e.g., life purpose, transformation, growth).

Leisure-spiritual coping is illustrated by the following case study based on the personal experience of the first author of this chapter (20). Fifteen years ago the first author was diagnosed with cancer, which was followed by surgery to remove a cancerous tumor and subsequently chemotherapy to eradicate the cancer that had spread elsewhere. At the time of diagnosis the author was experiencing multiple forms of stress. As executive director of an understaffed camp and conference center he was overworked and had no regular or consistent time off work. He had been experiencing overwork and burnout for a number of years. For the previous few years he had also been taking care of the affairs of an uncle with Alzheimer's disease who lived 160 kilometers away. Although this uncle died five months prior to the cancer diagnosis, the author had also become executor of the uncle's estate. He also had some responsibilities towards his father who was in his late 80s and lived alone in the family home 100 kilometers away. The author had been primary caregiver to his mother who had died six years earlier of cancer.

In regards to the *attribution* stage of *spiritual appraisal,* the author was initially quite shocked and perplexed as he had been very healthy all his life. *Primary spiritual appraisal* involved the realization that death might be a reality in the near future. In terms of *secondary spiritual appraisal,* the author realized changes in his lifestyle were necessary and that spiritual resources were essential to bring about these changes. In terms of *person factors*, the author's beliefs (*religious denomination* and *doctrine*) were rooted in Christian spiritual faith, which provided the contextual framework for understanding and responding to this stress. The author had been brought up in a Christian home and during his teenage years this faith became personalized into a faith of his own (*intrinsic religious orientation).*

From the time of diagnosis until the completion of chemotherapy, the author drastically cut his hours of work to a normal work week. This allowed more time than usual for spiritual practices of a traditional nature, but also *leisure-spiritual coping behaviors*. Although lacking the usual amount of energy, the author jogged two miles each day during chemotherapy, which acted as a *grounding* activity. Reduced working time led to opportunities to focus on spirituality through *sacralization* and *contemplation*. A specific example was participation in a weekend retreat on life changes at a spiritual retreat centre just prior to his surgery, which also offered the opportunity to *be away* to another setting. In terms of *leisure as space and time,* although the author strongly believed in the concept of *Sabbath* and had practiced it for most of his life, he had been unable to do so for the previous four years due to the nature of his work. During the period of cancer he returned to Sabbath keeping by abstaining from work on Sundays. Also during this time, the author experienced *being away* from his usual work setting of the remote camp and conference centre to his father's home in an urban area. While this change of environment related mainly to work and living situation, it also affected the context for leisure activities and provided for leisure opportunities that were not available in the remote setting.

In regards to *leisure-spiritual coping resources,* although opportunities for *connection with nature* were less accessible in the urban environment, the author, when possible, continued to participate in nature-based recreation which usually provided opportunities for meditation, prayer, and reflection that strengthened the *connection with the Transcendent other* (God) and thereby played a significant role in coping with this situation. *Connections with others,* which were now easier to pursue due to the urban setting, were also enhanced during this time. Spiritual friendships that were a source of inspiration and comfort were renewed and strengthened. Some of the opportunities for connections with others were within the leisure context. A particular highlight was a weekly Saturday morning hockey game with others from the same faith community.

All of the components of the leisure-spiritual model had an influence upon *meaning making,* which led to a reappraisal of beliefs and attitudes, and the author's ability to cope. In fact the author sometimes refers to this period in his life as a holiday, as his stress level was drastically reduced from previous levels. During this time the author re-evaluated the priorities in his life—developing connections with God and with others took on greater value while continuing in the job he held was questioned. He decided to resign from the position he held with no definite next step. Meaning making also fed back to spiritual appraisal: while others suggested possible reasons for the cancer, he accepted it as a mystery, and to some extent a gift, for which only God knew the reason why it occurred.

Implications for Recreation and Leisure Services

Empirical knowledge on leisure and spiritual health is valuable to recreation practitioners. Findings from Heintzman and Mannell's (7) study on leisure style and spiritual well-being regarding the importance of personal development activities, stimulus-avoidance motivations and leisure in one's own home to spiritual well-being, suggests that the role of recreation professionals may be more of leisure referral and education than leisure activity provision or management. The findings on leisure-spiritual coping with stress are of relevance to therapeutic recreation practitioners (20). Individuals who are experiencing stressful life events or who are marginalized may be provided with appropriate leisure pursuits that assist spiritual coping and the opportunity to obtain spiritual meanings. Creating leisure oases or leisure spaces, that is, opportunities of "being away" from the stresses of daily life to a different environment can be encouraged and provided to enhance spiritual rejuvenation for those experiencing stress.

Heintzman (13) has identified eight implications that arise from the empirical data presented on the leisure factors that help or hinder spiritual health. The first three are of primary relevance to leisure education and leisure counseling. First, educate individuals to create time and space for leisure activities with a spiritual dimension. Second, encourage balance in life especially for those who experience time pressure and work-related stress. Third, encourage people to explore leisure settings of personal or human history. The next five implications are of relevance not only to leisure educators and leisure counselors but also to all leisure practitioners as they develop and implement recreation activities and programs. Fourth, facilitate an attitude of receptivity, gratitude and celebration within partici-pants. Fifth, develop and implement programs where people explore nature and develop a relationship with it. Sixth, provide opportunities to be away to a different environment. Seventh, incorporate times for solitude and personal reflection within activities and programs. Eighth, include activities that help people explore and develop their connections with each other.

While these implications arise from research it is important to remem-ber the complexity of the relation between leisure and spiritual health. Models of leisure and spiritual well-being (e.g., Heintzman 15) suggest that this complexity includes several dimensions of leisure style (e.g., activity, motivation, setting, time), several components of spiritual health (e.g., transcendental dimension, connections with self, others and God/higher power; meaning in life), and numerous linkages (e.g., leisure spiritual pro-cesses). Differences exist between individuals (7, 9) and between different population groups (e.g., women, men, youth). Recreation practitioners need to be sensitive to the specific needs and characteristics of the individuals or groups that they are working with. Practitioners also need to recognize that in addition to leisure enhancing spiritual health, leisure may also repress spiritual health (16, 18).

Implications for Public Health

Although public health literature does not usually mention leisure or spiritual health, these concepts are implied in the public health goal of increasing the quality of life. The notion of quality of life may be defined as "a general sense of happiness and satisfaction with our lives and envi-ronment" (21) (p. 10). While general quality of life includes characteristics such as one's culture, values, recreation, and health, "health related quality of life reflects a personal sense of physical and mental health and the ability to react to factors in the physical and social environments" (21) (p. 10). Primary health quality of life indicators include global assessments of one's perception of health, healthy days, and years of healthy life. Both leisure and spiritual health could be considered when assessing these quality of life indicators.

Research in public health has often conceptualized leisure in terms of physical activity and other individual health behaviors. For example, Simoes and colleagues (22) conducted a study on leisure-time physical activity and dietary fat intake. Likewise, in a special issue of *Leisure Sciences* on leisure research, active lifestyles, and public health, the focus was on physical leisure activities (23). Unfortunately, recent public health research is still focused on leisure as a physical activity and no public health research exists on the specific relationship between leisure and spiritual health, a relationship which can significantly impact public health. Continuing to focus on only the physical dimension in public health alienates the whole person and this focus is not very applicable to the public health goal of quality of life. Therefore, an expansion is needed in research and practice. Public health practitioners and researchers need to learn from, and collaborate with, leisure studies researchers. The evidence-based work on leisure and spirituality by leisure researchers is critical to meeting public health goals. From this multidisciplinary research, public health training programs and interventions can be targeted and/or tailored to positively impact community behaviors, develop, and advocate for supportive health policies, and improve the environmental health on which we are all dependent.

References

1. Hawks S. Spiritual health: Definition and theory. *Wellness Perspectives* 1994;**10**:3–13.
2. Donatelle RJ. *Access to Health* (10th ed). Pearson/Benjamin Cummings: San Francisco, 2008.
3. Heintzman P. Putting some spirit into recreation services for people with disabilities. *J Leisurability* 1997;**24/2**:22–30.
4. Ragheb MG. Step-wise regression analysis of leisure domains and the reported contribution of leisure activities to individuals' well-being: An exploratory study. *Society and Leisure* 1989;**12/2**:399–412.
5. Ragheb MG. Leisure and perceived wellness: A field investigation. *Leisure Sci* 1993;**15**:13–24.
6. Tsai CY, Wu MT. Relationship between leisure participation and perceived wellness among older persons in Taiwan. *J ICHPER* 2005;**41/3**:44–50.
7. Heintzman P, Mannell R. Leisure Style and Spiritual Well-being. In Stewart W, Samdahl D (eds), *Abstracts from the 1999 Symposium on Leisure Research*. Ashburn, VA: National Recreation and Park Association, 1999, p. 68.
8. Heintzman P. Spiritual well-being: Theoretical links with leisure. *J Leisurability* 1999;**26/2**:21–32.
9. Heintzman P. Leisure and spiritual well-being relationships: A qualitative study. *Society and Leisure* 2000;**23/1**:41–69.
10. Heintzman P. Men's Wilderness Experience and Spirituality: A Qualitative Study. In Burns R, Robinson, K (comps), *Proceedings of the 2006 Northeastern Recreation Research Symposium*. Newton Square, PA: U.S. Department of Agriculture, Forest Services, Northern Research Station Gen Tech Rep NRS-P-14, 2007, pp. 216–225.
11. Heintzman P. Men's Wilderness Experience and Spirituality: Further Explorations. In LeBlanc, C, Vogt C (eds), *Proceedings of the 2007 Northeastern Recreation Research Symposium*. Newton Square, PA: U.S. Department of Agriculture, Forest Services, Northern Research Station Gen Tech Rep NRS-P-23, 2008, pp. 55–59.
12. Schmidt C, Little DE. Qualitative insights into leisure as a spiritual experience. *J Leisure Res* 2007;**39/2**:222–247.
13. Heintzman P. The spiritual benefits of leisure. *Leisure/Loisir* 2009;**33/1**:419–445.
14. Heintzman P. Nature-based recreation and spirituality: A complex relationship. *Leisure Sci* 2010;**32**:72–89.
15. Heintzman P. A conceptual model of leisure and spiritual well-being. *J Park Recreation Adm* 2002;**20/4**:147–169.

16. Heintzman P, Mannell R. Leisure-spiritual Health Processes: A Social Scientific Study. In Havitz M, Floyd M (eds), *Abstracts from the 2001 Symposium on Leisure Research*. Ashburn, VA: National Recreation and Park Association, 2001, p. 85.

17. Doi AS. Spiritual Well-being and Leisure Preferences in College Students. Unpublished Master's Thesis. Springfield College, Springfield, MA, 2004.

18. Heintzman P, Mannell R. Spiritual functions of leisure and spiritual well-being: Coping with time pressure. *Leisure Sci* 2003;**25**:207–230.

19. Iwasaki Y, MacKay KJ, Mactavish JB, Ristock J, Bartlett J. Voices from the margins: Stress, active living, and leisure as a contributor to coping with stress. *Leisure Sci* 2006;**28**:163–180.

20. Heintzman P. Leisure-spiritual coping: A model for therapeutic recreation and leisure services. *Therapeutic Recreation J* 2008;**42/1**:56–73.

21. U.S. Department of Health and Human Services (DHHS). *Healthy People 2010: Understanding and Improving Health (2nd ed)*. U.S. Government Printing Office: Washington, DC, 2000.

22. Simoes EJ, Byers T, Coates RJ, Serdula MK, Mokdad AH, Heath GW. The association between leisure-time physical activity and dietary fat in American adults. *Am J Public Health* 1995;**85/2**: 240–244.

23. Sallis JF, Linton LS. Leisure research, active lifestyles, and public health. *Leisure Sci* 2005;**27**:353–354.

Chapter 9
Physical Activity and Cognitive Health

Darla Castelli

A child jumps off a piece of equipment with another chasing close behind as a game of tag breaks out on a playground. A neighborhood basketball court is teeming with activity as the regular Saturday afternoon adult "pick up" game begins. Hand-in-hand, older adults walk through a garden admiring the flora. Regular engagement in physical activity during leisure time is associated with reduced risk for cardiovascular disease (1). Further, play and participation in sport activities has been linked to enhanced quality of life, prevention of disease, and better mental health (2). Physical activity can help people feel good about themselves by reducing anxiety and can increase cognitive abilities in youth and older adults. Specifically, regular engagement in physical activity (3) and the attribute of cardiorespiratory fitness (4) are associated with cognitive performance. The purpose of this chapter is to provide an overview of how physical activity and fitness may contribute to cognitive health across the lifespan.

Normal cognitive health, efficiently thinking, knowing, and remembering is something that we take for granted until we begin to experience regular decrements due to aging, such as forgetting where we put our keys and not remembering where we parked the car. Cognitive health has an excess of definitions which evolve by age. For instance, cognitive health in a school-aged child is characterized by grades in school, standardized test scores, and attention allocated to a specific task; whereas, a cognitively healthy adult is identified by carrying out activities of daily living or maintaining a sense of purpose. The study of cognitive health can focus on attention, memory, fluid intelligence, or executive control which is defined as a subset of cognitive processes related to sequencing, discrimination, and inhibition (5). Although the primary measure of executive control focuses on reaction time and accuracy, it has also been associated with performance in mathematics and reading (6). Measurement of these qualities can be completed through paper and pencil testing, reaction time and accuracy of computer tasks, electroencephalogram (EEG) as an assessment of the neural-electricity in the brain, and functional magnetic resonance imaging (fMRI) or neural imagery of brain function. This broad spectrum of evaluative tools permits interpretation ranging from medical diagnosis to translation for educational use.

Brain development begins prior to birth and because of environmental interactions, continues rapidly during the first few years of life. The size of the brain changes little between the ages of 7 and 14 except the *pruning* of irrelevant or disconnected associations, with a cognitive peak being attained between the ages of 21 and 27 (7). Young adults display quicker response or reaction times and exhibit greater accuracy than older adults, thus suggesting that executive control declines with age (8). This is often experienced as memory loss (9), reduced attention (10), or dementia (11). A longitudinal study of 294 Catholic nuns discovered that, "individuals having both low education and small head circumference were four times as likely to be demented as the rest of the sample" (12). These findings thereby underscore the importance of schooling and promotion of physical development. Human cognitive decline begins long before it is consciously acknowledged; however, steps (both figuratively and literally) can be taken to maintain good cognitive health throughout life.

Physical activity is any behavior that requires energy expenditure beyond rest. Activities such as walking, sport participation, gardening, and play all have different physiological demands, but are still considered types of physical activity. Fitness is a set of physiological attributes influenced by genetics, maturation, and behavior. Given the reciprocal, indirect relationship between physical activity and fitness, each variable must be examined as an independent mediator of cognitive performance. Additionally, mediating or indirectly contributing variables such as sleep and diet can circuitously influence cognitive performance.

Regular physical activity and fitness are associated with enhanced cognitive function across the lifespan (11, 13). The strength of the relationship is influenced by age, methodology, and the outcome variable. Specifically, it is widely accepted that brain function in older adults can be enhanced by regular physical activity engagement, and that this behavior can offer some protection from disease (14). Among children, the association is less clear, as study of this phenomenon has been inhibited by the developmental stages of growth and maturation as well as measurement issues. The lack of clinical trials has slowed the delivery of sweeping policy recommendations because of the void of causal evidence. Nonetheless, positive associations and trends among recent research findings suggest that this line of research warrants further investigation.

Historical Perspective

Research in this area has been problematic. Early research on physical activity and cognitive performance was predominately cross-sectional and lacked the necessary rigor to be generalized to large portions of the population (15). Some studies conducted in the laboratory setting, although scientifically sound, lacked contextual relevance preventing its application to authentic settings such as schools, parks and recreation programs, or national physical activity guidelines for daily living (16). Further, initial data revealed inconsistencies due to employment of varied methodologies (17).

However, evidence has been mounting of the connection between physical activity and cognitive function. Waneen Spirduso, a researcher at The University of Texas at Austin, is credited with establishing a line of research that examined the effects of physical activity on cognitive performance when she conducted a study that compared reaction time of active and inactive adults. Her seminal study demonstrated an association between the regularity of sport participation and reaction time (speed of response using microswitches) among 60 adult males who were categorized into: (a) older active sportsmen, (b) older nonactive males, (c) young active sportsmen, and (d) young nonactive males. Findings suggested that daily vigorous exercise might mediate the decline of reaction time with age (18). Since Dr. Spirduso's initial research nonhuman animal research by Isaacs, Anderson, Alcanatara, Black, and Greenough (19) has provided evidence of changes in brain structure and function, resulting from the observation of exercising rats. Beyond the obvious advantages of animal research (i.e., randomization, minimal subject burden, euthanizing to examine brain structure and weight), rodents are unique in that they engage in physical activity without prompting; when the animal is free of disease, the mere presence of a running wheel results in exercise participation. Issacs et al. compared the effects of different types of training protocols (optional exercise on a wheel, paced exercise on a wheel, exercise on a wheel and through a maze). Aerobically fit, motor-competent rats exhibited the greatest changes in brain structure, thus suggesting that enhanced cognitive function was related to the type and intensity of the physical activity. Further, it was also demonstrated that physically active mice grew new nerve cells, neurogenesis, through increased levels of brain-derived neurotrophic factor (BDNF) (20). By stimulating the hippocampus, BDNF helps neurons to survive, thrive, and regenerate, therefore playing an important role in cognitive health. Rats who completed several days of voluntary wheel running exhibited higher BDNF (21), which was sustained for several weeks post exercise (22). In general, aerobic training among nonhuman animals, results in enhanced brain function, elasticity, and the growth of new brain cells (19, 20). If these findings hold true in humans, it could have a profound impact on learning, but to date these data have only been replicated for specific tasks and age groups.

Adults and Cognitive Health

During the third decade of life, post-cognitive peak, brain tissue deterio-
rates and therefore motor and cognitive performance begins to decline
(23). However, a meta-analysis by Etnier and colleagues found that highly
fit adults outperformed less fit individuals on a variety of cognitive tasks
(24). The effect size (ES = .25) of the analyses of 134 studies suggested
that fitness mediated cognitive performance in adults. Despite these findings, the effects of fitness remained unclear because preexisting cognitive
abilities may have led the adults to concentrate on fitness for the health
benefits. Given that there was an identified association, but the directional
and causal effects were ambiguous, researchers initiated studies centered
on brain function and structure.

In a study of 55 older, high-functioning adults, it was discovered that
loss of brain tissue was moderated by cardiovascular fitness, across multiple regions of the brain (23). Although this particular study only examined
cognitive performance in healthy older adults, a subsequent meta-analysis
confirmed these findings across adults in varied stages of health. By 2003,
an additional 18 intervention studies had been enacted beyond those previously identified (24), thus providing enough studies to conduct analyzes on
physical activity type (aerobic activity alone or a combination of aerobic
and nonaerobic activity), duration, and cardiovascular improvement.
Regardless of training type, participant characteristics, or cognitive task,
physically active participants outperformed control participants with the
greatest difference being among tasks requiring executive control (3).

To examine the impact of specific exercise protocols, Chang and Etnier
(25) had 68 adults complete low, medium, and high intensity bouts of resistance training and measured its effects on performance during the Stroop
test. The Stroop test measures the time and accuracy of an individual
identifying the color of ink used when reading a list of color words (e.g.,
red written in blue ink, blue written in green ink) where the brain must
override the semantic meaning with the word and identify the ink color
instead. From this study on the acute effects of resistance training it was
shown, that a 30-minute bout at 70% of maximum effort had the greatest
impact on executive control and information processing of color words
(i.e., blue, green, red; 25). Given the present body of literature, it would
appear that individuals can influence their own cognitive health through
their mental, social, and physical behaviors (26) and it is safe to recommend that engagement in moderate physical activity be utilized as method
of maintenance of cognitive health and prevention of cognitive decline
(27). Seemingly, both aerobic and nonaerobic physical activities are viable
vehicles to enhance cognitive health and prevent deterioration. In general,

it has been concluded that submaximal exercise lasting up to 60 minutes may enhance cognitive performance in adults (4). Ongoing research is attempting to refine the dose-response relationship to make specific recommendations beyond adherence to the national physical activity guidelines (28) related to physical activity and health. These guidelines recommend 10,000 steps per day or 150 minutes (75 minutes of a moderate to vigorous intensity) of physical activity per week. Aerobic activities suggested in the national physical activity guidelines (28) include anything from brisk walking at least 3 miles per hour to aerobic dancing. Supplementary to the aerobic activity should be some form of strength-enhancing activities such as weight training for specific muscle groups.

Youth and Cognitive Performance

Development of the brain is heterochronous (milestones occur at different times for each child) and is influenced by intelligence quotient (IQ) and the environment. After age two, the critical events related to childhood brain development are: (a) myelination (formation of the sheath around nerve endings) and (b) pruning, also known as the competitive elimination of unused synapses. Because a child's brain is still developing, cognitive performance such as reaction time and accuracy are inferior to healthy adults in their twenties. Hillman and colleagues used a Flanker's computer stimulus-response task and EEG measures to compare brain function of high and low fit young adults and children (13). As predicted, adults had better reaction time (response to the computer stimuli) than children did; however, surprisingly, high fit children were just as accurate as the high fit adults were. While there were similarities in cognitive performance in high fit individuals across the lifespan, this effect seems to be moderated by age. In children, there are more general effects on cognitive performance, such as greater neural activation and enhanced attention (13).

In children, researchers and educators alike focus on brain growth and refinement of efficiency, most often displayed through attention, memory, report card grades, and performance on standardized tests as a measure of academic achievement. Increased identification of children with Attention Deficit-Hyperactivity Disorder (ADHD) and an inability for children to focus or sit still in the classroom has produced a growing desire to quantify and qualify the relationship between physical activity, fitness, and academic achievement and thus previous adult research paradigms are currently being applied to youth.

To examine the result of 44 studies pertaining to physical activity and cognition in children, a meta-analysis was employed to identify the effects of individual characteristics, type of physical activity, and cognitive assessment method, on cognitive performance. The meta-analysis concluded that there was a significant positive relationship between physical activity and cognition in children (effect size = .32), particularly among elementary and middle school students (29). The researchers cautioned that their review did not document causality between the variables in this population and that statistically robust intervention studies would be necessary to establish the extent to which a causal relation between physical activity and enhanced cognition exists in children.

Studies of cognition in children have two foci: (a) prolonged influence of physical fitness on academic achievement and (b) impact of a single bout of physical activity on cognitive performance. Work by Castelli and colleagues suggest that aerobically fit children are more likely to perform better on standardized testing in mathematics and reading (30). Although cross-sectional, this study was the first to account for the potential effects of socioeconomic status on cognitive performance. Since this study, these findings have been replicated in California (31), New York (32), Massachusetts (33), and Texas (34); however, these studies have received varying levels of peer-review.

Physical Education, Afterschool Fitness Interventions and Cognitive Performance

Because physical education provides physical activity opportunities for children during a school a day, researchers have examined the impact of these behaviors on performance on academic achievement. In Trois-Rivieres, Canada researchers enacted a longitudinal study of elementary school children that increased the amount of time spent during physical education to examine its impact on academic performance (35). The 60-minute program enhanced aerobic capacity over that of the 40-minute control group (35); however, there were no significant differences in cognitive performance in mathematics or reading. On the other hand, increasing physical activity time during the school day did not show any inhibition of academic achievement.

In the School Health, Academic Performance, and Exercise (SHAPE) study directed in South Australia, the impact of enhanced physical education among 546 fifth-graders was examined. Randomly assigned treatment group participants who experienced a 14-week physical activity program conducted during physical education exhibited no significant difference on the ACER and GAP academic tests from that of the control group, despite the fact that experimental students spent almost five times longer engaging in regular physical education and conversely considerably less time in academics (15).

A United States physical activity intervention entitled *Sports, Play and*

Active Recreation for Kids (SPARK), compared the effectiveness of varied teacher/leader training on program effectiveness and academic achievement among 759 fifth- and sixth-grade students. In general, the specialists delivered more effective programs when compared to control participants (36). Comparison of the treatment and control groups MAT test scores was inconclusive, suggesting that increased time spent in physical education class was not detrimental to academic achievement.

Enrollment in physical education was further examined by Coe (37) and her colleagues to determine its relation to standardized testing and school report card grades in 214 sixth-graders in Michigan. This study expanded previous work by measuring the amount and intensity of physical activity engagement during physical education classes, concluding that only associations were found among who were vigorously physically active and grades (37). An epidemiological evaluation of 5316 children enrolled in kindergarten through fifth grade during the 1998–1999 school year, suggested that physical education enrollment may have cognitive benefits for girls, but not boys (38). These findings warrant further investigation.

In addition to school day physical education, afterschool programs can also contribute to school-agers' physical activity (39). A randomized controlled design assigned 94 sedentary children to no exercise, 20-, or 40-minutes of physical activity in an afterschool intervention. Those who were in the nonexercise or 20-minute groups, participated in seated activities during their program. After 15 weeks, the active groups significantly outperformed the inactive group in fitness tests and the 40-minute group had higher scores on the cognitive task than the inactive group (40), thus moving the body of literature a step closer to the identification of a cause and effect relationship.

Acute Physical Activity and Cognitive Performance in Children

A promising area of research has begun to examine the impact of single bouts of physical activity on cognitive performance in children. As of the writing of this chapter, there are only three known studies that appear in peer-reviewed journals examining the immediate effects of a single bout of physical activity on executive function (normal weight children (41); overweight children (42) and attention (43)).

In Hillman's study using a within subject design, 20 participants completed a maximal fitness test and a battery of IQ and other psychosocial assessments. The participants were then randomly assigned to a counterbalance of exercise and cognitive testing (i.e., modified Flanker's task and Wide Range Achievement Test). The exercise task consisted of a 20-minute walk on a treadmill at 60% of the maximal heart rate. Those who completed the cognitive tasks after the acute bout of physical activity significantly outperformed their seated counterparts in executive function task accuracy and academic testing in reading, but not mathematics or spelling (41). Contrary to these findings, 69 overweight and inactive children failed to demonstrate cognitive performance difference after a 23-minute treadmill walking session involving visual task switching (a numbers memorization task followed by questions (46)). However, it should be noted that although both of the cognitive tasks elicited characteristics of executive function, they were different and therefore direct comparison should be reserved until additional studies have been published.

Finally, in Germany, 115 healthy adolescents ages 13–16 were randomized into a 10-minute physical education lesson, bilateral coordinated exercise, or regular school lesson groups and completed baseline testing on attention and concentration with post exercise or rest testing. The bilateral coordinated exercise group exhibited significantly higher attention and concentration, even though both active lessons resulted in the same mean heart rate (47).

Although only one acute physical activity study was conducted in an authentic setting, these findings suggest that acute (single sessions of physical activity, such as recess, an activity break during academic time or a physical education class) is positively associated with enhanced cognitive performance in healthy children. The effects of these physical activity sessions appear to be different for those who are overweight.

Given the paucity of research examining the dose-response relationship between physical activity and cognition, recommendations for children are nonspecific and reflect current best practice. That is, children need to have opportunities to play, before, during, and after school. Active transportation, or walking/biking to school, is a way for children to begin their day with a moderate amount of physical activity. Releasing students from academic study for periodic physical activity breaks and formal instruction on health-related fitness such as that provided during physical education is valuable and does not appear to inhibit academic performance.

In Summary

In summary, physical activity engagement is an effective strategy in attaining, regaining, or maintaining cognitive health from birth to adulthood. Although, the specific cerebral benefits may differ by age, there are no known adverse effects affiliated with the reduction of academics or cognitive time to pursue physical activity opportunities. The provision of physical activity opportunities through formal (i.e., physical education, youth sports, and senior games) and informal structures (i.e., parks, green space, access to physical activity facilities) seem to accentuate our professional responsibility to promote physical activity engagement as an important part of daily life. At present, national guidelines (28) indicate that adults should be engaged in at least 150 minutes of physical activity to reap chronic cognitive benefits; however, brief single bouts of physical activity are also beneficial. For children, a minimum of 60 minutes per day of physical activity is recommended in national guidelines for health. The dose-response relationship of physical activity and fitness is clearly still underdevelopment. Given the unique characteristics of childhood physical activity engagement, brain structure and function, it has been difficult to pinpoint underlying mechanisms facilitating cognitive health. We know that regular physical activity engagement has numerous physical, social, and emotional benefits and is therefore worthy of our investment. Additionally, we know that physical activity participation enhances cognitive health, and even reverses disease in adults and believe this notion to be true in children as well.

References

1. Kaplan GA, Strawbridge WJ, Cohen RD, Hungerfor LR. Natural history of leisure-time physical activity and its correlates: Associations with mortality from all causes and cardiovascular disease over 28 years. *Am J Epi* 1996;**144**:793–797.
2. Strong WB, Malina RM, Blimkie CJ, et al. Evidence based physical activity for school-age youth. *J of Pediatrics* 2005;**146**:732–737.
3. Colcombe S, Kramer AF. Fitness effects on cognitive function of older adults: A meta-analytic study. *Psychol Sci* 2003;**14/2**:125–130.
4. Tomporowski PD. Effects of acute bouts of exercise on cognition. *Acta Physiol* 2003;**112**:297–324.
5. Norman W, Shallice T. Attention to action. In Davidson RJ, Schwartz GE, Shapiro D (eds), *Consciouness and Self Regulation: Advances in Research and Theory (vol. 4)*, New York: Plenum, 1986, p. 1–18.
6. Bayliss C, Jarrold DM, Gunn AD, Braddeley AD. The complexities of complex span: Explaining individual differences in working memory in children and adults. *J Exp Psychol Gen* 2003;**132**:71–92.
7. Giedd JN, Blumenthal J, Jefferies NO, Castellanos F, Zijdenbos A, Paus T, Evans AC, Rapoport JL. Brain development during childhood and adolescence: A longitudinal MRI study. *Nat Neurosci* 1999;**2**:861–863.
8. Kramer AF, Hahn S, Gopher D. Coordinative executive processes during task switching. *Acta Physiol* 1999;**101**:339–378.
9. Federmeier KD, McLennan DB, De Ochoa E, Kutas M. The impact of semantic memory organization and sentence context information on spoken language processing by younger and older adults: An ERP study. *Psychophysiology* 2002;**39**:133–146.
10. Milham MP, Banich MT, Webb A, Barad V, Cohen NJ, Wszalek T, Kramer K. The relative involvement of anterior cingulated and prefrontal cortex attentional control depends on nature of conflict. *Cog Brain Res* 2001;**12**:467–473.
11. Kramer AF, Erickson KI, Colcombe SJ. Exercise, cognition, and the aging brain. *J Appl Physiol* 2006;**101**:1237–1242.
12. Mortimer JA, Snowdon DA, Markesbery WR. Head circumference, education and risk of dementia: Findings from the Nun Study. *J Clin Experi Neuro* 2003;**25/5**: 671–679.
13. Hillman CH, Castelli DM, Buck SM. Aerobic fitness and neurocognitive function in healthy preadolescent children. *Med Sci Sport Exerc* 2005;**37**:1967–1975.
14. Rovio S, Kareholt I, Helkala E-L, Viitanen M, Winblad B, Tuomilehto J, Soininen H, Nissinen A, Kivipelto M. Leisure time physical activity

at midlife and the risk of dementia and Alzheimer's disease. *Lancet* 2005;**4**:705–711.

15. Dwyer RT, Coonan WE, Leitch DR, Hetzel BS, Baghurst PA. An investigation of the effects of daily physical activity on the health of primary school students in South Australia. *In J Epidemiol* 1983;**12**:308–313.

16. Hillman CH, Weiss EP, Hagberg JM, Hatfiled BD. The relationship of age and cardiovascular fitness to cognitive and motor processes. *Psychophysiology* 2002;**39**:303–312.

17. Chodzko-Zajko WJ, Moore KA. Physical fitness and cognitive functioning in aging. *Exerc Spor Sci Rev* 1994;**22**:195–220.

18. Spirduso WW Reaction and movement time as a function of age and activity level. *J Gerontol* 1975;**30**:435–440.

19. Isaacs KR, Anderson BJ, Alcanatara AA, Black JE. Exercise and the brain: Angiogensis in the adult rat cerebellum after vigorous physical activity and motor skill learning. *Int J Cerebral Blood Flow Metabolism* 1992;**12**:110–119.

20. Cotman CW, Berchtold NC. Exercise: A behavioral intervention to enhance brain health and plasticity. *Trends Neurosci* 2002;**25**:295–301.

21. Neeper SA, Goauctemez-Pinilla J, Choi J, Cotman C. Exercise and brain neurotrophins. *Nature* 1995;**373**:109.

22. Neeper SA, Gomez-Pinilla F, Choi J, Cotman CW. Physical activity increases mRNA for brain-derived neurtrophic factor and nerve growth factor in rat brain. *Brain Res* 1996;**726**:49–56.

23. Colcombe SJ, Erickson KI, Raz N, Webb AG, Cohen NJ, McAuley E, Kramer AF. Aerobic Fitness Reduces Brain Tissue Loss in Aging Humans. *J of Gerontol: Bio Med Sci* 200;**58A/2**:176–180.

24. Etnier JL, Salazar W, Landers DM, Petruzzello SJ, Han M, Nowell P. The influence of physical fitness and exercise upon cognitive functioning: A meta-analysis. *J Sport Exerc Psychol* 1997;**19**:249–277.

25. Chang YK, Etnier JL. Exploring the dose-response relationship between resistance exercise intensity and cognitive function. *J Sport Exerc Pscyh* 2009;**31**:640–656.

26. Hertzog C, Kramer AF, Wilson RS, Lindenberger U. Fit Body, Fit Mind. *Sci Am Mind* 2009;**6**:24–31.

27. Erickson K, Kramer AF. Exercise effects on cognitive and neural plasticity in older adults. *Br J Sports Med* 2008;**10**:1–3.

28. U.S. Department of Health and Human Services. 2008 Physical Activity Guidelines for Americans. http://www.health.gov/paguidelines/. Accessed on October 1, 2009.

29. Sibley BA, Etnier JL. The relationship between physical activity and cognition in children: a meta-analysis. *Pediatr Exerc Sci* 2003;**15**:243–256.

30. Castelli DM, Hillman CH, Buck SE, Erwin HE. Physical fitness and academic achievement in 3rd and 5th grade students. *J Sport Exerc Psych* 2007;**29**:239–252.
31. Grissom, JB. Physical fitness and academic achievement. *J Exerc Phs–online* 2005;**8/1**:11–15.
32. Egger JR, Bartley KF, Benson L, Bellino D, Kerker B. Childhood obesity is a serious concern in New York City: High levels of fitness associated with better academic achievement. 2009;**8/1**:1–4.
33. Chomitz VR, Sling MM, McGowan RJ, Mitchell SE, Dawson GF, Hacker KA. Is there a relationship between physical fitness and academic achievement? Positive results from public school children in the Northeastern Unites States. 2009;**79/1**:30–37.
34. The Cooper Institute. Texas education agency releases Fitnessgram results. http://www.cooperinstitute.org/news/eventDetail.cfm?news_id=47. Accessed on October 1, 2009.
35. Lavallee H, Shephard RJ, Jequier JC. A compulsory physical activity program and out-of-school free activities in the Trois-Rivieres longitudinal study. In Lavallee H, Shephard RJ (eds), *Child growth and development*. Trois-rivieres: Editions du Bien Public. 182: pp. 61–71.
36. Sallis J, McKenzie TL, Kolody B, Lewis M, Marshall S, Rosengard P. Effects of health-related physical education on academic achievement: Project SPARK. *Res Quart Exerc Sport* 1999;**70/2**:127–134.
37. Coe DP, Pivarnik JM, Womack CJ, Reeves MJ, Malina RM. Effect of physical education and activity levels of academic achievement in children. *Med Sci Sport Exerc* 2006;**38/8**:1515–1519.
38. Carlson SA, Fulton JE, Lee SM, Maynard M, Brown DR, Kohl HW, Dietz WH. Physical education and academic achievement in elementary school: Data from the early childhood longitudinal study. *Am J Public Heal* 2008;**98/4**:1–7.
39. Beets MW, Beighle A, Erwin HE, Huberty JL. After-school program impact on physical activity and fitness: A meta-analysis. *Am J Prev Med* 2009;**36/6**:527–537.
40. Davis CL, Tomporowski PD, Boyle CA, Waller JL, Miller PH, Naglieri JA, Gregoski M. Effects of aerobic exercise on overweight children's cognitive functioning: A randomized controlled trial. *Res Quar Exerc Sport* 2008;**78/5**:510–519.
41. Hillman CH, Pontifex MB, Raine LB, Castelli DM, Erickson EE, Kramer AF. The effect of acute treadmill wlaking on cognitive control and academic achievement in preadolescent children. *Neuroscience* 2009;**159**:1044–1054.

42. Tomporowski PD, Davis CL, Lambourne K, Gregoski M, Tkacz. Task switching in overweight children: Effects of acute exercise and age. *J Sport Exerc Psych* 2008;**30**:497–511.
43. Budde H, Voelcker-Rehage C, Pietraβyk-Kendziorra S. Acute coordinative exercises improves attentional performance in adolescents., *Neuroscience Letters* 2008;**441**:219–223.

Chapter 10
Leisure and Social Health

Colleen Keller
Julie Fleury
Carol Rogers

In the U.S., 52.5% of older adults report no leisure time physical activity (LTPA), falling far short of Healthy People 2010 target objectives. Among Americans, those who report the least amount of LTPA include ethnic minorities, women, and persons with lower education and income levels (1). The benefits of LTPA, that includes at least moderate levels of intensity, include decreased risk for cardiovascular disease, chronic illness such as diabetes, and reduced all-cause mortality (2). LTPA is defined as physical activity that increases major muscle movement, encompasses a wide variety of activities ranging from sport activity to house and garden work, and represents an avenue to increasing active lifestyles in persons of all ages and backgrounds (3, 4). Of equal importance, LTPA has been shown to facilitate coping, skill development in people with disabilities, adjustment to healthy aging, and enhanced self-esteem and self-concept. Researchers have emphasized the importance of formal and informal community structures and supportive resources that increase LTPA and other health-promoting behaviors. Understanding the nature of supportive resources is particularly important to clarify factors that optimize involvement in LTPA, and represent critical areas of intervention for LTPA research and practice. This chapter addresses the role of supportive resources as an important factor in increasing LTPA.

Defining Supportive Resources

Supportive resources have been documented as contributing to physical activity and LTPA. Supportive resources include social support as well as social norms, social networks, and the neighborhood environment. Supportive resources play a dominant role in influencing individual and community goals, strategies, and opportunities for behavioral change. The context of support offered may have a differential influence on the relationship between social support and LTPA. For older adults, the support of friends is important, while for adolescents, parental support is most important, and for women with children, spousal support is paramount.

Individual support resources are shown to be influenced by behavioral counseling to promote engaging support of a family member or friend (5).

Individual resources include characteristics such as socioeconomic status, perception of health, and motivational factors, such as self-efficacy. Social norms provide standards for behavior and contribute to the development of common symbols, values, and behaviors. Salient correlates of LTPA include social norms that include knowing and observing others who engage in physical activity. Peers who model exercise behavior serve as a normative group that aids in feeling that exercise is an acceptable behavior, given that others like oneself are doing it.

Family, Kinship, and *Friend Social Resources* are interpersonal resources and include culturally relevant social support as well as social norms, social networks, and family relationships that may facilitate opportunities to recognize and create resources for physical activity, the performance of physical activity, and LTPA across the lifespan, in rural and urban settings, and across racial and ethnic groups (6, 7).Social support is one aspect of social resources, and is defined as aid and assistance exchanged through social relationships and interpersonal transactions, and includes four types of support: (a) emotional support, including expressions of empathy, trust, caring, (b) instrumental support, including tangible aid or service, (c) appraisal support, including information that is used for self evaluation, and (d) informational support, including advice, suggestions, and information (8). Social support from family and friends has been consistently and positively related to physical activity (9–11).Social support is recommended as an effective intervention for increasing physical activity, with evidence showing that when social support is present, time spent in physical activity increases by 44% and the frequency of physical activity increases by 22% (12). Social support is an invaluable resource that can be used to enhance participation in LTPA.

To maximize social support through counseling and teaching strategies that enhance social support, it is beneficial to consider social support from a broad perspective. Some investigators and theorists define social support as social capital, an array of social contacts that give access to social, emotional, and practical support. This broader context includes social and kinship ties, neighbors, members of social organizations, clubs, friends, parents, and spouses. Social capital is regarded, then, as an asset for both the individual and the group that provides information, access, and assistance. For example, the presence of social capital may foster LTPA through community-based walking groups, generation of resources for LTPA such as walking trails, and social organizations that provide information on LTPA and encourage LTPA program development.

Environment and Neighborhood Social Resource

There is no question that the environment influences the availability and the context of social support that is available to enhance LTPA. Environment and neighborhood social resources, including community resources, and factors specific to the built environment, may have a significant impact in creating a supportive personal and physical environment to promote physical activity. For example, access to safe, affordable facilities has been identified as an important correlate of participation in physical activity, particularly among elderly, poor, and minority women. Living in urban or rural areas influences the nature, source, and strength of social support for LTPA. For example, concerns about neighborhood safety may limit interaction among those living in urban areas. Similarly, distance and lack of sidewalks may limit interaction and support among those in rural areas. The neighborhood environment has been identified as an important supportive resource for LTPA, although higher levels of neighborhood poverty significantly reduce the likelihood of resources available for physical activity. Moving from a high poverty area to a low poverty area was associated with a 50% increase in the availability of physical activity resources as measured by observational data (13). In an examination of associations between neighborhood demographic characteristics, such as socioeconomic status and ethnicity, and the availability of commercial physical activity-related outlets by zip code across the United States, Powell and colleagues found that facilities were less likely to be present in lower-income neighborhoods and in neighborhoods with higher proportions of residents with Hispanic ethnicity (13). In a review of policy and environmental interventions, Matson-Koffman and colleagues noted that improving access to places and opportunities for physical activity were effective in increasing physical activity (14). Further research is needed to better quantify the role of environment and neighborhood social resources for LTPA, and to develop and implement relevant interventions to promote LTPA in community settings.

Supportive Resources for LTPA

To enhance the understanding of how social resources play out in the real world, their assessment, influence, strategies for implementation and evaluation methods will be discussed, including strategies that enhance social resources. The four areas of assessment include individual and family/kinship support resources, social norms, and neighborhood resources. To facilitate a greater understanding of their application, we will discuss the influence of each assessment category, strategies employed to impact change, and methods of evaluation (see Table 10.1 on p. 102).

Table 10.1 Social Resources for Leisure-Time Physical Activity

Assessment	Influence	Strategy	Evaluation
Individual support resources	Motivational strategies: Goal setting, instrument adjuncts such as pedometers, reducing perceived barriers such as time, unsafe LTPA environments	Behavioral counseling Culturally specific LTPA activities such as dance Computer-based instruction	Reduced perceived barriers
Social family and kinship social resources	Identification of family, kinship resources for engaging in LTPA Friends and family walking time Walking and planned exercise	Culture and gender relevant LTPA Development of skills to assess and develop social resources for LTPA Identify family and social networks for walking support	Enhanced physical activity Increase in group, family, and friend partnering for LTPA
Environment and neighborhood resources	Walking for leisure and transport Change environment access to parks and public recreation facilities Safe walking and exercise access	Assessing a safe environment Cooperation/joint agreement between public institutions such as schools and industry Increasing park features that appeal to public such as trails and equipment Developing relationships with key players and networks among policy groups within communities	Enhanced physical activity Increase in group, family, and friend partnering for LTPA

Individual Social Resources

Research has shown that culturally specific dance choreographed to gospel music increases LTPA, and influences self-efficacy and social support, while increasing neighborhood resources among African-American women (7). In this research, classes were taught in a church setting to address the barrier of an unsafe environment and build on neighborhood resources. Computer-tailored messages have also been employed to improve LTPA, and have included awareness of opportunities for physical activity, social influence from family and friends, pros and cons of physical activity, and self-efficacy enhancing information (15). Castro and colleagues used a behavioral counseling intervention to increase self-efficacy and social support for walking through telephone counseling and informational mailings; social support increased over time, and change in self-efficacy was associated with increases in walking (16).

Family, Kinship, and Friend Social Resources

For many people, LTPA occurs in a context of friends, family members, and social settings that contribute to the behavior change process. Integration in a social network which includes supportive friends, family, and neighbors, has been shown to provide a sense of purpose, recognition of self-worth, ability to meet expectations, motivation for self-care, and identification and use of resources. Social support systems are consistent with both cultural factors and social norms linked to health behavior change. Social support has been shown to be especially relevant, and perhaps a more potent factor in health promotion among ethnically diverse populations, and particularly among women. Marquez and McAuley found that social support to exercise from friends contributes to participation in leisure time physical activity (17). The lack of social networks was a primary barrier to physical activity among minority women.

Some community interventions among minority groups include multi-level interventions including *Promotoras de salud*, or Lay Health Advisors (LHA) as a mechanism for social support and reinforcement related to physical activity. LHA interventions have garnered increasing recognition as an influential health promotion and disease prevention strategy (18). *Promotora*-led interventions are based on the premise that LTPA might be best encouraged via programs designed to enhance awareness and develop resources within a context of community support. Community-based interventions which address social and cultural resources offer important opportunities to decrease premature morbidity, disability, and enhance the health status of underserved populations. The involvement of LHA or "natural helpers" in the design, delivery, and evaluation of LTPA interventions has been proposed as a mechanism to ensure that preventive programs address issues of importance to the community and promote sustainable, community-wide change (19).

Time, place, and circumstances contribute to the impact that enhancing supportive resources have on increasing and sustaining LTPA. For example, social support has been used to enhance participation in cultural dancing among regionally and racially diverse groups (7, 20). Interventions that have targeted social support systems, particularly those within the family and community, as a mechanism for increasing physical activity levels, have shown some effect. Grassi and colleagues found that a community-based intervention which focused on existing support mechanisms of Hispanic family and community members resulted in enhanced participation in intervention activities and a decrease in perceived barriers to physical activity (21). Nader and colleagues found that Mexican Americans who participated in a family-centered program to increase physical activity gained significantly more knowledge of the skills required to change exercise habits than did those in the control groups (22). Poston and colleagues conducted a culturally relevant intervention with strategies derived from social support theory, including peer leaders, verbal and written bilingual educational materials, and social activities that included sharing culturally relevant snacks (23).

Environment and Neighborhood Social Resources

The neighborhood environment, including the built environment, may have a significant impact in creating a supportive personal and physical environment to promote physical activity. The built environment is defined as the physical surroundings that form the physical characteristic of a city or town, such as roads, sidewalks, walking trails, and parks. The built environment also includes crime and safety, weather, and streetlights. Access to safe, affordable facilities has been identified as an important correlate of participation in physical activity, particularly among the elderly, the poor, and minority women. Data indicate that low-income and racial/ethnic minority populations have limited access to environments which promote physical activity compared to other populations, and specific concerns address safety, and lack of community physical activity settings. Other data suggests that architectural features, such as front porches on homes and greenways within neighborhoods that facilitate visual and social contacts may be perceived as a protective factor for encouraging people to walk in neighborhoods.

Of particular interest was the report that limited public transportation was associated with increased LTPA (24).While a lack of transportation has been reported to be a barrier to physical activity, it increases walking for leisure. Satisfaction with the quality of local facilities such as parks, sports venues, and fitness centers is important to increasing LTPA, as well as feeling safe within the neighborhood, satisfaction with pedestrian crossings, presence of traffic slowing devices, such as stop signs and well-marked speed limits, in the local streets and slow traffic patterns in the neighborhoods. Resources for public transportation and trusting many people in the neighborhood increased leisure time walking among young mothers (24).

To increase LTPA levels, community officials around the U.S. have identified public parks as a convenient, low-cost resource to enable active living. In some surveys, park visitors who were observed in park environments, which contained playgrounds, sport courts, and paths, were significantly more active than visitors in settings without these features. Park-built features that support physical activity across the life span (paths and courts in particular) should be considered by community leaders seeking relatively low-cost mechanisms to promote physical activity among residents (25, 26). Opportunities for increasing the use of public parks for recreation and leisure include joint use agreements between cooperating institutions such as high schools and community park and recreation agencies (27). The first step by which environmental health professionals can influence the built environment in communities is to build relationships with the individuals who make the plans, as well as those who make the decisions, use the places, and engage in related public health work.

Policy-influence activities might include talking to persons such as city council members or county commissioners who make decisions about zoning, planning, and development. Building relationships among relevant community members or groups such as parks and recreation managers, neighborhood association members, advocacy groups, and community service organizations enhances policy-making decisions to positively impact resources for LTPA. Building relationships with city and county planners, leaders, decision makers, community groups, and public health colleagues, especially those in physical activity, nutrition, and school health, help to set the stage for influence within communities.

Social resources for increasing leisure time physical activity can be developed from a variety of sources. Individual counseling, motivational enhancement, computer-based instruction that employs group activities, networks and contacts have been shown to increase LTPA. Increasing group and community efforts, through media, neighborhood activities, and reducing barriers such as unsafe areas enhances participation in LTPA. The larger influence on LTPA can be achieved through efforts such as policy enhancement, increasing access, safety, and variety in parks and recreation sites.

References

1. Hughes JP, McDowell MA, Brody DJ. Leisure-time physical activity among U.S. adults 60 or more years of age: Results from NHANES 1999–2004. *J Phys Activ Health* 2008;**5**:347–358.
2. Peterson JJ, Lowe JB, Peterson NA, Nothwehr FK, Janz KF, Lobas JG. Paths to leisure physical activity among adults with intellectual disabilities: Self-efficacy and social support. *Am J Health Promot* 2008;**23**:35–42.
3. U.S. Department of Health and Human Services and U.S. Department of Agriculture. *Dietary Guidelines for Americans (6th ed)*. U.S. Government Printing Office: Washington, DC, 2005.
4. U.S. Department of Health and Human Services. *The Surgeon General's Call to Action to Prevent and Decrease Overweight and Obesity*. U.S. Department of Health and Human Services, Public Health Service, Office of the Surgeon General: Washington, DC, 2001.
5. Costanzo C, Walker SN. Incorporating self-efficacy and interpersonal support in an intervention to increase physical activity in older women. *Women Health* 2008;**47/4**:91–108.
6. Choi J, Wilbur J, Miller A, Szalacha L, McAuley E. Correlates of leisure-time physical activity in Korean immigrant women. *West J Nurs Res* 2008;**30**:620–638.
7. Murrock CJ, Madigan E. Self-efficacy and social support as mediators between culturally specific dance and lifestyle physical activity. *Res Theor Nurs Pract* 2008;**22**:192–204.
8. Heany CA, Israel BA. Social networks and social support. In Glanz K, Rimer BK, Lewis FM (eds), *Health Behavior and Health Education: Theory, Research and Practice (3rd ed)*. San Francisco: Jossey-Bass, 2002.
9. Keller C, Allan J, Tinkle MB. Stages of change, processes of change, and social support for exercise and weight gain in postpartum women. *Journal of Obstetric, Gynecologic, & Neonatal Nursing* 2006;**35**:232–240.
10. Sallis JF, Cervero RB, Ascher W, Henderson KA, Kraft MK, Kerr J. An ecological approach to creating active living communities. *Annu Rev Publ Health* 2006;**27**:297–322.
11. Weyerer S, Kupfer B. Physical exercise and psychological health. *Sports Med* 1994;**17**:108–116.
12. Task Force on Community Preventive Services. *The guide to community preventive services (community guide)*. http://www.thecommunity-guide.org/index.html. Accessed June 21, 2010.
13. Powell KE, Martin LM, Chowdhury PP. Places to walk: Convenience and regular physical activity. *Am J Publ Health* 2003;**93**:1519–1521.

14. Matson-Koffman DM, Brownstein JN, Neiner JA, Greaney ML. A site-specific literature review of policy and environmental interventions that promote physical activity and nutrition for cardiovascular health: What works? *Am J Health Promot* 2005;**19**:167–193.

15. Smeets T, Brug J, de Vries H. Effects of tailoring health messages on physical activity. *Health Educ Res* 2008;**23**:402–413.

16. Castro CM, Sallis JF, Hickmann SA, Lee RE, Chen AH. A prospective study of psychosocial correlates of physical activity for ethnic minority women. *Psychol Health* 1999;**14**:277–293.

17. Marquez DX, McAuley E. Social cognitive correlates of leisure time physical activity among latinos. *J Behav Med* 2006;**29**:281–289.

18. Walker DG, Jan S. How do we determine whether community health workers are cost-effective? Some core methodological issues. *J Community Health* 2005;**30**:221–229.

19. Marin G, Burhansstipanov L, Connell CM, Gielen AC, Helitzer-Allen D, Lorig K, et al. A research agenda for health education among underserved populations. *Health Educ Q* 1995;**22**:346–363.

20. Brown CA, McGuire FA, Voelkl J. The link between successful aging and serious leisure. *Int J Aging Hum Dev* 2008;**66**:73–95.

21. Grassi K, Gonzalez G, Tello P, He G. La vida caminando: A community-based physical activity program designed by and for rural latino families. *Health Educ J* 1999;**30**:S13–7.

22. Nader PR, Sallis JF, Patterson TL, Abramson IS, Rupp JW, Senn KL, et al. A family approach to cardiovascular risk reduction: Results from the san diego family health project. *Health Educ Q* 1989;**16**:229–244.

23. Poston WS II, Haddock CK, Olvera NE, Suminski RR, Reeves RS, Dunn JK, et al. Evaluation of culturally appropriate intervention to increase physical activity. *Am J Health Behav* 2001;**25**:396–406.

24. Cleland VJ, Timperio A, Crawford D. Are perceptions of the physical and social environment associated with mothers' walking for leisure and for transport? A longitudinal study. *Prev Med* 2008;**47**:188–193.

25. Kaczynski AT, Potwarka LR, Saelens BE. Association of park size, distance, and features with physical activity in neighborhood parks. *Am J Publ Health* 2008;**98**:1451–1456.

26. Shores KA, West ST. The relationship between built park environments and physical activity in four park locations. *J Publ Health Manag Pract* 2008;**14**:e9–16.

27. Maddock J, Choy LB, Nett B, McGurk MD, Tamashiro R. Increasing access to places for physical activity through a joint use agreement: A case study in urban Honolulu. *Preventing Chronic Disease* 2008;**5**:A91.

Chapter 11
The Effect of Leisure Environments on Dimensions of Health and Wellness

Andrew J. Mowen
Ariane L. Rung

Introduction

The physical environment is an essential part of the leisure experience and contributes to a wide range of individual, social, and community health outcomes. Indeed, some of the more common leisure experiences and activities (e.g., walking, family gatherings, picnicking, attending sporting events, bicycling, swimming) require some type of built or natural environmental setting in which to participate. The characteristics, design, and availability of these built and natural environments serve as facilitators to healthy leisure participation and contribute to improved human health for a variety of populations across the lifespan. A wide range of built and natural leisure environments have the potential to influence individual, social, and community health. Within the leisure service delivery system, these environments typically include parks, preserves, playgrounds, public plazas, trails, and community centers.

In an increasingly urbanized nation, the best access that people have for nature contact is through their local parklands. Indeed, parks are found in almost every type of community. Parks vary in size, shape, quality, and character and provide a wide spectrum of opportunities for promoting individual, social, and community health. Park settings and facilities are often managed by trained park and recreation professionals who work for local, state, and federal organizations within government as well as the commercial and nonprofit sector. When considering all major U.S. cities, there are approximately 20,000 individual parks and over 10,000 playgrounds (1). The total area covered by urban parkland in the United States exceeds one million acres. These figures represent only major cities, and are likely much higher when taking suburban and rural park settings into account.

The enormous capacity of parks can be better leveraged to promote enhanced health and well-being across a broad population. Understanding how parks contribute to specific health and wellness outcomes is essential if professionals are to convey the value of preserving, designing, and improving these environments. With this evidence, park professionals are better positioned to advocate for preservation, maintenance, and construction of their settings and facilities. Recently, studies conducted by interdisciplinary research teams from leisure studies, community planning, and public health have pioneered new ways of assessing the linkages between leisure environments and health. Based on this emerging evidence, some general conclusions regarding the role of park settings in promoting health and wellness can now be made. Moreover, park, recreation, and leisure service organizations are now incorporating environmental strategies in their efforts to specifically promote health and wellness outcomes. The emerging park and recreation professional should be aware of the current evidence concerning the leisure environment and health and should understand how parks can be managed and designed to improve health. According to the World Health Organization (WHO), health is defined as a "state of complete physical, mental, and social well-being and not merely the absence of disease or infirmity" (2). Based on this broader view of health, the contributions of park and leisure environments upon four health domains include: Mental Health, Physical Health, Physical Activity, and Social Benefits.

Leisure Settings and Mental Health

Mental health restoration (e.g., stress/anxiety reduction) is perhaps the most well-recognized and established health benefit associated with park, outdoor, and nature settings. Years of environmental psychology research have shown that exposure to natural environments and contact with nature result in psychological regeneration (3). Contact with nature can specifically promote psychological well-being (4), reduce stress (5), and can support healing among psychiatric and other patients (6). These mental health benefits can occur across a variety of populations. For example, studies among workers, college students, hospital patients, inner-city girls, public housing residents, and apartment residents have found a variety of psychological, emotional, and mental health benefits based on exposure to the outdoors.

There are numerous psychological benefits for visitors that stem from exposure to park environments specifically. For example, Godbey and Blazey found that stress reduction (i.e., stress relief, clearing one's mind, feeling good) and exercise were the most common benefits reported by older park users, and approximately half of these park users reported that they were in a better mood after visiting parks (7). In a separate study, Hull and Michael sought to determine if parks and outdoor areas played a significant role in shaping people's moods. Interviews with 186 nature recreationists revealed that the longer the participants stayed at the park, the less stressed they became (8). Additionally, they found that respondents felt significantly calmer and less anxious at parks than in their home environments. Overall, these studies indicate that visits to parks are associated with positive moods and decreased anxiety levels.

New evidence also indicates that the setting context may be a more important contributor of mental health restoration than the leisure activities themselves. For example, a study commissioned by the Mind Institute compared mall walkers to park/nature walkers in terms of depressive symptoms and other emotional measures. Findings revealed that walkers in park/nature settings were more likely than mall walkers to report a boost of self-esteem after their walk, while mall walkers reported a decrease in feelings of self-esteem. Feelings of depression, anger, and tension were reduced more dramatically among those who had walked outdoors, compared to mall walkers. Moreover, when comparing a walk in a natural setting (e.g., a park), a walk in an urban setting, and relaxing in a comfortable chair, mental fatigue was most successfully relieved by a walk in a park (9). Park settings may also play a mentally-restorative role in populations that have been affected by large-scale disasters and stressful events. For example, a New Orleans study of park visitors after Hurricane Katrina found that visitors from flooded neighborhoods ranked the importance of "escape" reasons for visiting parks (e.g., using the park to forget about everyday responsibilities) higher than visitors from non-flooded neighborhoods (10). Results such as these suggest that parks may help communities cope with stressful events by providing individuals an outlet for psychological restoration.

People place value on the existence of parks and natural settings even when they do not use them (11). For example, studies have shown that "having the park there" is the biggest source of pleasure for residents living near a small park (12). Furthermore, a nationwide survey of Americans' use of local park and recreation services found that 71% of park nonusers reported receiving social, personal, and economic benefits from their local parks (11).

Leisure Settings and Physical Health

In addition to enhancing mental health and reducing stress, the availability and utilization of leisure environments can also contribute to improvements in both perceived and physiological health indicators. As discussed previously, certain environments are more conducive to restorative experiences than others. Parks, green space, and outdoor settings, in particular, have been associated with favorable health status and these health contributions can occur across different age groups that use parks for both inactive and active recreational pursuits. These natural landscapes have an apparent beneficial effect on physical health indicators such as blood pressure, heart rate, mood, day-to-day effectiveness, social behavior, cognitive functioning, and work performance. One landmark study demonstrated that exposure to natural settings and views was associated with shorter hospitalizations, reduced prescription drug use, and fewer negative evaluative comments (13). Furthermore, just the act of driving by parks and green spaces has been associated with stress relief. For example, one study exposed subjects who had just experienced an induced stressful event to one of four different simulated drives (forest/rural areas, golf courses, urban scenery and mixed roadside scenery). Subjects who engaged in a nature-based simulated drive (forest/rural areas, golf courses) recovered more quickly from stressful situations than those whose drives were dominated by built structures (14). Finally, a survey of older adults and park use found that users of local parks reported fewer visits to a physician for purposes other than checkups than did park nonusers, even when controlling for the effects of age, income, education level, health status, and other possibly influencing factors (15). Moreover, individuals living within walking distance of a park were in better condition (based on a number of physical health indicators) than those without a park nearby (15). As for personal health ratings, active park users had better self-reported health and showed other indicators of better health than did passive users and nonpark users (15). A separate study examining the relationship among stress, park-based leisure and physiological and psychological health indicators among older adults, found that older adults who stayed longer in parks had lower levels of systolic blood pressure (16). In urbanized areas, parks comprise much of the existing green space available for leisure experiences. Maas and colleagues explored the role of green space in shaping public health perceptions and found that the amount of green space in one's immediate living environment was positively correlated with self-reports of general health (17). This relationship was stronger for lower socioeconomic groups and for youth and the elderly.

Leisure Settings and Physical Activity

In addition to their physiological health benefits, there is increasing evidence that time spent in outdoor environments is associated with engaging in higher amounts of physical activity. For example, three studies of preschool children have found that being outdoors was the strongest correlate to their level of physical activity (18). Parks are a specific type of outdoor environment that contribute to increased physical activity levels for a variety of populations. Proximity to these settings is associated with higher use levels and increased physical activity levels across a range of populations. In a recent review conducted of the park and physical activity literature, Kaczynski and Henderson found that 8 of 13 articles reported at least some positive associations between park proximity and physical activity (19). Moreover, a national survey of U.S. adults examined both environmental determinants of physical activity and found that perceived access to parks and recreational facilities was significantly related to physical activity levels (20). Those who felt that parks and recreation facilities were accessible were almost twice as likely to meet recommended levels of physical activity.

Living far from safe and well-designed parks, trails, and public open spaces may be considered as a factor that contributes to chronic disease caused by physical inactivity (21). However, the availability of parks and leisure settings is not consistent across neighborhoods of differing socioeconomic and racial/ethnicity status, with minority neighborhoods less likely to have at least one park or recreation facility in their community compared to non-minority neighborhoods (22). Studies show that low-income communities of color are disproportionately affected by higher rates of health problems and often have poor access to physical activity settings such as parks, playgrounds, trails, community gardens, and other open spaces. For example, a study of over 4,000 youth in California found that having safe access to a park was associated with regular physical activity for youth from low-income families and urban communities, but not for youth from high-income families or rural communities. These results suggest that the availability of safe parks is particularly important in promoting physical activity among low-income and urban youth (23).

In addition to general park proximity, having access to a wide variety of leisure settings is also related to physical activity levels. For example, a study in West Virginia found that the number of recreation facilities and the total county acres devoted to water-based recreation were positively related to county-wide physical activity levels. Counties with more facilities and more acreage devoted to recreation had a lower proportion of the population reporting insufficient physical activity levels (24). Another study of six U.S. cities found that adolescent girls who had more parks within close proximity to their home (less than one mile) achieved higher levels of physical activity than girls who had fewer parks near home (25). Each park within one half of a mile of a girl's home was associated with an increase of 17 minutes of nonschool moderate/vigorous physical activity over a 6-day period (25).

Park settings can encompass a wide variety of activity-supporting features such as trails/paths, sport fields, open space for free play, playgrounds, and pools. The type and number of park features may, in turn, provide opportunities to be physically active while visiting. For example, Floyd and colleagues used observational methods to assess park-based physical activity and examine variations in energy expenditures across various park areas at 28 parks in Tampa, FL, and Chicago, IL. Across both cities, they found that park spaces with soccer fields; tennis/racquetball, basketball, and volleyball courts; and playgrounds were associated with moderate to vigorous levels of physical activity and overall higher levels of park-based energy expenditures (26).

Other studies have found that parks with more of a certain feature are more likely to be used for physical activity than parks with less of that feature. For example, one study reported that parks with paved trails were 26 times more likely to be used for physical activity than parks without paved trails (27). Proximity to specific types of park features has also been linked with the physical activity of adolescent girls. For example, girls living near parks containing features such as playgrounds, basketball courts, multipurpose rooms, walking, swimming, and track facilities had higher non-school physical activity levels than girls who did not (25). A practical application of these findings can be illustrated by ongoing efforts to renovate parks to provide more active features, particularly for youth. For example, in the city of Allentown, PA, a major park renovation project specifically targeted increased youth activity by incorporating active playground features, a new youth fitness/nature walk, improvements and extensions of the park's trail system, and the development of a youth sports complex. Based on these studies and practical examples, a general implication for promoting active parks would be to provide sufficient and convenient access to a number of park, recreation, leisure settings near communities where people of all ages and backgrounds live and work. Moreover, it appears that certain types of park features such as trails, sport complexes, or playgrounds might encourage more physical activity in these leisure settings.

Leisure Settings and Social Benefits

Parks have long been thought to influence the social fabric of community life. Early functions ascribed to parks included instilling values such as good citizenship, social consciousness, and democracy in the young, the poor, and among ethnic groups (28). Today, contemporary thinkers have evolved these notions to a phenomenon whereby parks may promote the social health of a community by fostering community cohesion, pride, and social relationships that in turn facilitate individuals' access to health-promoting resources.

Evidence for such a phenomenon comes from studies comparing housing residents living in places that are surrounded with greenery to those living surrounded by barren concrete. For example, one study found that exposure to green common spaces among elderly inner-city individuals was significantly related to higher levels of social integration among neighbors and friends (29). Researchers in New Orleans have taken this work a step further by attempting to define a construct called "Park-Based Social Capital" (30). Adapted from work on neighborhood social capital, the elements of park-based social capital include 1) park-based social cohesion, that is, the pattern of social interaction and values among park users within a park; 2) park-based social support and leverage, or resources and information that park users can draw upon within the park to cope with daily problems and advance socioeconomically; 3) park attachment, that is, being connected to and integrated in networks within the park that possess resources; and 4) park-based informal social control, or the ability of park visitors to collectively maintain social order and keep the park safe from criminal or delinquent activity. Researchers are finding that this construct of park-based social capital is indeed a collective park-based phenomenon; moreover, it is associated with increased frequency of park visitation, increased time spent in the park, as well as increased time spent engaging in moderate-to-vigorous physical activity in the park (30).

Social benefits also often arise in the context of community gardens. Advocates of community gardens say they increase residents' sense of community ownership and stewardship, provide a focus for neighborhood activities, expose inner city youth to nature, connect people from diverse cultures, reduce crime by cleaning up vacant lots, and build community leaders. For example, a recent study found that St. Louis neighborhoods with community gardens were more stable than other neighborhoods. In a city that lost nearly 50,000 residents between 1990 and 2000, neighborhoods with community gardens fared somewhat better in retaining their population, losing only 6% over a 10-year period compared with 13% for the city as a whole. More research is needed on the contributions of park and leisure settings on the social health of communities, because much of the existing evidence linking these settings to social health is preliminary or anecdotal.

Conclusion

Parks and outdoor environments contribute to both individual- and community-level wellness and may reduce the burden of medical care and treatment. Because these environments exist in rural, suburban, and urban communities, the capacity of parks to address contemporary health concerns (e.g., obesity, chronic stress) is considerable. Current research indicates that leisure participation in outdoor settings reduces stress and anxiety even more than indoor leisure activities. Moreover, park access, availability, and characteristics have been linked to enhanced park use as well as the achievement of recommended physical activity levels. Finally, emerging studies are exploring the role of parks as they contribute to social health. These early studies suggest that parks may play a role in the social health of our nation by providing opportunities for interpersonal interaction and enhanced social capital across visitors of different ages, interests, abilities, and backgrounds. Collectively, such evidence is inspiring today's park and recreation professional to purposively plan, design, and manage their parks in order to maximize health outcomes, particularly within urban park systems.

In summary, parks represent an ideal leisure setting from which to address contemporary mental, physical, and social health concerns. Investing in our nation's parks and leisure environments can pay handsome health dividends for a community and a nation. Having a large number of nearby parks increases the likelihood of being physically active, and parks that include certain active recreation features such as trails, playgrounds, and sport facilities may stimulate higher levels of park-based physical activity. Increasing the capacity of our nation's parks is consistent with a public health emphasis on community-level policies and interventions and can provide additional neighborhood resources from which to enhance health and wellness across a broader population.

References

1. City Park Facts. http://www.tpl.org/cityparkfacts/. Accessed May 2, 2009.
2. Constitution of the World Health Organization. The World Health Organization: New York, 1946.
3. Maller C, Townsend M, Pryor A, Brown P, St. Leger L. Healthy nature, healthy people: Contact with nature as an upstream health promotion intervention for populations. *Health Promot Int* 2005;**21/1**:45–54.
4. Kaplan R, Kaplan S, Brown, T. Environmental preference: A comparison of four domains of predictors. *Environ Behav* 1989;**21/5**:509–530.
5. Ulrich RS, Addoms DL. Psychological and Recreational Benefits of a Residential Park. *J Leisure Res* 1981;**13/1**:43–65.
6. Beck AT, Steer RA, Garbin MG. Psychometric properties of the Beck Depression Inventory: Twenty-five years of evaluation. *Clin Psychol Rev* 1988;**8/1**:77–100.
7. Godbey G, Blazey M. Old people in urban parks: An exploratory investigation. *J Leisure Res* 1983;**15/3**:229–244.
8. Hull RB, Michael SE. Nature-based recreation, mood change, and stress restoration. *Leisure Sci* 1995;**17**:1–14.
9. Hartig T, Mang M, Evans GW. Restorative effects of natural environment experience. *Environ Behav* 1991;**23/1**:3–26.
10. Rung AL, Broyles ST, Mowen AJ, Gustat J, Sothern MS. Escaping to and Being Active in Neighborhood Parks: Park Use in a Post-Disaster Setting. *Disasters*, In press.
11. Godbey G, Graefe A, James S. The Benefits of Local Recreation and Park Services: A Nationwide Study of the Perceptions of the American Public. National Recreation and Park Association: Washington, DC, 1992.
12. Kaplan R (1981). Evaluation of an urban vest-pocket park. Research Paper NC-195. U.S. Dept. of Agriculture, Forest Service, North Central Forest Experiment Station: St. Paul, MN, 1981.
13. Ulrich RS. View through a window may influence recovery from surgery. *Science* 1984;**224/4647**:420–421.
14. Parsons R, Tassinary LG, Ulrich RS, Hebl MR, Grossman-Alexander M. The view from the road: Implications for stress recovery and immunization. *Journal of Environmental Psychology* 1998;**18**:113–140.
15. Payne LL, Orsega-Smith E, Roy M, Godbey GC. Local park use and personal health among older adults: An exploratory study. *Journal of Park and Recreation Administration* 2005;**23/2**:1–20.

16. Orsega-Smith E, Mowen A, Payne L, Godbey G. The interaction of stress and park use on psycho-physiological health in older adults. *J Leisure Res* 2004;**36/2**:232–256.
17. Maas J, Verheij RA, Groenewegen PB, de Vries S, Spreeuwenberg P. Green space, urbanity, and health: How strong is the relation? *J Epidemiol Community* 2006;**60/7**:587–592.
18. Sallis JF, Prochaska JJ, Taylor WC (2000). A review of correlates of physical activity of children and adolescents. *Med Sci Sports Exerc* 2000;**32/5**:963–975.
19. Kaczynski AT, Henderson KA. Environmental correlates of physical activity: A review of evidence about parks and recreation. *Leisure Sci* 2007;**29/4**:315–354.
20. Brownson RC, Baker EA, Housemann RA, Brennan LK, Bacak SJ. Environmental and policy determinants of physical activity in the United States. *Am J Publ Health* 2001;**91/12**:1995–2003.
21. Kahn EB, Ramsey LT, Brownson RC, Heath GW, Howze EH, Powell KE, et al. The effectiveness of interventions to increase physical activity: A systematic review. *Am J Prev Med* 2002;**22/4S**:73–107.
22. Gordon-Larsen P, Nelson MC, Page P, Popkin BM. Inequality in the built environment underlies key health disparities in physical activity and obesity. *Pediatrics* 2006;**117/2**:417–424.
23. Babey SH, Hastert TA, Yu H, Brown ER (2008). Physical activity among adolescents: When do parks matter? *Am J Prev Med* 2008;**34/4**:345–348.
24. Rosenberger R, Sneh Y, Phipps T, Gurvitch R. A spatial analysis of linkages between health care expenditures, physical inactivity, obesity and recreation supply. *J Leisure Res* 2005;**37/2**:216–235.
25. Cohen DA, Ashwood JS, Scott MM, Overton A, Evenson KR, Staten LK, et al. Public parks and physical activity among adolescent girls. *Pediatrics* 2006;**118/5**:e1381–9.
26. Floyd MF, Spengler JO, Maddock JE, Gobster PH, Suau LJ. Park-based physical activity in diverse communities of 2 U.S. cities. *Am J Prev Med* 2008;**34/4**:299–305.
27. Kaczynski AT, Potwarka LR, Saelens BE. Association of park size, distance, & features with physical activity in neighborhood parks. *Am J Publ Health* 2008;**98/8**:1451–1456.
28. Cranz G. *The Politics of Park Design: A History of Urban Parks in America.* The MIT Press: Cambridge, MA, 1982.
29. Kweon B-S, Sullivan WC, Wiley A. Green common spaces and the social integration of inner-city older adults. *Environ Behav* 1998;**30/6**:832–858.

30. Broyles ST, Mowen AJ, Theall KP, Rung AL (2009). Socializing and Softball: A Conceptual Model for Integrating Social Capital into a Park Use and Active Living Framework. 2009 Active Living Research Annual Conference, February 18–20: San Diego, CA.

Chapter 12
Leisure as a Context for Prevention

Linda L. Caldwell
Melissa A. Tibbits

Think for a minute about all of the things you have done today, or will do, that have an element of risk. Did you go through that very yellow light? Did you cross the road on the "do not walk" sign? Did you forget to put on sunscreen before you went out to play golf or went for a run? We all do risky things in our daily lives, most of the time with little consequence. Imagine, however, someone who engages in risky behavior on a regular basis, and who does the same type of risk behavior continually. For example, consider someone who regularly does not wear a seat belt. The chances of that behavior resulting in major, negative consequences are high given what we know about the protection provided by wearing a seat belt.

Now think of all the things you have done today, or will do, that will contribute to your health and well-being. Will you take a long, brisk walk on a rail trail? Have you had a meaningful conversation with a loved one? Have you practiced some form of meditation? People who do these things on a regular basis also experience major consequences, but positive ones.

This chapter will introduce the notion of risk and protective factors in one's life that contribute to long-term health and well-being. The long-term pattern of one's behavior is of critical importance to consider with regard to positive and negative health outcomes. We will also introduce and discuss the notion of prevention, which goes hand in hand with concepts of risk and protection. We will then describe how leisure is an important context for prevention and then end the chapter with examples of preventive interventions that promote health and well-being through leisure.

Risk and Protective Factors and Prevention

Risk factors are characteristics that *increase* the likelihood of a particular negative outcome, whereas protective factors are characteristics that *reduce* the likelihood of a particular negative outcome. In order to illustrate the notion of risk and protective factors, we will give an example of one particular type of health outcome: heart and vascular diseases. Later in the chapter we will examine substance use and misuse in relation to leisure related risk and protective factors.

Heart and vascular diseases include conditions such as high cholesterol, heart attacks, high blood pressure, obesity, and so on. These conditions are often interrelated, and typically affect women and men in middle age or later. The treatments for these conditions are costly and often not always able to "fix" the entire problem. Treatments may include inserting stents, bypass surgery, and being on lifelong medications. Given the high prevalence of heart and vascular diseases and the emotional, physical, and monetary costs of these disorders, public health professionals have (a) tried to determine the risk and protective factors for heart and vascular diseases and (b) tried to implement programs aimed at decreasing risk factors and increasing protective factors for heart and vascular diseases.

One factor known to play a role in heart and vascular diseases is diet. Diets high in saturated fats and low on "the good foods" (such as leafy green vegetables, fruits, and foods high in fiber) increase the likelihood of heart and vascular diseases such as high cholesterol and heart attack over the long term, whereas diets low in saturated fats and high on "the good foods" decrease the likelihood of these diseases. Thus, unhealthy diet is considered a *risk factor* for heart and vascular diseases, whereas healthy diet is considered a *protective factor*. Another important risk/protective factor for heart and vascular diseases is level of physical activity (i.e., low physical activity is a risk factor and moderate to high physical activity is a protective factor).

Although diet and physical activity are largely under the control of an individual, other risk and protective factors for heart and vascular diseases are often beyond the individual's control and may be genetic, environmental, or social in nature. For example, individuals may have more or less access to healthy foods and opportunities to participate in physical activities in their community. Similarly, the individual's family or friends may or may not model or support healthy eating habits. This raises the point that individuals often have both risk factors *and* protective factors for a particular health outcome (e.g., a healthy diet but few opportunities for physical activity). Thus, negative health outcomes occur when the number and severity of risk factors outweigh the number of protective factors.

Although treating individuals who already have health conditions such as heart and vascular diseases is undoubtedly important, preventing these conditions eliminates the need for risky and costly procedures and is thus the preferred approach. For example, compared to inserting stents into a patient's heart, promoting healthy dietary habits and physical activity through workplace promotions is relatively inexpensive and can be effective.

The first step in designing an effective preventive intervention is to identify the risk and protective factors for the outcome of interest. As noted, preventive interventions aim to increase the number of protective factors and decrease the number of risk factors. Therefore, knowledge of risk and protective factors helps intervention developers understand the variables that should be targeted in the intervention. For example, interventions aimed at preventing heart and vascular diseases often try to increase access to healthy foods and opportunities for physical activity and change individuals' attitudes about eating healthy foods and engaging in physical activity.

Types of Prevention

Primary prevention focuses on preventing something from occurring (e.g., heart and vascular diseases). There are three basic types of primary preventive interventions: universal, selected, and indicated. There are also secondary and tertiary prevention programs that focus on mitigating the effects of a problem once it has occurred, but that is beyond the scope of this chapter.

Universal preventive interventions are designed to promote health and prevent problems by targeting everyone in a population regardless of level of risk and protection. An example is the Wise Kids program developed by the Säjai® Foundation. Wise Kids aims to increase healthy eating and physical activity in primary school children. Through schools, recreation and park departments, YMCA/YWCAs, etc., Wise Kids is given to all kids in after school programs during the school year, or at day camps during the summer. Thus, everyone who goes to the after school program or day camp receives the program.

Like universal preventive interventions, selected preventive interventions also are designed to prevent problems before they happen. Selected interventions differ from universal interventions, however, in that they are only delivered to those groups of people who have risk factors for the outcome of interest in general. Further, the content matter of selected interventions often is specific to the group being targeted, whereas the content matter of universal interventions is often more broad. To revisit the Wise Kids example, research suggests that prevalence rates of suboptimal physical activity are especially high among African-American and Hispanic youth compared to White youth. Thus, modifying the Wise Kids intervention to target the risk factors for suboptimal physical activity specific to African-American and Hispanic youth and selectively targeting schools or districts with high proportions of African-American and Hispanic youth to deliver the Wise Kids intervention may deliver a lot of bang for the buck.

Whereas selected preventive interventions target those with risk factors for a particular problem, indicated preventive interventions are targeted at individuals who possess risk factors *and* early signs of the problem. Consider a school nurse who identifies youth in his or her school who are particularly at-risk of suboptimal physical activity *and* who are already overweight (an early sign of heart and vascular disease). In this case, a full-blown heart or vascular condition has not yet happened, but the odds of having problems are increased given the presence of risk factors and early signs of the problem. Thus, an indicated program might be to invite those specific youth and their parents to attend after school or weekend activities designed to promote family fun through physical activity.

Leisure: A Context of Risk, Protection, and Prevention

Leisure is considered one of the more "free" contexts in a person's life and potentially contains a number of health-promoting characteristics. Most people engage in leisure activities out of some sense of personal choice because the activities are inherently interesting (and therefore intrinsically motivating) or because they serve some future purpose (and are self-endorsed). In turn, intrinsic motivation is associated with health and well-being; at the same time, being nonintrinsically motivated (e.g., by some external reward like doing something to please someone else or because there is nothing else to do) is associated with negative health outcomes. In addition to intrinsic motivation, several other characteristics of leisure make it a unique context of protection. The following list of leisure-related characteristics have all been shown to be associated with many types of positive health (e.g., mental, physical, social, spiritual):

- Social support, friendships, and social acceptance are endemic to most leisure activities, and are important factors in the initiation and maintenance of health behaviors.
- Competence and self-efficacy are often derived from leisure participation.
- Leisure provides opportunities for experiences of challenge and being totally absorbed in leisure activity.
- Leisure provides opportunities for being self-determined and in control.
- Leisure activities provide a range of many types of opportunities for a number of experiences, including feeling relaxed, disengaged from stress, and being distracted from negative life events to being challenged and having high levels of excitement and risk.
- Nature-based and outdoor recreation experiences promote many forms of health. For example, being close to parks and trails are associated with higher levels of physical activity.

Although leisure has many health-promoting characteristics as just identified, it also is imperative to consider that leisure is a context for risky

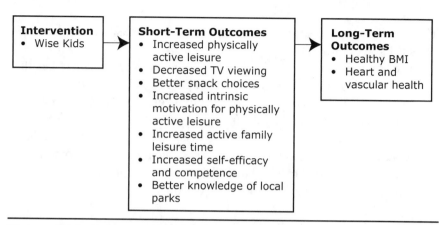

Figure 12.1 Outcomes Example

behaviors, such as substance misuse/abuse, acts of vandalism or violence, sexual risk, or being sedentary. Thus, prevention and promotion efforts that involve leisure must take into consideration the paradox that leisure can both promote health and reduce risk, yet also provide a context for risky and/or unhealthy behavior.

Leisure-Related Prevention Outcomes. As we have indicated, prevention efforts are deliberate attempts to reduce risk factors and promote protective factors. In prevention language, these factors are called outcomes: what we want to have happen as a result of what we do. Typically we target a long-term outcome (e.g., heart and vascular health) and a set of short-term outcomes that we think will lead to the long-term outcome (e.g., healthy diet and regular physical activity). You can think about the short-term outcomes as happening right after the intervention is completed, and the long-term outcomes as happening 6 to 12 months post-intervention. Preventive interventions specifically attempt to impact the short-term outcomes with the thought that they will cause the long-term outcome to happen. We have provided an example in Figure 12.1 using the Wise Kids program we previously mentioned, which includes only a partial list of potential short-term outcomes.

There are many possible types of leisure interventions that target a combination of individual, social, or environmental risk and protective factors. Common forms of these interventions are educational programs (e.g., school-based programs), media campaigns, or workplace promotions aimed at individual behavior or social groups. For example, prevention programs aimed at families may be more effective than programs that only try to change individual youth behavior. Other preventive interventions may focus on policies or opportunities and thus address environmental factors. As an example, it is common knowledge that the closer one is to a playground, park or trail, the more one is likely to routinely engage in physical activity.

Thus, policies or infrastructure development that increases access to these areas is likely to promote change.

The previous list of leisure-related characteristics that relate to health provides a starting point to consider developing leisure-based preventive interventions at individual, social, or environmental levels. As previously mentioned, first understanding the underlying etiology and causal pathways leading to the targeted health outcome is essential. Then, one can develop or choose a prevention program that targets reducing risk and promoting protective factors specifically related to that outcome. In the next section, we provide an example to consider from our own work.

Adolescents, Leisure, and Substance Use

One thread of our own work is rooted in the desire to prevent risky substance use and sexual risk behavior using a prevention curriculum designed to decrease related risk factors and increase leisure-based protective factors. We have developed, implemented, and evaluated two related universal primary preventive interventions: TimeWise: Taking Charge of Leisure Time, and HealthWise: Life Skills for Adolescents. Both of these address risk behaviors by educating youth to make healthy and good choices in their leisure time. TimeWise has been implemented in rural and urban Pennsylvania and HealthWise, which uses TimeWise as a basis but includes more focus on health behaviors and facts, was implemented and evaluated in Cape Town, South Africa. In general, both prevention programs were developed based on the leisure characteristics previously listed that connect to health.

We began by reviewing literature so that we could (a) determine appropriate theories of adolescent substance use (e.g., why adolescents do or do not use or misuse substances) and (b) establish risk and protective factors to target in the programs. When developing a new intervention, this always should be the first step. If the developers of an intervention cannot clearly articulate why they are taking a particular strategy based on theory and past research, it is much less likely that the program will be effective. Furthermore, if you are in the position to choose an existing preventive intervention, make sure this step was taken and there is evidence (i.e., a rigorous evaluation) that the intervention has been successful. This is termed an evidence-based intervention.

Based on a review of the literature and preliminary studies we did ourselves, we knew that leisure boredom was associated with substance use and misuse among adolescents. We also knew that if adolescents were *not* generally intrinsically motivated in their leisure activities, they were more likely to have problems such as substance use and mental health issues. For example, using self-determination theory, one study (1) found that college student athletes and exercisers who were extrinsically (as compared to intrinsically) motivated to participate were more likely to consume more alcohol, binge drink, use marijuana, and chew tobacco. Thus, TimeWise and HealthWise had lessons related to reducing boredom, increasing leisure interests, and teaching about the importance of being intrinsically motivated and the dangers of being amotivated (i.e., doing something without a purpose and feeling empty) and extrinsically motivated. Thinking back to our previous example of outcomes, in this case, boredom/interest and motivation were two of our short-term outcomes thought to influence our long-term prevention outcome: reducing substance misuse.

Selected TimeWise Results. One set of results from the TimeWise program came from approximately 600 rural middle school youth (2). We compared those who got the intervention (from four schools) to those who did not get the intervention (five schools) and collected data on them over a period of three years (beginning of 7th grade through the end of 9th grade). Findings indicated that those who received TimeWise were less amotivated and more intrinsically motivated. They were also better able to restructure boring situations into something more interesting and participated in new interests, sports, and nature-based activities. Marijuana and inhalant use was significantly lower for males, and although there were no other significant differences between youth who received TimeWise and youth who did not, the effects on substance use were consistently in the desired direction. From this study we can conclude that TimeWise did what it was supposed to do in terms of influencing protective and risk factors in the desired directions: more intrinsic motivation and interest, less boredom and amotivation.

The results on substance use were not surprising since at that age, very few rural youth have begun to use substances. But, that is the point! We wanted to get to them early and prevent the behavior from occurring. This brings us to an important prevention point: intervene as early as you can to prevent the risk behavior from occurring. You will need to know the typical trajectory of the health behavior in order to make that decision (i.e., understand the etiology). Do not wait until it has already occurred (then you have to think about treatment rather than prevention).

Of course, the dilemma here is: how do I know if I really prevented anything from occurring if I cannot see it? In our case, ideally we would have been able to follow the youth in our study through their high school years. In that way, we could have known for sure whether TimeWise was successful in preventing substance use. At least we took comfort in that our results were in the right direction.

Selected HealthWise Results. Now let us take a look at some of the findings from the HealthWise intervention. This intervention was delivered to students in four schools in Mitchell's Plain, South Africa (right outside of Cape Town), and students from five schools participated as a comparison group who did not receive the intervention. We collected data from the youth for a three-year period, starting at the beginning of 8th grade, and ending at the beginning of 11th grade. This long-term perspective allowed us to look at *patterns* of behavior across time, as well as take snapshot pictures of what they were doing at each time point. Once again, we were interested in leisure activities, leisure motivation, and how youth experienced their leisure (e.g., boredom). Of course we were interested in many other things, but we will focus on these for this chapter.

In her dissertation work using the HealthWise data, Tibbits (3) was interested in whether a youth's type of motivation and level of interest in a specific activity was associated with alcohol and tobacco use. She hypothesized that it was not the activity *per se* that was important, but rather whether or not one was internally motivated and interested in what one was doing that was associated with smoking and drinking. Tibbits found that, compared to youth who participated in one or more leisure activities but were motivated and interested, youth who participated in several leisure activities but were amotivated and bored in all of them had highest likelihood of alcohol and tobacco use. Furthermore, females who only spent leisure time in social activities and were amotivated and bored while doing so had a much higher likelihood of alcohol and tobacco use than females who only spent time in social activities but were interested and motivated.

We mentioned that patterns of behavior (in this case leisure motivation and boredom) over time are important to examine in terms of risk and protection. Another one of the HealthWise studies examined patterns of youth smoking over a period of three years. We found that youth who were extrinsically motivated, amotivated, and bored had higher odds of either starting to smoke, or of smoking consistently across time (4). Another HealthWise study also gave us some insight about the importance of understanding changes in leisure boredom across time (5). We found that a one unit increase in leisure boredom from the beginning of 8th grade to the beginning of 10th grade was associated with increased odds of using alcohol, cigarettes, and marijuana (14%, 23%, and 36%, respectively).

Conclusions from TimeWise and HealthWise. This brief discussion of results was provided to illustrate the notion that leisure can be an important context for examining risk and protective factors around adolescent substance use and misuse. These results also suggest that we can improve what we are doing. For example, we found gender differences in much of what we have studied. This means that to do an even more effective job, we should consider these gender differences. We might need to focus on some topics in a different way for boys and girls. Or, we might want to develop mini-sections of the intervention to target specific groups (an indicated prevention program within a universal program). Perhaps females in our HealthWise study who were in social situations and bored and amotivated may be a particularly significant group for whom to develop a more targeted intervention based on their needs and risk factors.

Co-morbidity of Health Risk Behaviors

There is another consideration when thinking about preventive efforts. Problem behaviors often co-occur. That is, health risk is influenced by a number of factors (e.g., personal, interpersonal, environmental) that combine to cause some people to be at various levels of risk. Although some prevention programs just target one specific issue (e.g., substance use or sedentary behavior), some people argue that effective prevention programs target personal, interpersonal, and environmental risk and protective factors associated with the onset and escalation of a particular health outcome or set of outcomes in a more comprehensive manner.

Research has shown, for example, that there is an association between substance use and depression, although the mechanisms that underlie these are associated are unknown (6). Depressed or stressed adolescents may use smoking, alcohol or drugs for their pharmacological effects. We also know that depression is strongly related to lack of motivation (6). Hopefully you can see by this brief example how important a more complete understanding of how health risk factors interrelate can better inform preventive interventions.

Summary and Conclusion

In this chapter, we have introduced you to a number of related topics: risk and protective factors, prevention, and how leisure is a context for prevention by reducing risk and promoting health factors. The following points summarize the major topics of our discussion.

1. Individuals have both risk and protective factors in their lives, some of which are under their control and some of which are not. This balance represents a risk/protection profile and can help health care providers assess someone's risk of a disease or negative health condition.

2. It is more cost effective and typically healthier to prevent something from happening than to treat it after it happens. Prevention efforts

require that appropriate risk and protective factors are identified.

3. Leisure promotes many types of protective factors, but also is a context for risk factors. This makes leisure a particularly important context for prevention.

4. It is important to understand the theory behind what leisure risk and protective factors might contribute to the outcome of interest and to choose prevention programs or develop your own program that targets those specific factors. If you choose an existing program, make sure it is evidence-based.

5. It is best to intervene as early as possible to prevent the targeted behavior from occurring. This requires knowledge of the etiology of the targeted behavior.

6. Leisure may have the most benefit to prevention and promotion of health if human motivation and experiences associated with leisure activities are considered. It is also important to take a long-term perspective to understand patterns of activity and experiences.

7. Consider for whom and under what conditions the prevention intervention might work. It may work better for males than females, or for middle school youth rather than high school youth.

8. Usually health risk behaviors or the underlying risk factors co-occur. Thus, sometimes the best method of prevention is not to single out a particular risk factor (e.g., alcohol misuse) but to target a group of related risk factors (e.g., smoking, alcohol misuse, and physical inactivity) or protective factors (e.g., social support through leisure and increasing intrinsic motivation).

References

1. Rockafellow BD, Saules KK. Substance use by college students: The role of intrinsic versus extrinsic motivation for athletic involvement. *Psychol Addict Behav* 2006;**20**:279–287.
2. Caldwell LL, Baldwin CK, Walls T, Smith EA. Preliminary effects of a leisure education program to promote healthy use of free time among middle school students. *J Leisure Res* 2004;**36**:310–335
3. Tibbits MK. Engagement within and across leisure activities in adolescence: Implications for substance use and sexual activity. Dissertation: Pennsylvania State University, 2009.
4. Palen L, Smith EA, Caldwell LL, Bray BC, Flisher AJ. Longitudinal patterns of cigarette use and their relations to free time engagement among youth in Cape Town, South Africa. *Journal of Health Psychology*. Submitted for publication.
5. Sharp EH, Coffman DL, Caldwell LL, Smith EA, Wegner L, Flisher AJ, et al. Predicting substance use behavior among South African adolescents: The role of free time experiences. *Journal of Developmental Psychology*. Submitted for publication.
6. Kelder SH, Murray NG, Orpinas P, Prokhorov A, McReynolds L, Zhang Q, et al. Depression and substance use in minority middle-school students. *Am J Publ Health* 2001;**91**:761–766.

Chapter 13
Leisure and Becoming Physically Active

Melissa Bopp
Andrew T. Kaczynski

Introduction

The connection between health and physical activity is well-documented and this relationship is emphasized almost daily in laments about issues such as childhood obesity and the physical inactivity of North American populations in general. Low levels of physical activity have been linked to many physical and mental health problems and a lack of physical activity is, along with poor nutrition and smoking, among the top three modifiable risk factors for chronic disease and premature death (1). Consequently, improving population-level physical activity rates has consistently been identified as a top public health priority.

This book is a testament, of course, to the many health-related benefits leisure behaviors and settings can confer to both individuals and communities. One of these benefits, and an increasingly valued and recognized one, is the promotion of physical activity. Interestingly, leisure researchers and practitioners have, until recently, tended to focus on other benefits of leisure, including those related to psychological and spiritual health or economic or social concerns (2). This may have been an attempt over the past half century to differentiate the fields of leisure studies and services from their roots in physical education in order to better establish the unique contributions of this relatively youthful area of research. However, as is described later in this chapter, leisure behaviors and settings are now acknowledged to be integral to physical activity by researchers and professionals both within and beyond the domains of leisure, parks, and recreation.

Physical Activity Recommendations

There are several and significant health benefits that have been attributed to increased physical activity levels, and much attention has been devoted to developing clear guidelines for the public about the recommended types and quantity of physical activity. Current guidelines for physical activity are a compilation of many decades of research investigating the frequency, intensity, duration, and type of physical activity that results in positive health outcomes. Guidelines have evolved over several decades, moving from more intense, performance-based outcome recommendations focusing primarily on leisure-time activities and structured exercise to current guidelines which are more health-oriented and include less structured approaches. To that end, occupational, household, and transportation-related physical activity are all emphasized in addition to the traditional notion of leisure-time activity. The U.S. Department of Health and Human Services' recent recommendations for adults indicate that 150 minutes per week of moderate intensity aerobic activity (e.g., brisk walking) will result in health benefits, including a reduced risk of disease as outlined earlier (1). Alternatively, benefits can also be obtained with 75 minutes per week of vigorous aerobic physical activity. Additionally, it is important to note that even small amounts of physical activity have been shown to be beneficial compared with being completely sedentary, and physical activity levels beyond the stated guidelines can result in additional benefits. Specific guidelines for older adults indicate that 150 minutes of physical activity are also beneficial for this age group, although special considerations may be needed related to chronic health conditions that are often found among older adults. Children and adolescents are recommended to perform 60 minutes of physical activity daily, which should include aerobic activity of moderate or vigorous intensity to improve cardiorespiratory fitness, as well as activity that will result in muscle and bone strengthening.

Prevalence of Physical Activity

Trends in physical activity participation have remained relatively stable over the past 10–20 years. Although there are differences between different countries in the portion of the population that is meeting recommendations, overall differences between population subgroups remain relatively similar worldwide. Physical activity participation decreases with age, with a significant decline in older age, precisely during a time when individuals could benefit the most from regular activity. On average, men are more active than women, a trend that begins in childhood and translates into similar patterns in adulthood. Individuals from ethnic or racial minority groups are less likely to be active when compared with Caucasians, and education and income are positively related to physical activity levels. In the United States, self-reported data from national surveys indicate that approximately half of the population (48.8%) is meeting current recommendations for physical activity (1). Of those who are not meeting recommendations, approximately 14% are completely sedentary (less than 10 minutes of physical activity/week). Current recommendations include physical activity from leisure-time, occupational, household and transportation domains; however, it is noteworthy that approximately 25% of the population does not even engage in any leisure-time physical activity. Among youth, self-report data indicates that 38.5% of high school students in the U.S. are currently meeting recommendations.

Data from other national surveys using objective forms of physical activity measurement (e.g., accelerometers) suggest that the number of individuals meeting current recommendations is substantially lower than those described with self-report methods. This more recent finding suggests that physical inactivity is a much larger problem than was previously understood, re-confirming the notion that large scale, public health approaches incorporating multilevel strategies are increasingly important.

Social Ecological Influences on Physical Activity

As physical activity research and promotion have expanded to emphasize activity that occurs in diverse settings and at different levels of intensity, social ecological models have been widely adopted to better understand the myriad of factors that can influence active behaviors. Several authors have described the utility of social ecological models to active living and health promotion more broadly (3, 4). Much of this work is based on a model developed by McLeroy et al. (5) which proposes five classes of factors that affect how or why a person might participate or fail to participate in a healthy behavior such as physical activity. These levels are labeled intrapersonal, interpersonal, institutional, community, and public policy factors (Figure 13.1). Social ecological models emphasize that complex health

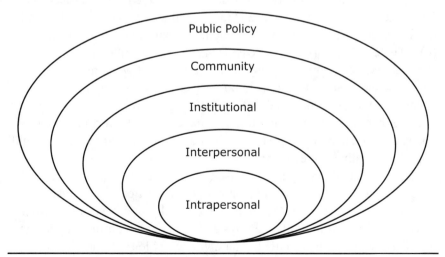

Figure 13.1 Social ecological model to explain influences on physical activity behaviors

behaviors such as physical inactivity are best understood and addressed using a multilevel approach. Further, interactions between levels should also be taken into account (e.g., how confidence in one's ability to be more active may be influenced by living close to an attractive park). Finally, targeting multiple types and levels of influences is a daunting task and will require collaboration among both academics and professionals from numerous disciplines to plan, implement, and evaluate comprehensive efforts to increase physical activity participation.

Within the social ecological model, *intrapersonal* factors include the knowledge, skills, attitudes, behaviors, and other individual traits of potential physical activity participants. This level of influence also includes demographic variables such as age and race/ethnicity, the impact of which are described elsewhere in this book. Medical history and personal experience with physical activity are also possible intrapersonal influences. Physician counseling, mass media campaigns, and peer support groups are examples of common physical activity intervention strategies that are sometimes delivered at a level greater than the individual, but that are nevertheless directed at influencing intrapersonal characteristics in order to evoke the desired behavior change.

Numerous intrapersonal factors that influence physical activity have been studied at length, but a few traits have demonstrated a consistent association with initiating and maintaining a more physically active lifestyle. In particular, psychological factors are a frequent target within physical activity intervention programs, and have often shown strong relationships with behavior. For example, of all the constructs associated with physical activity, likely the most widely studied is self-efficacy. Self-efficacy can be defined as an "individual's beliefs in his or her abilities to execute necessary courses of action to satisfy situational demands (6)." Therefore, a person will possess varying levels of self-efficacy for different behaviors (e.g., physical activity, healthy eating, public speaking, etc.). Self-efficacy is hypothesized to be a strong influence on behavior because higher levels of self-efficacy are related to a propensity to undertake more challenging tasks, to expend more effort in pursuit of goals, and to demonstrate greater resilience in the face of aversive stimuli (e.g., bad weather, time constraints).

Some of the defining characteristics of leisure settings make them especially conducive to the development of self-efficacy for physical activity (7). For example, leisure pursuits usually involve *freely-chosen* activities which an individual enjoys and is likely to continue to engage in. Likewise, this enjoyment and maintenance of leisure pursuits also results from activities being *intrinsically-motivated*, rather than prompted by incentives that are external to the individual. Finally, because their activities are freely-chosen and intrinsically-motivated, people are likely to experience increased feelings of *control* during their leisure time. All of these characteristics that are inherent within or accrue from leisure settings and activities provide an especially fertile playground for the development of self-efficacy. For example, a child who is permitted to se- lect an outdoor activity of his or her choice may develop an intrinsic lust for that activity along with greater perceptions of control and autonomy. These feelings can all lead to increased self-efficacy for physical activity and a greater likelihood of continued participation. At the same time, self-efficacy is just one factor within a host of psychological variables that have demonstrated strong relationships with physical activity partici- pation. Enjoyment of physical activity, perception of barriers for physical activity participation, and knowledge and valuation of benefits are some other intrapersonal influences.

Interpersonal factors within the social ecological model include rela- tionships with family members, friends, coworkers, neighbors, and other acquaintances. The opinions and support of these people in encouraging or discouraging physical activity participation has been widely documented. Social support can be provided in many different forms, including instru- mental support, informational support, emotional support, or modeling (8). Instrumental support can involve an offer to participate in the activity with the person being supported or assistance with fees, transportation, or other auxiliary concerns. Informational support may include sharing knowledge about benefits of or opportunities for physical activity. Emotional support encompasses encouragement and interest in the person engaging in physi- cal activity. Finally, social support for exercise and physical activity can also occur through seeing another person model exercise participation and an overall active lifestyle. In general, the social nature of many leisure pursuits offers an inherent strength for developing social support that can help in initiating and maintaining physical activity behaviors. For example, individuals may create a formal or informal neighborhood walking group to encourage physical activity participation. Likewise, friendships developed in other non-active leisure settings or activities might lead to the sharing of emotional and informational support that can benefit physically activity pursuits as well.

Of course, not all interpersonal interactions are equally beneficial for physical activity. Participating in physical activity with a spouse or chil- dren may have numerous familial benefits, but the level of challenge or the choice of activity may have to be adjusted to accommodate the presence other family members. Similarly, parents often have to subvert their own physical activity participation altogether to cater to their child's activity preferences. One solution may be to better design multigenerational physical activity facilities, such as playgrounds that incorporate a walking track around them for parents who might otherwise be watching their children play while being inactive on a bench. Other ideas should also be investigated for positively manipulating the interpersonal components of physical activities or contexts.

The third level of influence which may impact health behaviors are *organizational or institutional* factors. Organizational settings such as schools, churches, healthcare settings, and workplaces provide the context for much of the activities people engage in during the course of a day. These settings are unique in that they include physical and social environments as well as policies that impact physical activity. A setting may include a physical environment that is arranged to promote physical activity (e.g., an office building with signs next to the elevator encouraging taking the stairs), or a social environment where the norm is physical activity (e.g., an office that encourages "walking meetings"). Policies pertaining to physical activity may also influence behavior for those individuals within an institution (e.g., a school that takes away a student's physical education class as a disciplinary measure).

Perhaps the greatest influence organizations have on physical activity participation is the potential to offer programs and interventions with a large reach. There are a number of advantages to offering interventions in these settings, including an established system for flow of information (e.g., emails, newsletters, and websites), access to safe facilities for holding activities, and increased potential for sustainability of the intervention by training individuals within the setting to conduct the intervention. Setting-based intervention strategies have the ability to target multiple levels of factors influencing physical activity, including intrapersonal factors (e.g., educational materials and classes), interpersonal factors (e.g., activities to enhance social support), and institutional factors (e.g., policies developed to promote physical activity). Although leisure may not have as direct of an impact on this level as others in the social ecological model, the potential for impacting physical activity behavior through setting-based interventions is substantial.

Community factors are also important influences on health behavior. One way that parks and recreation promote physical activity is through their integral role in creating neighborhoods and communities that are more "activity-friendly." In the broader physical activity field, considerable emphasis is now placed on the role of built, physical, and social environments in either facilitating or discouraging physical activity. For example, having sidewalks, streetlights, trails, and nearby stores or workplaces to walk or bike to are just some of the ways we can better design our surroundings to encourage physical activity as part of daily routines. Within this urban planning paradigm, parks and recreation facilities are acknowledged as important behavior settings for physical activity. Kaczynski and Henderson (9) conducted a review of 50 studies that had investigated whether proximity to parks and/or recreation facilities was related to increased physical activity levels of residents who participated in the studies. They found that 80% of the articles reported at least some positive associations between the parks and recreation and physical activity variables that were examined. A rapidly growing body of research is also documenting the types and intensities of physical activities that occur in parks and recreation contexts as well as the characteristics and features of these settings that are more conducive to promoting physical activity.

Community factors may also impact physical activity participation via the effective coordination of multiple agencies' efforts and through the exertion of power and influence in setting and addressing public health priorities. For example, a bond proposal to build a new recreation center using public tax money may be more likely to succeed if it is developed, supported, and advocated for by the local public health department, parks and recreation agency, and police force. Each of these agencies may have a different motivation for wanting to see the facility built (e.g., reducing health care costs, increasing quality of life, reducing youth crime), but their joint efforts to promote its construction and use for physical activity and other pursuits is an example of how community factors can impact health priorities and behaviors. Likewise, recreation agencies and school districts often develop formal or informal joint-use agreements in which the parties share facilities (e.g., school gyms, municipal arenas) during the hours when such resources might otherwise sit empty. Other examples like this exist whereby communities can come together to more effectively foster physical activity participation among adults and children alike.

Finally, *public policy* plays a critical role in maintaining population health and preventing the further spread of infectious and chronic diseases. Laws and regulations can deter certain behaviors (e.g., smoking) that are deemed sufficiently detrimental through both positive and negative actions (e.g., increased taxes on cigarettes; smoking bans in public places). Similarly, public policy can promote a positive behavior, such as physical activity, through government funding and ordinances (e.g., providing bike lanes on all major streets), while also discouraging it through other regulations (e.g., zoning laws that segregate land uses so that people live too far to walk to stores or restaurants).

With respect to leisure, parks, and recreation, numerous opportunities exist to develop policies that can encourage physical activity. Tax incentives can be an effective economic tool to influence behaviors. In some states and provinces, income tax deductions are permitted for purchases of physical activity equipment (e.g., bikes) or for enrolling youth in recreation programs that will contribute to improved cardiovascular health. Likewise, many jurisdictions have implemented ordinances disallowing smoking in public parks or near playgrounds, thereby creating a more pleasant physical activity environment for children and other park users. At a fundamental level, most cities have land dedication policies that stipulate that a certain percentage of land that is to be developed for residential or commercial uses must be set aside as open space. However, challenges exist in ensuring that the dedicated land is suitable for physical activity and that concomitant funding is also available to properly design and maintain the space for active use.

Parks and recreation agencies also need to examine the level of equity that exists in the distribution of parks and recreation facilities across their communities and adjust policies and allocation practices accordingly. Extensive research shows that persons from disadvantaged and under-represented groups (e.g., low-income or racial minority backgrounds) exhibit lower rates of physical activity and higher incidences of obesity and chronic diseases (10, 11). Part of this may be attributed to the related concern that other research has reported that areas with higher minority and/or low income populations generally have fewer parks and recreation resources (and that these areas are often perceived as being poorer quality or less safe) (12, 13).This phenomenon has been referred to as "deprivation amplification" (14) in that persons with fewer *personal* resources that might support physical activity (e.g., income, knowledge of physical activity benefits) also tend to reside in areas that are more deprived of *neighborhood* physical activity resources (e.g., sidewalks, parks). For example, one national study reported that high-minority/low-education areas were half as likely to have at least one physical activity facility as low-minority/high-education areas (15). Further, among adolescents in the study, having just one facility nearby was associated with a 3% increase in achieving five or more bouts of physical activity per week and a 5% decrease in the odds of being overweight. When translated to the larger population, these differences have significant health implications. Overall, initiatives and policies such as those described above have significant potential to impact the promotion of physical activity through leisure, parks, and recreation.

While physical activity is a complex behavior, there are many influences that could impact participation. A summary of influences can be found in Table 13.1. Interventions, programs, or services, including those involving leisure and public health activities or settings, should be cognizant of these influences in developing targeted and tailored programs for promoting physical activity adoption and maintenance.

Table 13.1 Social ecological model to explain influences on physical activity behaviors

Level of Influence	Definition Related to Physical Activity	Examples of Influences
Intrapersonal	Biological and psychological behavioral influences that are unique to the individual	• Demographic (age, gender, race/ethnicity) • Medical history (disease status, weight) • Psychological (self-efficacy, perceived barriers, enjoyment)
Interpersonal	Interpersonal groups and relationships that create a social environment and provide social support	• Family • Friends • Co-workers • Acquaintances • Healthcare provider
Institutional/ setting	Organizations that include policies and environments that can promote or discourage behaviors	• Schools • Workplaces • Churches/faith organizations
Community	A network of multiple institutions, can include geographically defined areas	• Social and physical resources • Access and opportunities
Policy	Local, state, or federal policies, laws, and legislations that can support or impede health behaviors	• Laws or ordinances that promote access to physical and activity programs • State or local resource allocations to support activity-friendly environments

Future Directions for Physical Activity, Parks and Recreation, and Public Health

This chapter has discussed the issue of physical activity, including its health benefits, recommended levels, and prevalence, as well as factors that affect physical activity participation across the levels of influence in the social ecological model. Although this chapter focused on physical activity, it is noteworthy to consider the effect of sedentary leisure activities on active behaviors. Considerable evidence suggests that growing participation in screen time (e.g., television, video games) among children, adolescents, and adults is related to reduced time spent being active. This may be due to some of the attractive properties of these electronic activities, including their ability to facilitate feelings of either flow or relaxation, or the potential for social interaction and the development of sub-cultures and social worlds. Future research and health promotion interventions need to consider how such intra- and interpersonal factors can be combined with broader environmental and policy influences to either change the relative attractiveness of sedentary or active pursuits or make them work cooperatively to create a more balanced lifestyle. For example, in one experimental study in which families were paid to adhere to a reduced screen time protocol, all children reduced their electronic media use to more acceptable levels and exhibited higher levels of physical activity, but children living closer to parks experienced an even greater increase in active behaviors (16). Certainly, other opportunities exist as well to take advantage of the potential for cross-fertilization between research in leisure studies and public health (17, 18). As mentioned previously, leisure researchers have largely avoided topics related to physiological health, including physical activity, in favor of investigating the wide-ranging psychological, social, and economic impacts parks, recreation, and leisure can have on individuals and communities. However, tremendous opportunity exists for those who study parks, recreation, and leisure behavior to contribute to the public health dilemma of physical inactivity.

For example, most research in public health on the built environment and physical activity that adopts a social ecological perspective is inherently spatial. Very often, it addresses issues related to distance, direction, size, and shape, but is generally isolated from cultural and social interpretation. In contrast, researchers in leisure and environmental studies, among other fields, have a significant grounding and particular interest in the meanings people instill on cherished spaces, such as parks, through the study of constructs related to "place." In future, research on the influence of parks and recreation facilities on physical activity can benefit from combining the perspectives of both place and space to better understand the many factors that shape active behaviors in these settings.

Other concepts in leisure studies also show parallels with ideas from public health. For instance, the notion of constraints in leisure studies—including intrapersonal, interpersonal, and structural constraints—closely mirrors the different levels of the social ecological model at which exercise and health behaviors have been studied. For example, self-efficacy (or a lack thereof) is one type of intrapersonal constraint on physical activity, while poor social support and neighborhood walkability may be seen as interpersonal and structural constraints, respectively. The theoretical underpinnings of most constraints and physical activity research also overlap with both being largely grounded in social cognitive theory (SCT) (19). Researchers from exercise sciences have used SCT variables and principles in studying physical activity, but leisure constraints researchers have likewise made significant conceptual advances in the application of SCT to physical activity through ideas such as negotiation. Given that they have such a great amount of common ground, it is not hard to envision constraints and exercise behavior researchers coming together more frequently and productively in future to better understand people's participation or nonparticipation in physically active leisure.

Finally, one last area of mutual interest of leisure and health practitioners is the value of further exploring notions of community in relation to physical activity and overall health. A growing body of epidemiological research in public health has provided evidence of a positive link between various indicators of social capital and physical activity. These studies show that people who are more engaged politically and socially in their communities exhibit more physically active behavior and less sedentary behavior. Some research has also established a connection between living in a more walkable neighborhood and increased perceptions of social capital. Therefore, the mutually beneficial relationship between walkable neighborhoods, social capital, and recreational and utilitarian physical activity merits further exploration as a means to promote the physical and social health of residents. Leisure studies researchers have made significant conceptual and practical advancements in examining ideas related to community and social capital, perhaps due to the suggestion that leisure is central to the bonding and bridging behaviors necessary to develop community connectedness. However, when further exploring these linkages in future, an increased focus on outcomes related to physical activity and physical health may prove fruitful.

In summary, the public health issues of physical activity and inactivity will grow in importance in the 21st century as rates of obesity and chronic diseases continue to escalate. In the coming years, aspects of leisure, parks, and recreation are likely to become even more central to understanding and addressing such concerns. By working together, researchers and professionals in public health and leisure services can strive toward the goal of a healthier population and a reduction in chronic disease.

References

1. Physical Activity Guidelines Advisory Committee. Physical Activity Guidelines Advisory Committee Report, 2008. U.S. Department of Health and Human Services: Washington DC, 2008.
2. Driver BL, Bruns DH. Concepts and uses of the benefits approach to leisure. In Jackson EL, Burton TL (eds), *Leisure Studies: Prospects for the Twenty-First Century*. State College, PA: Venture Publishing, Inc., 1999, pp. 349–369.
3. Sallis JF, Owen N, Fisher EB. Ecological Models of Health Behavior. In Glanz K, Rimer BK, Viswanath K (eds), *Health Behavior and Health Education. Theory, Research and Practice* (4th ed.). San Francisco: Jossey-Bass, 2008, pp. 465–485.
4. Sallis JF, Cervero RB, Ascher W, Henderson KA, Kraft MK, Kerr J. An ecological approach to creating active living communities. *Annu Rev Public Health* 2006;**27**:297–322.
5. McLeroy KR, Bibeau D, Steckler A, Glanz K. An ecological perspective on health promotion programs. *Health Educ Q* 1988;**15/4**:351–377.
6. McAuley E, Pena MM, Jerome GJ. Self-Efficacy as a Determinant and an Outcome of Exercise. In Roberts GC (ed), *Advances in Motivation in Sport and Exercise*. Human Kinetics, Champaign, IL, 2001, pp. 235–261.
7. Mannell RC, Kleiber DA. *A Social Psychology of Leisure*. Venture Publishing, Inc.: State College, PA, 1997.
8. Duncan SC, Duncan TE, Strycker LA. Sources and types of social support in youth physical activity. *Health Psychol* 2005;**24/1**:3–10.
9. Kaczynski AT, Henderson KA. Environmental correlates of physical activity: A review of evidence about parks and recreation. *Leisure Sci* 2007;**29/4**:315–354.
10. Trost SG, Owen N, Bauman AB, Sallis JF, Brown W. Correlates of adults' participation in physical activity: Review and update. *Med Sci Sports Exerc* 2002;**34/12**:1996–2001.
11. U.S. Department of Health and Human Services. *Healthy People 2010. 2nd ed. With Understanding and Improving Health and Objectives for Improving Health*. U.S. Government Printing Office: U.S. Department of Health and Human Services: Washington, DC, 2000.
12. Moore LV, Diez Roux AV, Evenson KR, McGinn AP, Brines SJ. Availability of recreational resources in minority and low socioeconomic status areas. *Am J Prev Med* 2008;**34/1**:16–22.
13. Powell LM, Slater S, Chaloupka FJ, Harper D. Availability of physical activity-related facilities and neighborhood demographic and socioeco-

nomic characteristics: a national study. *Am J Public Health* 2006;**96/9**:1676–80.

14. Macintyre S. Deprivation amplification revisited; or, is it always true that poorer places have poorer access to resources for healthy diets and physical activity? *Int J Behav Nutr Phys Act* 2007;**4**:32.

15. Gordon-Larsen P, Nelson MC, Page P, Popkin BM. Inequality in the built environment underlies key health disparities in physical activity and obesity. *Pediatrics* 2006;**117/2**:417–24.

16. Epstein LH, Raja S, Gold SS, Paluch RA, Pak Y, Roemmich JN. Reducing sedentary behavior: the relationship between park area and the physical activity of youth. *Psychol Sci* 2006;**17/8**:654–9.

17. Godbey GC, Caldwell LL, Floyd M, Payne LL. Contributions of leisure studies and recreation and park management research to the active living agenda. *Am J Prev Med* 2005;**28/2** (Supp 2):150–8.

18. Ainsworth BE, Mannell RC, Behrens TK, Caldwell LL. Perspectives of public health and leisure studies on determinants of physically active leisure. *J Phys Act Health* 2007;**4** (Supp 1):S24–35.

19. Mannell RC, Loucks-Atkinson A. Why Don't People Do What's "Good" for Them? Cross-Fertilization Among the Psychologies of Nonparticipation in Leisure, Health, and Exercise Behaviors. In Jackson E (ed), *Constraints to Leisure*. State College, PA: Venture Publishing, Inc., 2005, pp. 221–232.

Chapter 14
Leisure and Stress Reduction

Yoshitaka Iwasaki

Introduction

What triggers your mind when you think of "stress"? Have you ever felt
that your life is stressful? Is stress bothering you or taking over your life
lately? Stress is a very prevalent and pervasive issue for many of us in
contemporary life. Not only do high pressure and demand in our life (e.g.,
education, work, financial, family, and relationship issues) make us feel
stressed, but our social system also presents structural stress due to various
types of "isms" (e.g., sexism, racism, classism, ableism, ageism, hetero-
sexism/homophobia) concerning discrimination and oppression based
on power imbalance (e.g., men vs. women, white vs. colored). Because
life without stress is almost impossible, we must find ways to effectively
manage stress, including the reduction of stress through various methods
for our survival and thriving. One of the key stress reduction methods
for many of us appears to be the constructive use of leisure in our daily
life. For example, yoga that values the harmony among body, mind, and
spirit seems to have stress-reducing benefits, while some people find that
a leisure-time physical activity such as walking or running helps reduce
stress. Addressing issues relevant to those who may be under high stress,
this chapter focuses broadly on the role of leisure in the reduction of stress.

What is Stress?

First, we wonder what stress is. We often feel stressed when our perceived
ability is thought to be insufficient or limited to deal with or overcome a
taxing or challenging experience (1). For example, an interpersonal conflict
in a relationship with your partner or friend may cause stress, while being
stuck in a bumper-to-bumper traffic before going to an important appoint-
ment (e.g., job interview) may make you stressed. A feeling of stress, however, can be triggered by a variety of stressors including both micro (e.g.,
daily hassles) and macro stressors (e.g., structural discrimination) in various life domains (e.g., personal, family, community, work, educational).
For instance, time pressure to complete a work-related task (i.e., deadline)
or a parent's struggle to discipline one's child can be a daily hassle,
whereas racism experienced among racial/ethnic minorities or ableism
experienced by persons with disabilities can be more societal and political

by limiting their rights to pursue life opportunities from a macrostructural perspective. Besides chronic stressors such as chronic illnesses or diseases (e.g., diabetes, arthritis), significant life events can cause stress including traumatic events such as abuse (e.g., physical, sexual), death of significant others, or natural disasters. Being distinguished from stressors (i.e., sources or causes of stress), consequences of stress include both psychological (e.g., distress, depression, anxiety) and physiological (e.g., elevated blood pressure, heart rate, cortisol response) stress responses. In some situations, however, stress may be felt as positive, particularly when the occurrence of an event is considered desirable or exciting (e.g., wedding ceremony, sport competition). Nevertheless, this chapter deals with the ways in which leisure may contribute to reducing negative stress.

How Can Leisure Help People Feel Less Stressed?

Considering the focus of this entire book on the connections of leisure to health and well-being, what role can leisure play in managing stress and then maintaining/promoting good health? The notion of how leisure can help people cope with stress will be discussed in the next chapter, whereas the present chapter focuses on the reduction of stress through leisure.

Freely Chosen Enjoyable Activity to Gain Meanings of Life

First, a key aspect of this stress-reduction process via leisure is that leisure can provide a unique opportunity to engage in a relatively freely chosen enjoyable or pleasurable activity that can help people gain valued meanings of life. As a result of involving in such an enjoyable and meaningful activity by choice, one of the key outcomes often includes stress reduction. For example, a nature walk within wilderness may provide such an enjoyable and peaceful opportunity to gain a spiritual meaning as a way of spiritual renewal and stress reduction. In fact, Hull and Michael's study on nature-based recreation showed that stress reduction appears to result while people recreate in the natural environment (2). Their conclusion was based on mood changes observed at the start, middle, and end of their participants' leisure experiences. For example, they found that "anxiety decreased during the park visit, and this was more so for highly stressed persons than for less stressed persons" (p. 12). Showing the connection of gaining a spiritual meaning to stress reduction, Unruh, Smith, and Scammell found that gardening as a leisure activity acts as a spiritual enabler to facilitate stress reduction and meaningfulness under extremely stressful circumstances such as dealing with cancer (3). Godbey summarized the research literature on the health benefits of outdoor recreation (e.g., peaceful stress reduction) including how children's health problems (e.g., child obesity) could be mitigated through outdoor play, sports, and nature study (4).

Stress-Reducing Capacity of Leisure Based on Activity Typology

Researchers have also used the typology or activity classifications of leisure to examine the stress-reducing capacity of leisure. For example, Caltabiano examined the dimensionality of leisure based on perceived capacity of leisure activities to reduce stress (5). According to her factor analysis of 83 leisure activities (e.g., jogging, camping, visiting friends, listening to music) reported by 340 respondents in Cairns, Australia, three groups of activities were identified (including outdoor-active sport, social, and cultural-hobbies leisure) and were "perceived to be equivalent in potential to reduce stress" (p. 17). On the other hand, Iwasaki, Mannell, Smale, and Butcher's short-term longitudinal study with 132 police and emergency response services workers in Winnipeg, Canada provided evidence that the type of leisure activity matters in predicting better adaptational outcomes including stress reduction (6). Specifically, of the seven major groups of leisure activity examined (e.g., physically active leisure, social leisure), relaxing leisure was found to be the strongest predictor of stress reduction. Greater "enjoyment" in relaxing leisure also had a positive and significant association with stress reduction, alluding to the need for giving attention to the quality of leisure experiences (e.g., enjoyment, satisfaction), as opposed to activity/behavior per se for better understanding the ways of stress reduction through leisure. These results are consistent with the major findings of Trenberth, Dewe, and Walkey study on the role of leisure in dealing with work stress among 695 principals of secondary schools in New Zealand (7). They found that the passive and recuperative type of leisure had a stronger impact on reducing or managing work stress than did the active and challenging type of leisure. To relax and to do something quiet and peaceful were key aspects of the passive and recuperative type of leisure in their study. Likewise, Zuzanek, Robinson, and Iwasaki suggested on the basis of their analyses of the 1990 U.S. National Health Interview Survey (n=31,868) that high stress levels may be better countered by "leisurely" activities involving relaxation and recuperation than by physical exercise alone (8).

The idea of stress reduction is also signified in Mair's discussion of health and wellness tourism as a key illness prevention strategy (9). Due to a rising demand for and interest in alternative medical treatments, health tourism (i.e., travel for health and well-being) is a growing industry world-wide (10). One major motivation for such form of tourism seems to be the reduction of stress for a health and wellness purpose. On the other hand, *stress-reduction,* calming, and relaxation effects of just watching fish were highlighted as major benefits reported by home aquarium owners as a way of lessening anxieties and creating a sense of serenity (11). More broadly, the ownership of and interaction with a pet may generate a benefit of stress reduction.

There is also research evidence that working adults (n = 32,229) participating in moderate amounts of leisure-time physical activities (LTPA) or exercise have about half the rate of perceived stress as non-participants, showing a strong relationship between LTPA and stress reduction (12). Consistent with this finding, Zuzanek et al.'s analysis of a U.S. population health survey suggested that the subjective perception of being physically active was significantly associated with lower levels of stress for both women and men (8). Also, Iwasaki found that leisure palliative coping (i.e., taking a break to "breathe" from stressors and restore one's energy to "regroup") significantly predicted perceived stress reduction among Canadian university students (13). For example, going for a walk or eating out with friends to have a time-out and refresh one's mind is considered a way of leisure palliative coping to reduce perceived stress. Furthermore, speaking of the benefits of leisure, Baum suggested that leisure is the antithesis of psychophysiological changes due to stress, claiming that one virtue of leisure is stress reduction (14). There is also research evidence that engaging in an Aboriginal dance (e.g., powwow), a "gay" holiday, or social leisure with friends who never talk about having a disability as an issue helps reduce perceived stress among those "marginalized" groups of individuals (i.e., Aboriginal/Indigenous persons, gays/lesbians, and individuals with disabilities, respectively) (15).

Stress Reduction Through *Therapeutic Recreation* (TR) Practices

Now, from a service-provision perspective, the idea of stress reduction is essential to *therapeutic recreation* (TR) practices (16, 17). For example, Kelley and Loy's intervention study with women who live with fibromyalgia (FMS) provided evidence that both aquatic- and land-based exercise had an impact on reducing salivary cortisol as a psychophysiological marker of *stress* (18). Also, Patterson and Fallu suggested that a casual leisure activity (as opposed to a serious type of leisure) can create a pleasurable experience in a relaxing yet at times stimulating environment as a way of reducing stress for individuals with severe developmental disabilities (19). Latimer, Martin Ginis, and Hicks' study showed the role of exercise in buffering or reducing the effects of *stress* on well-being among people with spinal cord injury (SCI) (20), while Griffin discussed a leisure-based psychoeducational group to address trauma issues in the treatment of posttraumatic *stress* disorder (PTSD) caused, for example, by childhood abuse (21). Furthermore, Hebblethwaite and Pedlar's interview study found managing or reducing *stress* as one of the major TR-driven factors to facilitate community reintegration among older adults with mental illness who have been discharged from a hospital (22). Alluding to the role of TR among children and youth, researchers including Cassidy and Passmore and French found that reduced psychological distress is a key outcome from leisure engagements among adolescents besides other benefits such as increased optimism and perceived competence or self-efficacy (23, 24). Finally, managing or reducing stress is a key concept covered in a recent special issue of the *Therapeutic Recreation Journal (TRJ)* featuring several innovative papers on "Mental health and transcending life challenges: The role of TR services." Implying the breadth of TR's contributions to stress reduction, a broad range of population groups were examined in this special issue including people who face acute or chronic life stressors (17), women living in a prison system (25), women and men who have encountered traumas (e.g., abuse, violence, rape, combat-related stress) (26), and, more broadly, those individuals who can take advantage of gaining TR support particularly through spiritual leisure (27).

Integrating Enjoyable and Meaningful Leisure into Daily Life for Stress Reduction

In summary, various types of leisure can act as a key mechanism for the reduction of stress, including: relaxing or recuperating leisure, leisure-time physical activity, outdoor recreation, health tourism, social leisure, spiritual leisure, cultural dancing, pet ownership, leisure "palliative" coping for taking a break/having a time-out, as well as more systematic TR practices. Evidence for this function has been reported by a variety of population groups, including nondominant or marginalized groups of individuals besides the general population using different research methods (e.g., large-scale surveys, qualitative methods). A key aspect of this mechanism appears to be that leisure represents a unique life domain in which people can freely choose to engage in an enjoyable or pleasurable activity that can generate meanings of life valued by people (e.g., spiritual meaning, social meaning). One of the key benefits gained from such pursuit seems to be the reduction of stress.

Consequently, integrating leisure into one's life (either personally or through a TR intervention) seems to be an effective way of fighting against and reducing stress in life, and is an essential mechanism for the promotion of health and wellness. Thus, stress reduction through enjoyable and meaningful leisure has broader implications for the enhancement of health and life quality for all people regardless of gender, race/ethnicity, age, social class, sexual orientation, disability/ability, and other human characteristics. Because leisure represents a less obligatory domain of life with a greater degree of freedom of choice, compared to the other domains such as work, even a small change in one's perspective about leisure can make a big difference, especially through increased realization about the role of leisure in stress reduction. One of the major benefits of leisure engagements seems to be the reduction of perceived stress through enjoyable leisure activities that can help people gain valued meanings of life emotionally, spiritually, and socially. Not only can leisure provide opportunities for breathing/taking a break, relaxing, or calming down, but it can also offer contexts for restoring one's energy and gaining a renewed perspective to live actively through better managing one's life, often bothered or overwhelmed by stress. Letting stress take over your life has negative consequences health-wise, which may compromise the overall quality of your life. The constructive use of enjoyable and meaningful leisure, however, has the potential to help you regain a sense of control over your life so that you can be the one who is in charge of your own life despite the prevalence of stress in our society.

References

1. Lazarus RS, Folkman S. *Stress, Appraisal and Coping*. Springer: New York, 1984.
2. Hull IV RB, Michael SE. Nature-based recreation, mood change, and stress restoration. *Leisure Sci* 1995;**17**:1–14.
3. Unruh AM, Smith N, Scammell C. The occupation of gardening in life-threatening illness: A qualitative pilot project. *Can J Occup Ther* 2000;**67/1**:70–77.
4. Godbey G. *Outdoor Recreation, Health, and Wellness: Understanding and Enhancing the Relationship*. Resources for the Future: Washington DC, 2009.
5. Caltabiano ML. Measuring the similarity among leisure activities based on a perceived stress-reduction benefit. *Leisure Stud* 1994;**13**:17–31.
6. Iwasaki Y, Mannell RC, Smale BJA, Butcher J. Contributions of leisure participation in predicting stress coping and health among police and emergency response services workers. *J of Hlth Psych* 2005;**10/1**:79–99.
7. Trenberth L, Dewe P, Walkey F. Leisure and its role as a strategy for coping with work stress. *International J of Stress Management* 1999;**6**:89–103.
8. Zuzanek J, Robinson JP, Iwasaki Y. The relationships between stress, health, and physically active leisure as a function of life-cycle. *Leisure Sci* 1998;**20**:253–275.
9. Mair H. *Tourism*, health and the pharmacy: Towards a critical understanding of health and wellness *tourism*. *Tourism* 2005;**53/4**:335–346.
10. Stathi A, Avgerinos A. Bathing in the healing waters: A case-study of the development of thermal spas in Greece. *World Leisure J* 2001;**43/1**:41–51.
11. Kidd AH, Kidd RM. Benefits, problems, and characteristics of home aquarium owners. *Psych Reports* 1999;**84/3**:998–1004.
12. Aldana SG, Sutton LD, Jacobson BH, Quirk MG. Relationships between leisure time physical activity and perceived *stress*. *Perceptual & Motor Skills* 1996;**82/1**:315–321.
13. Iwasaki Y. Roles of leisure in coping with stress among university students: A repeated-assessment field study. *Anxiety, Stress & Coping* 2003;**16/1**:31–57.
14. Baum A. A psychophysiological perspective, with emphasis on relationships between leisure, stress, and well-being. In Driver BL, Brown PJ, Peterson GL (eds), *Benefits of Leisure*. State College, PA: Venture Publishing, Inc., 1991, pp. 407–410.

15. Iwasaki Y, MacKay K, Mactavish J, Ristock J, Bartlett J. Voices from the margins: Stress, active living, and leisure as a contributor to coping with stress. *Leisure Sci* 2006;**28**:163–180.
16. Carruthers CP, Hood CD. The power of the positive: *Leisure* and well-being. *Therapeutic Rec J* 2004;**38/2**:225–245.
17. Hutchinson SL, Bland AD, Kleiber DA. Leisure and stress-coping: Implications for therapeutic recreation practice. *Therapeutic Rec J* 2008;**42/1**:9–23.
18. Kelley C, Loy DP. Comparing the effects of aquatic and land-based exercise on the physiological stress response of women with fibromyalgia. *Therapeutic Rec J* 2008;**42/2**:103–118.
19. Patterson I, Fallu M. Snoezelen as a casual leisure activity for people with a developmental disability. *Therapeutic Rec J 2004;***38/3**:289–300.
20. Latimer AE, Martin Ginis KA, Hicks AL. Buffering the effects of *stress* on well-being among individuals with spinal cord injury: A potential role for exercise. *Therapeutic Rec J* 2005;**39/2**:131–138.
21. Griffin J. Recreation therapy for adult survivors of childhood abuse: Challenges to professional perspectives and the evolution of a *leisure* education group. *Therapeutic Rec J* 2005;**39/3**:207–228.
22. Hebblethwaite S, Pedlar A. Community integration for older adults with mental health issues: Implications for therapeutic recreation. *Therapeutic Rec J* 2005;**39/4**:264–276.
23. Cassidy T. Leisure, coping and health: The role of social, family, school and peer relationship factors. *Br J Guid Counsell* 2005;**33/1**:51–66.
24. Passmore A, French D. A model of leisure and mental health in Australian adolescents. *Behav Change* 2000;**17/3**:208–220.
25. Pedlar A, Yuen F, Fortune D. Incarcerated women and leisure: Making good girls out of bad? *Therapeutic Rec J* 2008;**42/1**:24–36.
26. Arai SM, Griffin J, Miatello A, Greig CL. Leisure and recreation involvement in the context of healing from trauma. *Therapeutic Rec J*, 2008;**42/1**:37–55.
27. Heintzman P. Leisure-spiritual coping: A model for therapeutic recreation and leisure services. *Therapeutic Rec J* 2008;**42/1**:56–73.

Chapter 15

Making the Best of Bad Situations: The Value of Leisure in Coping with Negative Life Events

Douglas A. Kleiber
Susan L. Hutchinson

It seems generally understood that leisure activities mitigate the aggravations, frustrations, and stresses of everyday life. But what about bigger, more seismic, events that seem to change life altogether? Do you know someone—a friend, a family member, a co-worker—who has experienced a traumatic life event? It may have been the unexpected or unwanted end to a cherished relationship, or even the death of a loved one. It may have been a severe injury or chronic illness. It may have been the loss of a job. It may have been a crisis that devastated an entire community, like war, violence, or severe weather (e.g., massive flooding). These types of negative life events not only cause significant psychological or emotional distress, they also disrupt all aspects of people's lives, including their routines, their roles, their relationships, and even how people see and feel about themselves.

For example, imagine you are an athlete. Maybe you don't consider yourself an "elite" athlete, but participating in this sport is a central and defining part of your life. Imagine then that you are suddenly injured, and this injury has made it impossible for you to continue to play this sport you love. How would this affect:

- Your everyday life (e.g., If most of your time was spent training or working out, what would you do with your time?)
- Your friendships (e.g., If most of your friends are still training/competing, how would you relate to them?)
- How you see yourself (e.g., Would you still feel like the same person or would much of your identity be tied up in your vision of yourself as an athlete?)
- How others see and treat you (e.g., Would you still be popular or would people shy away if you had to now use a cane or wheelchair to get around?)

Or perhaps you've seen someone lose a job and experience not only financial stress but also being stigmatized (as "unemployed"), feeling useless, and being disconnected from valued social connections (1, 2, 3). Together these stressors can pile up and negatively affect a person's physical and mental health.

How, if at all, is leisure relevant in such situations? Indeed, it may be the loss of leisure–valued capacities and opportunities and companionable relationships–that may be a large part of the distress associated with such experiences. The sorrow and devastation experienced may make leisure seem like a thing of the past. But in coping with, adjusting to, and ultimately adapting to such events, leisure becomes relevant in at least five ways:

- For positive distraction and escape
- As a source of hope
- In restoring a sense of self
- In promoting personal transformation
- As a resource of strength and support

Leisure as a Source of Positive Distraction and Escape

As was noted at the outset, leisure is clearly a source of positive distraction that can help almost everyone manage day-to-day stresses. Likely there are occasions when one feels the need to escape or turn off their problems, even if it is just for a short time. When people do take some time for themselves they will often report feeling more relaxed, calmer, and less stressed. While long-term escape or avoidance may be unhealthy (e.g., not answering your phone or leaving your room for days on end), there is now strong evidence that "healthy distractions" are important for effectively managing stressful situations (4, 5) In the past, people might have felt guilty in taking time for themselves, and even now some people (e.g., older adults or overachievers) still do. Yet positive distractions such as reading a good book, listening to a favorite song, taking the dog for a walk, or even going for coffee with a friend have proven to be effective in helping people cope with immediate stress. While this is true for people managing everyday stress, there is also evidence that it is true for people managing more acute or traumatic life events. Why is this? There is evidence that, in the face of negative life events, positive distractions can:

- Substitute positive feelings for negative ruminations or feelings of anxiety and distress
- Provide some distance from the event
- Have the effect of dulling the pain

In other studies, we have highlighted the ways positive distractions helped people manage an unwanted divorce, living with a chronic illness or spinal cord injury, and the stress of being in the hospital following a traumatic injury (6, 7, 8). Are there any similarities between these studies in terms of the types of activities that are most beneficial in providing a positive distraction? Interestingly, we have found that almost any activity can serve this function.

Some activities provide a positive distraction by requiring high levels of physical intensity (e.g., playing a game of pickup basketball) or mental involvement (doing a Sudoku puzzle or reading an exciting novel), while others require relatively low levels of physical, emotional, or mental exertion (e.g., watching a favorite television show, playing with a pet). Though more intense forms of leisure may offer the preoccupying activity that keeps a person's mind off their troubles, the humor-generating aspects of casual, relaxing, and social aspects of many leisure situations can be "relativising" in a way that puts a problem into some more manageable perspective. In a recent study comparing humor (e.g., watching a standup comedy video) with a bout of exercise, the former was found to be more effective in reducing anxiety (9). Activities done alone also seem to offer as much benefit at times as those done with others. For example, while one woman described redecorating her living room as a focus for her energy in the aftermath of her divorce, a student spoke of how important it was to her to have a "spa day" with her mother after her mother found out she was diagnosed with cancer. In other words, what seems to matter is not the type or intensity of the activity, or whether done alone or with others, but whether or not the suffering is at least temporarily interrupted.

Leisure as a Source of Hope

As we have just noted, using leisure to keep busy is a very common positive distraction strategy in coping with stress and loss for all people in times of stress, and takes on special significance in the face of ongoing stress that often accompanies a traumatic life event. But if such actions are primarily escapist and avoidant, they don't have the effect of enabling a person to accept or adjust more completely to an ongoing problem. To do this requires some reappraisal of the situation, "reframing" of a sort that leaves a person with a new view (10, 11). To see *oneself* as being able to enjoy activities and experience pleasure is to move from the general view that "life as I have known it is over" to one of more hope and optimism for the future (12). In particular, leisure activities or experience can be a source of hope when they:

- Remind people of the good things in their lives
- Remind people of their capabilities and strengths
- Give people something to anticipate or look forward to

When people have the opportunity to experience an emotional uplift as a result of a leisure activity or experience, this may provide the cognitive space for positive reappraisal ("maybe my life isn't *all* bad"). Some activities can even be so meaningful that they may lead to the reinterpretation of a negative event. For example, one mother, devastated by an unwanted divorce, found she was able to look at her situation differently after going biking with her son (6). She realized that she could focus her attention on building a relationship with him, which she came to see as an unexpected benefit of the divorce.

Having something to look forward to is also a major source of motivation for people who are facing seemingly insurmountable challenges. Again, in many studies with people who have experienced a negative life event, having something pleasurable and personally meaningful to look forward helped them have the emotional strength to persevere with the challenges they were experiencing (6, 7, 8). For example, a young woman who experienced a spinal cord injury talked about how much looking forward to a favorite television program each night helped her cope with the physical pain and frustrations she was experiencing during the day. Looking forward to spending time with others—whether visiting or hanging out at home or on an outing (e.g., to go shopping, for lunch)—often enables people to receive social support and reassurance without having to talk about problems (in addition to providing the positive distraction described previously (7)). Even the anticipation of being in a special place can help. For a woman with cancer who was a gardener, looking forward to planting or tending her garden helped her cope with the uncertainty of her future. Again, it seems that the type or intensity of activity is less important than having something that is personally meaningful and enjoyable to anticipate or look forward to, to plan for, and then reminisce about afterwards.

Leisure as a Source for Self-Restoration

When one is overcome with grief or in real physical pain, leisure activity would seem to be irrelevant. Indeed, the self-appraisal that takes place in such circumstances may focus more on the losses experienced than on any positive moments. Studies of negative life events such as spinal cord injury, the sudden onset of illness, or the loss of a loved one suggest that a loss of leisure abilities, leisure opportunities, and leisure companions are regularly part of the trauma that people endure (13, 14). In fact, previously enjoyed leisure activities will often become unappealing when people are no longer able to participate in the activities in the same way as before. For example, one young woman spoke of not wanting to go to the bar after her spinal cord injury because she couldn't wear high-heeled shoes anymore; this made this activity less "normal" and thus less desirable for her. People who have lost a spouse or child often talk about not wanting to visit favorite places or do familiar activities because they are painful reminders of what they have lost (15).

What may be less evident is that leisure activities may come into play in helping when life gets very difficult and threatening. In the face of these threats, leisure activities can help preserve or restore positive self-perceptions in the following ways:

- By reaffirming or validating personal values and beliefs
- By allowing people to express enduring personal characteristics and preferences
- By finding suitable substitute activities that approximate those no longer available
- By providing the social space for people to be themselves
- By helping people feel that they are essentially the same as before the disruptive event

Leisure may be the place where a sense of self is maintained regardless of the difficulties and losses that beset one in other aspects of life. The ability to draw on other activities in a repertoire or to substitute activities for those that are lost can preserve a sense of self and a sense of personal continuity (12, 13, 14). Indeed, to the extent that activity involvement is associated with personal identity, then maintaining those activities in some ways is crucially important to emotional stability.

What kinds of activities are or could be "identity affirming"? Consistent with the personal growth theories of leisure, it has been argued that some types of activity and involvement are better than others. As it relates to dealing with job loss, for example, Robert Stebbins (16) suggested that "serious leisure"—that which involves commitment, persistence, and identification with others who do the activity—can be important by providing work-like activity, offering a link with former work associates, current friends and relatives, expanding one's social circle, fostering responsibility, and creating the opportunity to feel needed by other people. Regardless of the intensity or type of activity, it seems that activities that hold personal meaning, in which people have a level of competence and skill, and in which there is relatively low levels of evaluation by one's self or others can be important in restoring a sense of self. Personal meaning is often reflected in one's *place attachment* as well (17, 18); identity can be reinforced and restored simply by being in a preferred place at times, whether it is in the woods and mountains of a particular state or in one's hometown library.

Leisure as a Source for Personal Transformation

While we most often think about leisure as a source for personal growth and development throughout the life course, leisure may also be the chosen venue for expressions of change and personal growth in the face of a negative life event (19, 13). Csikszentmihalyi (19), for example, has written about the ways in which flow-generating activities can lead to complexification of the self following trauma. In psychology literature, the concept of *post-traumatic growth* has been used to reflect the ways that people may change the ways they view themselves, their relationships, and their lives as a result of devastating loss (20, 21). This shift in thinking and life priorities often results in people being more "present-centered," appreciative, and responsive to others. In the wake of personal challenges and struggles, people may experience personal growth; leisure activities, experiences or interactions may be a large part of this self-expansion:"Greater appreciation" of one's life and relationships, opens one up to the benefits of relaxation, peacefulness, and contemplative leisure

- Activity experimentation facilitates recognition of new possibilities for one's life
- Innovative, self-expressive activities lead to new self-conceptions
- Disengagement from other demands in leisure affords greater interiority

Some of the more positive ways in which leisure experience can lead to self-expansion, however, may occur where least expected. People faced with difficult life circumstances and stressful life events—rather than giving into helplessness and relying on leisure only for escape—may take their conditions and circumstances as catalysts for change. Research on the role of leisure in response to negative life events suggests that not only are leisure activities sources of distraction, renewed optimism and self-restoration in response to the pain and loss as we've discussed above, they are also sometimes reflected in the ways people use the events to make a new life in some respects (12). For example, a young man whose automobile accident has deprived him of the sports that he has loved so much may turn to writing and finds that he has a gift for narrative and short story. Someone may find that his heart attack is a "wake up call" to spend more time with his family. The loss of a job may move another person from being stuck in a job she hates to take the risk to turn a hobby into a home-based business.

Researchers who have studied post-traumatic growth have observed that among the changes made by people who have experiences such injuries or losses are a change in perspective about living in and enjoying the present and turning to new expressive activities.

Leisure as a Source of Strength and Support

Finally, while the above functions described how leisure is actually used in the face of threat, injury, and loss, in a more general and perhaps less direct sense, can leisure help people be less *vulnerable* to the stress and trauma of a negative life event? There is evidence that leisure may both serve to "buffer" stress (come between the person and the stressor) but also promote resilience or the personal capacities to better withstand stress (22, 23, 24, 25). Though people may differ in terms of the types or forms of leisure they may turn to in times of stress, it seems that there are two relatively common resources or assets that are generated through leisure that may have the effect of reducing the impact of the stressors: *social support* and *self-determination.*

Coleman and Iso-Ahola (26) first introduced these ideas, noting that various life events, especially negative events such as losing a job and . financial debt, have been shown to lead to a higher incidence of mental and physical illness. In response to this stress, first they argued leisure participation can facilitate coping with stressful life circumstances when people believe that social support is available to them. In other words, leisure that is highly social in nature can facilitate the development of companionship and friendship, and consequently, social support. Second, enduring beliefs of self-determination have been found to contribute to people's coping capacity and health. When people feel that they generally have some ability to control the good and bad things that happen to them, they experience less mental and physical illness or ill health. The central characteristics of leisure, perceptions of freedom and control, allow the development and maintenance of stable self-determination dispositions; that is, feelings of being in control of one's life. These perceptions of social support and self-determination are described as buffers against life stress, and when life stress is high leisure's contribution to health is expected to be greater (26, 27, 28). Iwasaki (24, 25) found that it is more important that people believe they can draw on leisure-related resources (like leisure companions) in times of stress, than the actual strategies they use, in terms of improving health and well-being.

When people experience moments of enjoyment or positive distraction, when they have something to look forward to, when they are able to engage in activities that help them feel normal and even see things in new ways as a result of leisure participation, leisure experiences bolster people's resilience—or the beliefs they can manage stressful, unwanted negative events in their lives. Beliefs about access to social support and one's capacity to be self-determined enable one to be resilient and resourceful in the face of significant stressors. These beliefs may also determine people's motivations or reasons for engaging in leisure to cope with stress as well as the meanings or benefits they seek from their leisure in times of stress.

Conclusions and Implications

As people are dealing with immediate stressors, they may want to take a time out—mentally or physically—from their problems, to engage in a positive distraction or escape. If it is a "healthy pleasure" (and not an enduring form of escape) then this time out can give people a chance to recover and recharge so they feel better able to go back to the problem at hand. And enjoyable activities not only help people escape the pain; they also have mood- and morale-enhancing properties which help them feel better able to manage their problems. In situations where people are experiencing the negative effects of traumatic events, then leisure activities can be a source of hope, reminding them not only that they are capable or valued, but in giving people something to look forward to. Beyond coping with the immediacies of a situation, some events have created unalterable change: the end of a relationship, death of a loved one, loss of a job, permanent impairments as a result of a chronic illness or injury. In these cases people need to not only cope with immediate losses and stress but also must come to terms with it, either by accepting or changing the way they view the situation. Again, leisure can be a resource for not only restoring or preserving one's sense of self, but also in promoting personal growth.

What are the implications of this information—for how you lead your life, how you help those you care about, or how you prepare for your future work? First is to realize that stress is an inevitable part of life; it is how you manage it that matters. Making time to build personal and social resources will help protect you and others against future stress. When a stressful situation does arise, to the extent people intentionally choose leisure activities that they know will help them feel better and less stressed, they will likely feel better able to manage their problems. In turn, this will help them to feel more capable of managing other difficult challenges in their lives. Encouraging others in your family or with whom you work or go to school to engage in these leisure-based "self-care" strategies may help others more effectively manage stress in their lives. Promoting similar kinds of leisure education as part of workplace wellness, healthy aging, or chronic disease self-management programs would also contribute more broadly to realizing leisure's full potential in promoting health.

References

1. Havitz M, Morden P, Samdahl D. *The diverse worlds of unemployed adults: Consequences for leisure lifestyle and well being*. Waterloo, ON: Wilfred Laurier University Press, 2004.
2. Lobo F. *Leisure, Family and Lifestyle: Unemployed Young People*. Rawat Publications: Jaipur, India, 2002.
3. Lobo F. Coping with bulk unobligated time: The case of unemployment. *Society Leis* 1996;**19**:377–413.
4. Iwasaki Y. Counteracting stress through leisure coping: A prospective health study. *Psych Health Med* 2006;**11**/2:209–220.
5. Iwasaki Y, Mactavish J, Mackey K. Building on strengths and resilience: Leisure as a stress survival strategy. *Brit J Guid Couns* 2005;**33/1**:81–100.
6. Hutchinson SL, Afifi T, Krause S. The family that plays together fares better: Examining the contribution of shared family time to family resilience following divorce. *J Divorce Remar* 2007;**46/3–4**:21–48.
7. Hutchinson SL, Kleiber, DA. Gifts of the "ordinary": Considering the contribution of casual leisure to health and well-being. *World Leis J* 2005;**47/3**:2–16.
8. Hutchinson SL, Loy DP, Kleiber, DA, Dattilo J. Leisure as a coping resource: Variations in coping with traumatic injury and illness. *Leis Sci* 2003;**25/2–3**:143–161.
9. Szabo A. The acute effects of humor and exercise on mood and anxiety. *J Leis Res* 2003;**35**:152–162.
10. Folkman S. Positive psychological states and coping with severe stress. *Soc Sci Med* 2003;**45**:1207–1221.
11. Folkman S, Moskowitz JT. Stress, positive emotion and coping. *Curr Dir Psych Sci* 2000;**9**:115–118.
12. Kleiber DA, Hutchinson SL, Williams R. Leisure as a resource in transcending negative life events: Self-protection, self-restoration and personal transformation. *Leis Sci* 2002;**24**:219–235.
13. Kleiber DA. *Leisure Experience and Human Development: A Dialectical Interpretation*. Basic Books: New York, 1999.
14. Kleiber DA, Brock SC, Dattilo J, Lee Y, Caldwell L. The relevance of leisure in an illness experience: Realities of spinal cord injury. *J Leis Res* 1995; **27**:283–299.
15. Lopata HZ. Widows: Social Integration and Activity. In Kelly JR (ed), *Activity and Aging*. Newbury Park, CA: Sage, 1993, pp. 99–105.
16. Stebbins R. *Amateurs, Professionals, and Serious Leisure*. McGill-Queen's University of Press: Montreal, 1992.

17. Low SM, Altman I. Place Attachment: A Conceptual Inquiry. In Altman I, Low SM (eds), *Place Attachment*. New York: Plenum Press, 1992, pp. 1–12.

18. Williams DR, Patterson ME, Roggenbuck JW, Watson A. Beyond the commodity metaphor: Examining emotional and symbolic attachment to place. *Leis Sci* 1992;**14**:29–46.

19. Csikszentmihalyi M. *Flow: The Psychology of Optimal Experience*. Harper Perennial: New York, 1990.

20. Tedeschi RG, Calhoun LG. Postraumatic growth: Conceptual foundations and empirical evidence. *Psych Inq* 2004;**15**/11:1–18.

21. Tedeschi RG, Calhoun LG. *Trauma and Transformation: Growing in the Aftermath of Suffering*. Sage: Thousand Oaks, CA, 1995.

22. Coleman D. Leisure based social support, leisure dispositions and health. *J Leis Res* 1993;**25**:350–361.

23. Iso-Ahola SE, Park CJ. Leisure-related social support and self-determination as buffers of stress-illness relationship. *J Leis Res* 1996;**28**:169–187.

24. Iwasaki Y. Examining rival models of leisure coping mechanisms. *Leis Sci* 2003;**25/2–3**:183–206.

25. Iwasaki Y. Counteracting stress through leisure coping: A prospective study. *Psych Health Med* 2008;**11/2**:209–220.

26. Coleman D, Iso-Ahola SE. Leisure and health: The role of social support and self-determination. *J Leis Res* 1993;**25**:111–128.

27. Iwasaki Y, Mannell RC. Hierarchical dimensions of leisure-stress coping. *Leis Sci* 2000a;**22**:163–181.

28. Iwasaki Y, Mannell RC. The effects of leisure beliefs and coping strategies on stress-health relationships: A field study. *Leis/Loisir* 2000b;**24/1–2**:3–57.

Chapter 16
Building Self-Esteem and Self-Efficacy through Leisure

Steriani Elavsky
Shawna Doerksen

Introduction

You have heard these phrases before, "she is such a well-adjusted person" or "he just seems to have a good sense of himself." Have you ever thought about what it is that we are referring to when we make such statements about people? Chances are that at least to some degree these evaluations have to do with two important psychological characteristics, self-esteem and self-efficacy. *Self-esteem* is regarded as an important indicator of emotional and social adjustment and research shows that it plays a key role in explaining human behavior. People with higher levels of self-esteem appear to be more emotionally stable and more resilient to stress, possess higher motivation, strive to pursue more difficult goals, and persist in achieving those goals (1). People low in self-esteem, on the other hand, seem to be more susceptible to negative emotions and feelings such as depression, anxiety, body dissatisfaction, eating disorders and suicidal tendencies (2, 3). Low self-esteem is also associated with low perceived personal control and low self-perceived ability to accomplish a task, or self-efficacy. *Self-efficacy*, sometimes referred to as situation-specific self-confidence, is thought to influence how a person acts, what activities they choose to participate in, the amount of energy they put into the activities, how they face obstacles, and the level of success they achieve (4). High levels of self-efficacy are thought to play an important role in successful chronic disease management, maintaining overall health, and effective coping (5). Therefore self-esteem and self-efficacy—although not readily self-evident to most of us—are absolutely essential components for nurturing self-actualization, or in other words, for us to be all that we can be.

In addition to being essential elements of well-being and quality of life, self-esteem and self-efficacy also serve as important determinants of positive health behaviors and subsequent health outcomes. Undeniably, as individuals we tend to seek out situations and environments which reaffirm our sense of self, reinforce our sense of self-worth, and make us feel confident and in control. Although leisure, defined here as enjoyable and preferred activities that are part of one's everyday life (6), arguably represents an ideal context for studying and enhancing self-perceptions related to the sense of self-worth and competence, these constructs remain understudied in the leisure domain. The few studies that exist in the field of leisure have focused on concepts related to self-esteem and self-efficacy such as self-enhancement or empowerment. However, studies directly examining self-esteem and self-efficacy have been largely limited to research on physical activity, a sub-component of active leisure. The purpose of this chapter is to lay a conceptual basis for leisure research on self-esteem and self-efficacy by way of reviewing physical activity-related research on self-esteem and self-efficacy and presenting opportunities for enhancing self-esteem and self-efficacy in the broader context of active and passive leisure.

Physical Activity and Self-Esteem

Defining Self-Esteem

Although you may have seen them used interchangeably, self-esteem must be differentiated from the term self-concept. *Self-concept* refers to the description of the self, or one's identity. *Self-esteem,* sometimes called *self-worth,* refers to self-evaluation of how well the self is doing. That is, you may view yourself as an athletic person, for example; this is who you are and how you define yourself (i.e., your self-concept). Self-esteem is the degree to which you see yourself as a worthy and competent person, no matter your personal identity. The dimensions of self-love, self-acceptance, and a sense of competence are common to most definitions of self-esteem. For the purposes of this chapter, let us define self-esteem as the degree to which one feels positive or negative towards oneself, regardless of what criteria that individual uses to make that evaluation. In this sense, self-esteem is seen as encompassing two main processes: evaluation (where cognition plays the crucial role) and affection (which is driven by feelings and emotions) (7).

Contemporary Theories and Instruments

Have you ever asked yourself what it is that makes you feel good about yourself? You can probably come up with multiple reasons. You may be proud of your accomplishments at school, for example. This may be because you have high GPA or because you excel in a specific subject area (math, Spanish, etc.). Volunteering, showing empathy for others, or simply interacting with your family or friends may also make you feel good or proud. In other words, it is likely that your actions and experiences in different domains of your life make you who you are and how you feel about yourself. This is exactly how contemporary theories view self-esteem, as a hierarchical concept consisting of multiple domains. In the hierarchical model, general or global self-esteem occupies the top of the hierarchy. This is the general sense of self-worth you possess and reflects your self-esteem across multiple different domains (e.g., academic, social, physical self-esteem). Each of these self-esteem domains are then made up of even more specific areas. For example, your physical self-esteem may vary across various sub-domains, such as how you perceive your physical appearance, strength, or sport abilities. As one moves from the top to the baseline of the hierarchical structure, self-esteem becomes less stable (i.e., easier to change) and more situation specific.

In trying to understand how self-esteem changes, researchers have applied this hierarchical and multidimensional view of self-esteem in different domains. In the physical activity area, for example, initial work on how physical self-esteem changes focused on testing of the "self-enhancement" and "skill-development" hypotheses. According to the "skill development hypothesis," exercise participation leads to improvements in physical abilities and the estimation of the abilities is proposed to have a positive effect on self-esteem. The "self-enhancement hypothesis," on the other hand, proceeds in the opposite direction whereby self-esteem determines the involvement in exercise behavior. For example, imagine an individual with low self-esteem in the physical domain. This person does not believe they are good at sports. Because of this low perceived competence, he/she is less likely to engage in sports. On the contrary, an individual with high self-esteem most likely perceives his/her physical competence positively and would strive to engage in sports. Success experienced in the activity will in return boost his/her self-esteem. Support for both hypotheses has been however inconsistent and primarily based on cross-sectional evidence. Many consider both hypotheses to be rather general and inadequate for explaining the complexities of how and why self-esteem changes in the process of physical activity participation.

The most useful model explaining the mechanisms of change to date is the Exercise and Self-Esteem Model (EXSEM) (8). This model is hierarchical and multidimensional and shows how engaging in exercise or physical activity may lead to increased physical and global self-esteem. In the EXSEM model, positive changes in physical parameters associated with exercise (e.g., increased fitness or flexibility, or reduced body fatness) are hypothesized to lead to increases in the perceptions of self-efficacy (i.e., you become more confident that you can accomplish a specific task or behavior). Enhanced self-efficacy then leads to enhanced self-perceptions in various physical subdomains (e.g., self-esteem relative to strength, endurance, body) which in turn increase global physical self-esteem. A case study demonstrates how the EXSEM model can be used to study the effects of physical activity on self-esteem. Additionally, examples of commonly used measures of self-esteem in physical activity research are presented in Table 16.1.

Self-Esteem Case Study

In one study (9) researchers examined how self-esteem may be enhanced through exercise participation. A group of middle-aged sedentary adults (56 men and 58 women) were enrolled in a 20-week long structured walking program. Participants exercised under supervision three times per week, beginning at 10–15 minutes of exercise and progressing to 40 minutes of exercise per session by the midpoint of the program and this duration was maintained for the remainder of the program. All participants completed measures of fitness, self-esteem and self-efficacy at the beginning and end of the program. Both men and women improved their global self-esteem, physical self-esteem, and sub-domain self-esteem relative to physical condition following the program. More importantly, increases in aerobic fitness and self-efficacy led to increases in physical condition and body attractiveness self-esteem, both of which were associated with increases in physical and global self-esteem. In other words, participants who improved their aerobic fitness and self-efficacy ended up viewing their bodies and physical condition more positively which, in turn, increased their physical self-worth and global self-esteem, thus supporting the EXSEM hypothesis.

Physical Activity and Self-Efficacy

Defining Self-Efficacy

Self-efficacy is defined as the belief in one's abilities to perform a given task (4). In the physical activity context, for example, a person who is high in self-efficacy may believe that he/she can be active five or more days of the week for at least 30 minutes at a time regardless of the barriers that may get in the way like time management, bad weather, or fatigue (10). *Self-efficacy* is fundamental to behavior change in that confidence in ones' abilities can provide the motivation necessary to follow through with a change in behavior. Additionally, self-efficacy is important because it influences several other social cognitive variables. Individuals who are more efficacious are more likely to believe that the behavior will bring about positive consequences. That is, they have positive outcome expectations regarding the behavior of interest. If an individual has high self-efficacy, they believe that with personal effort, they can overcome the barriers to certain behaviors. Finally, those who have high self-efficacy also set higher personal goals and are more motivated to achieve these goals than those who have lower levels of self-efficacy (11).

Contemporary Theories and Instruments

Self-efficacy is the key component in social cognitive theory as it influences the amount of effort one puts forth to bring about a desired behavior (12). Based on social cognitive theory, human behavior is determined by reciprocal interaction between environmental (both social and physical) and personal (cognitive, affective, physiological) factors. That is, each factor (e.g., environmental, personal) influences each other and behavior. Behavior also influences both environmental and personal factors. Efficacy beliefs represent the active ingredient in the social cognitive theory in that they can impact cognitive and affective processes, interpretation of physiological states, and subsequent behavior. Self-efficacy can be enhanced by targeting the primary sources of efficacy information which include mastery experience, vicarious observation, social persuasion, and interpretation of affective and physiological stimuli (12).

Mastery experience involves previous performance of the desired behavior. Those individuals who have had success with the behavior in the past should have greater self-efficacy for performing this behavior in the future. For example, if a person completed a five mile run in the past, they will have greater confidence in their ability to complete a five mile run in the future. Vicarious observation involves watching another person perform a task successfully. If the individual completing the activity is thought to be similar to the person who is observing the behavior, the observer may have greater feelings of self-efficacy as they can relate to the performer's success. Social persuasion, or the input from important others such as friends, family members, or trusted professionals, is another method by which self-efficacy can be altered. If an individual receives positive encouragement from others their self-efficacy for a given task could be increased. Alternatively, if significant others provide negative feedback, the person may experience a decrease in self-efficacy for the task. Stimulation of the affective system is another source of self-efficacy and can be described as the emotions brought about by the thought of performing the behavior. Whether or not this stimulation will affect self-efficacy depends on how the emotional information is processed. If the person thinks these feelings are normal, his/her self-efficacy may remain stable. However, if these feelings are determined to be because of lack of skill, a person's level of confidence for the desired behavior will decrease (12). An example of a study that successfully changed self-efficacy using some of the above methods is discussed in the case study below.

Other models of health behavior such as the transtheoretical model and the theory of planned behavior, have sought to incorporate self-efficacy into their models; however, the measurement of self-efficacy in these frameworks has been different than that of self-efficacy from a social

Table 16.1 Examples of commonly used measures of self-esteem and self-efficacy in the physical activity literature

Name of Instrument	Subscales	Author of Instrument	Sample Item	Response Scale
Self-Esteem				
Rosenberg's Self-Esteem Scale	Global self-esteem	Rosenberg (1965)	I feel that I have a number of good qualities.	Likert: 1 (strongly agree) – 5 (strongly disagree)
Physical Self-Perception Profile	Physical self-worth and sub-domain self-esteem relative to attractive body, strength, physical condition, sport competence	Fox & Corbin (1989)	I feel that compared to most, I have an attractive body.	Likert: 1 (not at all true) – 4 (completely true)
Physical Self-Description Questionnaire	Global esteem, global physical self-concept, sub-domain esteem relative to health, strength, body fat, physical activity, endurance/fitness, sport competence, coordination, appearance	Marsh et al. (1994)	I feel confident when doing coordinated movements.	Likert: 1 (false) – 6 (true)
Self-Efficacy				
Exercise Self-Efficacy Scale		McAuley (1993)	I am able to continue to exercise five times per week at moderate or higher intensity, for 40+ minutes without quitting for the next month.	Likert: 0–100% confident
Barriers Self-Efficacy Scale		McAuley (1992)	I believe I could exercise 5 times per week for the next 3 months if the weather was very bad (hot, humid, rainy, cold).	Likert: 0–100% confident
Exercise Self-Efficacy Scale		Garcia & King (1991)	Over the next 6 months I could exercise when on vacation.	Likert: 0–100% confident

cognitive theory perspective, making it difficult to compare the roles of self-efficacy between the theories (13). The transtheoretical model involves stages of behavioral change and suggests that self-efficacy increases as a person moves forward in the stages of change (i.e., increases in their level of readiness to change behavior) or decreases if a person moves backwards through the stages. Self-efficacy (labeled as perceived behavioral control) was also incorporated into the theory of reasoned action, since referred to as the theory of planned behavior. In this theory, perceived behavioral control is thought to directly influence a person's intentions to participate in a behavior as well as the behavior itself, thus helping predict behavior by accounting for situations that may be beyond the individuals' control. Perceived behavioral control is marginally different from self-efficacy in that it describes the control one feels they have over the situation and not their confidence in their abilities; however, perceived behavioral control is often measured using items from self-efficacy measures. Examples of commonly used measures of self-efficacy specific to physical activity participation are presented in Table 16.1.

Self-Efficacy Case Study

The effect of efficacy manipulation on affect was examined in a study by McAuley and colleagues (14). Low-active, female college students (N=46) were randomly assigned to either a high or low efficacy condition. Each of the students completed a fitness test at the beginning of the study and then received bogus feedback regarding their performance. Those in the high efficacy condition were told that they were in the top 20% of their peers in terms of fitness whereas participants in the low efficacy group were told they were in the bottom 20% of their peer group. The students' self-efficacy was measured before and after they were given the feedback and those in the high efficacy group showed significantly higher self-efficacy for physical activity over those in the low efficacy group after the feedback. The students then returned for a second exercise session and those in the high efficacy group maintained their elevated levels of efficacy for physical activity over those in the low efficacy group. They also reported more positive emotions and lower fatigue after exercise whereas those in the low efficacy group reported higher levels of psychological distress. This study demonstrates the ability to manipulate self-efficacy by using social persuasion and mastery experience. It is possible that self-efficacy has an indirect influence on physical activity participation through positive affect. This indirect relationship through positive emotions may be one pathway through which efficacy influences this form of active leisure.

Self-Esteem and Self-Efficacy in the Leisure Context

So far, we have presented a brief review of the roles that self-esteem and self-efficacy were shown to play in the area of physical activity. As demonstrated by the EXSEM model, although both self-esteem and self-efficacy are individually important for behavior and its associated health and well-being outcomes, they are also linked in important ways. That is, to experience increases in self-esteem one must experience increases in self-efficacy, both of which occur in a domain-specific and hierarchical manner. Figure 16.1 represents a simplified, conceptual model of these relationships. Consider the example of a novice yoga participant. For this individual, over time, participation in yoga classes is likely to increase his/her confidence in their abilities to perform yoga due to gaining mastery experiences, vicarious learning, verbal support and encouragement from instructors or other participants, etc. As a result, this person may increase their yoga or other exercise participation and experience improvements in various physical outcomes (i.e., improved flexibility, strength) which, in turn, are going to positively impact his/her sense of physical

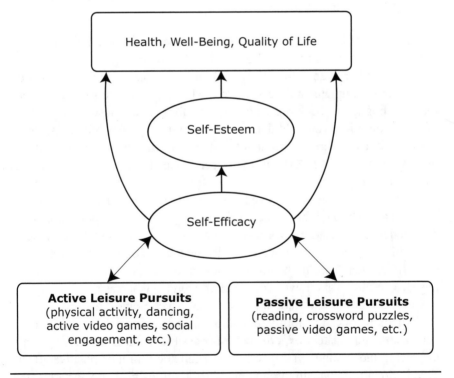

Figure 16.1 Conceptual framework for studying self-esteem and self-efficacy influences on health, well-being, and quality of life in the context of leisure

self-worth. It is important to note that the degree to which increases in physical self-esteem are going to impact global self-esteem will depend on the level of importance or value an individual places on that particular domain. The potential of physical activity to enhance self-efficacy and self-esteem thus begs the question of whether similar effects occur in the broader leisure domain.

Can Leisure Foster Growth in Self-Esteem and Self-Efficacy?

Before we explore the way in which different leisure contexts may be used to enhance self-efficacy and self-esteem, let us clarify our conception of leisure. Kleiber (15) defines leisure as enjoyable and preferred activities that are part of one's everyday life. From the psychological perspective leisure has been further qualified as the experience of the state of mind, one that has to be entered into voluntarily, and one that is intrinsically motivating in and of itself (16). As such, leisure activities are most typically divided into active and passive. Active leisure activities involve some exertion of physical or mental effort. These may include activities such as walking for pleasure, yoga, or other recreational activities such as playing chess or active video games (e.g., Wii Fit). Passive leisure activities (e.g., going to the movies, watching television, reading books) do not involve significant exertion of energy, yet they are important means of relaxation and enjoyment for some people. So what are the possibilities of using these different leisure contexts to enhance self-esteem and self-efficacy?

Because leisure by definition involves engagement in preferred, enjoyable, and intrinsically motivating activities, leisure offers the opportunity to turn to fulfilling and meaningful activities that are aligned with an individual's values, interests, and priorities. Activities that are most likely to enhance self-efficacy and self-esteem have to be of personal relevance or value but they must also have some inherent level of challenge. To result in increases in self-efficacy (rather than reductions), this level of challenge has to match up with individuals' capabilities. Therefore, the choice of activities, initial levels of self-efficacy and self-esteem, as well as personal abilities are going to determine the extent to which a particular leisure context is likely to foster growth in self-efficacy and self-esteem. In other words, participating in the same activity is going to produce different results depending on how relevant that activity is to a person's sense of self, what that individual's levels of self-efficacy and self-esteem in that domain are to begin with, as well as the person's relevant skills and abilities. A proficient chess player with a healthy level of self-esteem and high self-efficacy who plays against his less skillful peers, for example, is unlikely to increase self-esteem or self-efficacy even if playing chess is enjoyable and personally meaningful.

This may be different, however, if that person gets the opportunity to play chess against a more talented or professional chess player and wins or simply does well in the match-up. Thus, increasing self-efficacy and self-esteem in well-adjusted, normally functioning, healthy individuals is likely to occur through participation in enjoyable, personally important activities only if they are presented with increasing level or challenge or through participation in activities that are novel.

In the leisure context, the concept of balancing the level of challenge and skill has been studied in relation to the process of "flow." Here, rather than an outcome of leisure, self-efficacy is viewed as a source of enjoyment, a key aspect of intrinsically motivating behavior/activities. *Flow* is defined as a state wherein an individual is intrinsically interested in and fully absorbed by an activity or an intrinsically enjoyable experience (17). Balance of challenge and skill is seen as one of the key elements of flow along with other factors such as complete absorption in the activity, clear goals, merging of action and awareness, total concentration on the task at hand, loss of self-consciousness, and a sense of control. Of course, to maintain levels of self-efficacy and self-esteem (as opposed to increasing them), the balance of challenge and skill is not always necessary. Continuing engagement in preferred and fulfilling leisure activities irrespective of whether they present challenge may still serve as an effective buffer against losses in self-efficacy or self-esteem and allow for healthy levels of both to be maintained. However, those with low levels of self-esteem or self-efficacy may see improvements from participating in leisure interventions that promote flow.

Arguably, leisure may offer distinctive opportunities to intervene on self-efficacy and self-esteem in certain unique situations or with special population sub-groups. A number of researchers discussed the role of leisure across important life transitions. Because some life transitions impact self-esteem, they may represent important intervention targets. Examples of such life transitions include entering preschool, kindergarten, high school, adolescence, college, menopausal transition, or retirement. Kleiber and colleagues have also studied extensively the role of leisure in adjustment to disability and dealing with negative life events (6, 18). Disability, regardless of whether it occurs suddenly (e.g., as a result of accident) or over longer period of time (e.g., as a result of aging or chronic disease), may have negative impact on self-esteem and self-efficacy. Similarly, negative life events such as divorce or loss of job can have adverse effects on self-esteem and self-efficacy. Kleiber et al. argued that in these situations leisure may provide opportunities for self-enhancement or self-restoration (6). This self-development can occur through personal transformation or through social identity as a function of individuals discovering new interests and new opportunities for self-realization, meeting new people, or rediscovering meaningful, enjoyable activities or old circles of friends. Leisure may also enhance self-esteem and self-efficacy by acting as an important source of positive experiences and positive emotions. Son et al. (19) described how participation in leisure organizations may impact health and wellbeing in women. Specifically, they examined the experiences of women engaged in the Red Hat Society, a leisure organization for women with the goals to promote fun and new interests in women after fifty (although younger women may participate as well). Women described their participation in the society as important for enhancing their sense of self through creating happy moments, support networks, and providing opportunities to learn from and interact with others.

Summary

Currently, the literature has a narrow focus of self-esteem and self-efficacy with respect to leisure. That is, these constructs have been primarily studied in the context of physical activity which represents only one aspect of active leisure. Our focus on self-esteem and self-efficacy should broaden to encompass all components of leisure, both active and passive. As briefly presented here, self-esteem and self-efficacy have been shown to bring about positive changes in physical activity behavior as well as other health and wellbeing outcomes, which are all important public health concerns. Further research should be conducted to determine whether these relationships translate to other aspects of active and passive leisure as well. Additionally, further research is needed to characterize how self-esteem and self-efficacy are enhanced across different leisure contexts. For example, can hierarchical models similar to the EXSEM model be tested in other areas of leisure? Certainly, different leisure contexts or activities could be used to study the relationships among leisure, self-efficacy, and self-esteem so as to determine their impact on health, well-being, and quality of life (Figure 16.1).

In terms of practice, the evidence obtained from the psychological and physical activity literatures can be used to guide strategies for enhancing self-esteem and self-efficacy across different leisure contexts. In a general sense, it is important to choose activities that teach strategies that help individuals develop a realistic and accurate picture of themselves (i.e., aid in realistic self-appraisal), that provide accomplishments in areas that are considered meaningful but also help individuals maintain self-esteem and self-efficacy in the face of setbacks. Bearing with the fact that self-efficacy is situation-specific and self-esteem is hierarchical and complex, it is important to consider how improvements in a single area may generalize across areas and subsequently result in enhanced global self-esteem. Practical approaches may concentrate on targeting a single domain or multiple domains. The extent to which improvements in a single domain may translate to enhanced global self-esteem will depend on how important that domain is to the individual. For example, having older adults engage in mental activities such as Sudoku or memory-boosting games may enhance their self-efficacy relative to memory or cognitive functioning. Because these areas of functioning carry a high level of relevance for older adults, they may enhance their global self-esteem as a result. In addition to personal relevance, other evidence-based strategies for enhancing self-esteem and self-efficacy include providing mastery experiences, vicarious experiences (i.e., role modeling), verbal persuasion, and interpretation of physiological and affective arousal. Effective approaches should also respect personal preferences, offer choice of activities, provide space for self-expression, keep activities novel and interesting, and capitalize on the role that socialization may play in enhancing self-esteem and self-efficacy.

References

1. Biddle SJ. Cognitive Theories of Motivation and the Physical Self. In Fox KR (ed), *The Physical Self: From Motivation to Well-Being*. Champaign, IL: Human Kinetics, 1997, pp. 59–82.
2. Davis C. Body Image, Exercise, and Eating Behaviors. In Fox KR (ed), *The Physical Self: From Motivation to Well-being*. Champaign, IL: Human Kinetics, 1997, pp. 143–175.
3. Hattie J. *Self-Concept*. Erlbaum: Hillsdale, NJ, 1992.
4. Bandura A. *Self-Efficacy: The Exercise of Control*. W.H. Freeman and Company: New York, 1997.
5. Leventhal H, Weinman J, Leventhal EA, Phillips LA. Health psychology: the search for pathways between behavior and health. *Annu Rev Psychol* 2008;**59**:477–505.
6. Kleiber DA, Hutchinson SL, Williams R. Leisure as a Resource in Transcending Negative Life Events: Self-Protection, Self-Restoration and Personal Transformation. *Leisure Sci* 2002;**24**:219–235.
7. Fox KR. The Physical Self and Processes in Self-Esteem Development. In Fox KR (ed), *The Physical Self: From Motivation to Well-Being*. Champaign, IL: Human Kinetics, 1997, pp. 111–141.
8. Sonstroem RJ, Harlow LL, Josephs L. Exercise and Self-Esteem: Validity of Model Expansion and Exercise Associations. *J Sport Exerc Psychol* 1994;**16**:29–42.
9. McAuley E, Mihalko SL, Bane SM. Exercise and self-esteem in middle-aged adults: multidimensional relationships and physical fitness and self-efficacy influences. *J Behav Med* 1997;**20**:67–83.
10. McAuley E. The role of efficacy cognitions in the prediction of exercise behavior in middle-aged adults. *J Behav Med* 1992;**15**:65–88.
11. Bandura A. Health promotion by social cognitive means. *Health Educ Behav* 2004;**31**:143–164.
12. Bandura A. *Social Foundations of Thought and Action: A Social Cognitive Theory*. Prentice Hall: Englewood Cliffs, NJ, 1986.
13. McAuley E, Blissmer B. Self-efficacy determinants and consequences of physical activity. *Exerc Sport Sci Rev* 2000;**28**:85–88.
14. McAuley E, Talbot H-M, Martinez S: Manipulating self-efficacy in the exercise environment in women: Influences on affective responses. *Health Psychol* 1999;**18**:288–294.
15. Kleiber DA. *Leisure Experience and Human Development: A Dialectical Interpretation*. Basic Books: New York, 1999.
16. Neulinger J. *The Psychology of Leisure* (2nd ed.). C.C. Thomas: Springfield, IL, 1981.

17. Csikszentmihalyi M. *Flow: The Psychology of Optimal Experience*. Harper and Row: New York, 1990.
18. Kleiber DA, Reel HA, Hutchinson SL. When distress gives way to possibility: The relevance of leisure in adjustment to disability. *NeuroRehabilitation* 2008;**23**:321–328.
19. Son JS, Kerstetter DL, Yarnal C, Baker BL. Promoting older women's health and well-being through social leisure environments: What we have learned from the Red Hat Society. *J Women Aging* 2007;**19**:89–104.

Chapter 17
Leisure and the Development of Complexity

Roger C. Mannell
Stephen R. Manske

Ideas abound about the influence of people's leisure on their health and well-being. The things people choose to do during discretionary time have been linked directly to physical and mental health, as well as indirectly, through their influence on the vitality of people's interpersonal relationships, work and family lives and the organizations and communities of which they are a part (1). This chapter explores the idea that the leisure choices people make may contribute to their individual psychological health through the development of complexity. Furthermore, these choices, under some conditions, may promote the health of others in their community while providing optimal conditions for the development of individual complexity. Communities also can influence choices by strategically providing opportunities to develop complexity.

Complexity is a characteristic of biological, social, and psychological systems. More complex systems have greater numbers of distinct parts or elements, that is, they are more differentiated. More complex systems also are more integrated in that their distinct parts are well interconnected and organized. Psychological systems include personality and cognitive systems. These systems have been developed to characterize the way people structure and organize their perceptions and beliefs about themselves and their physical and social worlds and this complexity has important implications for health (2, 3, 4). An interesting question, then, is "how can leisure behavior promote the development of complexity?" Consider the following scenarios:

> *Scenario #1*: Kim and Ayesha hold similar positions in the tax division of an accounting firm that has had to cut staff and increase workloads, creating a stressful work environment. Of the two, Kim has better maintained her enthusiasm for work, appears less anxious, and has taken fewer sick days. If we take a closer look at the ways these women view themselves, that is, at their self-concepts, Ayesha sees herself primarily in terms of her work and family—a competent accountant and dedicated mother. Kim not only sees herself as a competent accountant and

parent but also an avid birder, committed volunteer and
member of a regular golf group.

In this scenario, Kim appears to have more roles and corresponding
sets of skills and knowledge than Ayesha. Complexity has been described
as an individual or personality difference and Kim could be characterized
as having higher complexity than Ayesha. Consequently, Kim is more
protected or buffered from work-related stress and less prone to depression
and anxiety. What is it about self-complexity that facilitates coping with
stress, how do people become more complex and do the leisure choices
people make contribute to the development of this type of complexity?

> *Scenario #2:* Early in his life, Liam's aunt taught him a
> few simple magic tricks, which he regularly practiced on
> family and friends. This pastime as an amateur magician
> eventually became a lifelong passion. When tricks no lon-
> ger challenged him, he read books, attended magic con-
> ventions and joined clubs finding and creating new more
> challenging tricks and performing for increasingly
> demanding audiences. On those occasions when he had the
> audience in the palm of his hand, flawlessly performed a
> difficult trick that tested his skills to the utmost and
> received immediate feedback on the quality of his perfor-
> mance, he experienced the best moments of his life—
> moments of intense enjoyment when he lost track of time,
> surroundings and sense of self. One moment flowed into
> the next and he experienced total involvement!

Liam's feeling of being in the flow, while meaningful in its own right,
is a motivational state that drives a process of healthy psychological
growth or increasing complexity. Here complexity refers to the continuous
development of new and more advanced skills, knowledge, and abilities
that provide a deep sense of enjoyment and enrich people's lives (2). In
Liam's case, a leisure activity is the vehicle for the experience of flow and
development of complexity. However, it is unlikely that all leisure activities promote flow and complexity. What characteristics are important and
how does leisure compare to work and other domains of life in providing
opportunities for the development of complexity? Can leisure activities
that are highly engaging and challenging but that are illegal or hurt others
promote complexity?

Scenario #3: Terry is recruited by a friend to help put up anti-smoking posters after school. Reluctantly, he agrees to do so but eventually becomes very involved with fellow students concerned with smoking behavior. The group eventually develops a school campaign that requires a lot of Terry's free time and, along with the others in the group, a great deal of effort, development of new skills in collaborating with others, problem solving, and creative thinking. In spite of the time, occasional setbacks and slow, hard work, Terry becomes extremely absorbed in the initiative and experiences many moments of real enjoyment. He also feels good about making a positive contribution to his new group of friends and the school community.

In this scenario, Terry experiences flow and an increase in complexity much as Liam did in scenario #2. However, the growth of complexity experienced by Terry and his personal goals become integrated with the goals of the group and the greater good of the school community. It has been argued that for the development of complexity that fully contributes to health and well-being, individual complexity must be linked or contribute to the greater social good and in this sense be a "positive" activity (2) that helps and does not hurt others. This scenario raises the question about how leisure activities can be structured to facilitate the development of individual complexity and well-being and at the same time promote a public good such as community or population health (i.e., improving the health of an entire population).

Complexity, Stress Coping, and Health

As we saw in scenario #1, Kim could be seen as having a higher level of complexity, which is consistent with the idea that the more constructs people use to describe or characterize themselves, the more complex their cognitive structure (3). Linville suggested that when a stressful event occurs, it affects that part of people's self-concept most pertinent to the stressor. For Kim and Ayesha, who are experiencing work-related stress, the attitudes, beliefs, and abilities associated with their work roles are most pertinent. For a person with numerous parts to their self-concepts such as Kim, the affected part is only one of many parts. Therefore, a relatively small proportion of her total self-concept will be negatively affected. By contrast, stress will negatively affect a greater proportion of the total self-concept in persons like Ayesha who have fewer aspects to their self-concept. Consequently, complexity can act as a buffer against stress-related illness and depression (4).

It is generally recognized that complexity is developed during socialization and direct experience with specific cognitive domains such as work, leisure, and family, but little or no research has been reported on this process. However, research on the development of leisure identities provides evidence that certain types of leisure can contribute to identity formation and affirmation and these leisure identities become important aspects of people's self-concepts (5). There is also support for the idea that beliefs developed through leisure involvements can act as a buffer to stress (6). For example, making choices during leisure can contribute to feelings of self-determination that characterize people who deal with stress more effectively. Also, given that much of leisure is social, the development of companionship and friendship in leisure can engender strong beliefs about available social support, beliefs that have been found to act as a buffer to stress. Leisure-generated self-complexity may also act as an additional type of buffer.

Flow, the Development of Complexity and Healthy Personal Growth

A view of complexity that has been more explicitly associated with leisure is illustrated by the experiences of Liam and Terry in scenarios #2 and #3. Here, complexity rather than being narrowly linked to stress coping is seen as an aspect of personal growth and healthy psychological development (2). In fact, flow experience, the result of the ongoing matching and inter-play of skills and challenges, is the "engine" that drives people to become more complex. The focus of this theory is not so much on individual dif-ferences in self-complexity as it is with the characteristics of flow and the conditions that foster it and the growth of complexity.

Flow has been frequently used as a model to describe the nature of the most positive and psychologically absorbing leisure experiences, and flow resulting from leisure engagements has been studied extensively. Csikszentmihalyi first developed the idea of flow following interviews with people engaged in their best leisure (rock climbers, basketball play-ers, recreational dancers, chess players) and work (surgeons). He found that situations providing participants with challenges that match their skills, clear and immediate feedback, and in which the participants lose track of their awareness of themselves are experienced as most rewarding. Subsequent studies have led Csikszentmihalyi to suggest that flow experi-ences are the best moments of people's lives and occur when body or mind are stretched to the limits in a voluntary effort to accomplish something difficult and worthwhile. Leisure or discretionary activities because of their voluntary nature have great potential for producing flow—people have greater opportunity to choose activities that allow them to maintain a match between the challenges encountered and their current skill level. Flow-producing activities are said to lead to increased complexity by encouraging the development of greater knowledge, skills, and abilities due to the constant improvement of skills and the subsequent search for greater challenges to maintain flow.

From Csikszentmihalyi's perspective, a more complex psychological system means that a person is differentiated to the extent that they have many different interests, abilities, and goals and to the extent that these are integrated. Finding new challenges, developing new skills, opening oneself to novel experiences—these are all differentiating functions. The incorporation of skills and experiences into a person's cognitive structure and personality enhances integration. Flow-complexity theory has similarities to social cognitive theories such as Deci and Ryan's (7) self-determination theory that suggests people are naturally inclined toward growth and development based on meeting the psychological needs of autonomy, competence, and social relatedness.

Csikszentimalyi has increasingly emphasized that positive growth and development depend on promoting complexity in society as well as the individual. People's highest potential involves developing to the fullest their individual uniqueness, that is, differentiation, yet at the same time, identifying with the larger processes at work in society. In other words, people must also learn to enjoy activities with increasingly complex goals that are also integrated with the goals of others.

Development of Complexity and Promoting Health through Leisure

The growth of time pressure, stress, and sedentary lifestyles associated with contemporary changes in work and the dominant role of technology in people's lives are contributing to unhealthy lifestyles and growing demands on health care systems. As well, excessive drinking, drug use, and other risky health behaviors are often engaged in during free time. In other words, they are types of leisure behavior. Consequently, the potential contributions of leisure to health are being viewed not only at the level of the individual but increasingly from a public and population health perspective. The ideas of complexity and health explored in this chapter are interesting, but are they useful in promoting individual health and healthy populations through leisure?

Of course, flow and the complexity it can produce are not uniquely developed through leisure. They can be fostered in work and other non-leisure domains. Not all leisure activities have the potential to provide increasing levels of challenge as people's skills increase, and consequently, continue to allow the experience of flow and promote complexity. Also, people do not automatically choose to engage in leisure activities that promote complexity and health. In fact, people frequently opt for less challenging and more relaxing and diversionary activities when making leisure choices. In contrast, more obligatory work and family activities often require participation in more demanding and challenging activities that require people to continually develop skills, knowledge, and abilities. Even the leisure activities people choose are more frequently challenging when they feel some sense of obligation to others or themselves associated with their participation (e.g., playing with grandchildren during a vacation, participating as a member of a sport team, volunteering with a club to maintain a hiking trail, participating in physically active leisure to maintain health) (8). In fact, theory and research (1) indicate that people's leisure repertoires must include more than simply pleasant, diversionary, escape-oriented experiences if discretionary activities are to contribute substantially to psychological well-being and personal growth. For example, the construct of serious leisure (9) suggests that people who experience higher levels of well-being and life satisfaction are more involved in freely chosen activities that require an investment of effort and that consequently enhance feelings of competency. Difficulties with mounting longitudinal studies have discouraged research that would document this process. However, with respect to flow experiences, there is research evidence that highly creative and fulfilled people report more frequent flow experiences in their daily lives (2) as do older adults with higher life satisfaction (1).

Recently, there has been a great deal of attention focused on positive youth development and the way voluntary or leisure activities need to be structured and provided. Larson (10) suggests that providers face the fundamental challenge of "allowing participants' actions to be self-directed, voluntary, and intrinsically motivated, yet also structured and challenging enough that participants are stretched into new domains of complexity" (p. 179). Activities engaged in during leisure have been shown to be ideal for these purposes if organized and given appropriate leadership (11).

Given the pervasiveness of public and private agencies that provide leisure services and educational opportunities, efforts to support participation in complexity-promoting leisure can be a significant part of a public and population health strategy. In this sense, community recreation agencies and organizations can promote public health and the increases in complexity that may result enhance coping with stress and lead to healthy development that can reduce the frequency of risky health behaviors. However, Csikszentmihalyi's view that the development of complexity is more than just an individual-oriented process and requires collaboration with others and the alignment of personal goals with community/societal goals has implications not only for the development of individual health but also public and population health.

The idea of individual leisure contributing to the social good was illustrated by Terry's experience described in scenario #3 and has also been discussed in other contexts where meaningful leisure is viewed as providing opportunities for exercising good citizenship in collaboration with others (12). For example, people who advocate for their own health and help create environments (social and physical) that encourage the health of others can facilitate the development of their personal complexity. Such opportunities apply to all ages. Older adults can develop complexity in the sense of leadership skills by volunteering to manage their health and that of their companions (13). At the other end of the spectrum, empowered youth have been found to develop leadership and related complexity in health promotion campaigns (e.g., Florida's Truth anti-smoking campaign) engaged in as volunteers during free time. Youth were engaged at state and local levels to define and implement the campaign. Broad participation led to edgy media spots (e.g., adding a laugh track to tobacco company executives swearing they did not know about the connection between smoking and health) and grassroots advocacy (e.g., demonstrating how non-normative smoking really is). These roles challenged participants and likely contributed to the development of complexity. These experiences had a dual function: identifying a common enemy (tobacco companies) while taking advantage of the adolescents' new peer and social connections to make healthy personal choices. Smoking rates in Florida dropped from 18.5 to 8.6 percent for middle school students in a 2-year period.

In a complementary vein, a local data collection system called SHAPES (School Health Action, Planning and Evaluation System—www.shapes.uwaterloo.ca) has been created and found to stimulate interest and mobilize youth action for health by generating information relevant to them (14). According to the SHAPES model, planning and action based on the school-specific data can lead to real change. When people (youth and adults) lead together, these processes result in social environments that provide opportunities for choice and the development of complexity. In turn, alignment of these experiences with broader social goals promotes individual development and health as well as population health. Research suggests that for these types of initiatives to work the activities need to be non-judgmental, provide opportunities to hear the voices of all stakeholders, create options and choices, encourage ownership and responsibility, and avoid approaches that marginalize individuals or that use coercive methods (Deci & Ryan, 2000). Individual involvement in these types of collective initiatives also encourages individual change and development. For example, in youth smoking prevention programs, where "older" youth prepare skits with the "stay smoke free" message, the older youth are often most affected themselves by their involvement – there is regular, intensive exposure to the message, ownership because it is self-created and adaptive. These changes have the earmarks of increasing complexity.

These examples focus on health promotion and population health initiatives and activities that often occur during discretionary time or leisure. Of course, there are other collective initiatives that may not be as clearly or directly related to health promotion interventions and yet could be fertile contexts for the promotion of complexity and healthy development during people's leisure (e.g., local community projects, sports clubs and volunteer tourism). Unfortunately, structured leisure or voluntary opportunities that promote the development of complexity do not present themselves spontaneously nor are they taken up automatically. Recreation and leisure, education, and health professionals need to design programs and policies that promote these types of involvement. Principles of community mobilization and community development are consistent with the current understanding of experiences that build complexity. Learning to do "with" rather than "to" may stretch both the professionals and the participants but the result will be resilient, complex individuals living in supportive environments.

References

1. Mannell RC. Health, well-being and leisure. *World Leisure Journal* 2007;**49**:114–128.
2. Csikzsentmihalyi M. *The Evolving Self: A Psychology for the Third Millennium.* Harper Collins: New York, 1993.
3. Linville PW. Self-complexity as a cognitive buffer against stress-related illness and depression. *J Pers Soc Psychol* 1987;**52**:663–676.
4. Rafaeli-Mor E, Steinberg J. Self-complexity and well-being: A review and research synthesis. *Personality and Social Psychology Review* 2002;**6**:31–58.
5. Coatsworth JD, Sharp EH, Palen L, Darling N, Cumsille P, Marta E. Exploring adolescent self-defining leisure activities and identity experiences across three countries. *Int J Behav Dev* 2005;**29**:361–370.
6. Iwasaki Y. Examining rival models of leisure coping mechanisms. *Leisure Sci* 2003;**25**:183–206.
7. Deci EL, Ryan RM. Self-determination theory and the facilitation of intrinsic motivation, social development, and well-being *Am Psychol* 2000;**55**:68–69.
8. Mannell RC, Zuzanek J, Larson R. Leisure states and "flow" experiences: Testing freedom and intrinsic motivation hypotheses. *Journal of Leisure Research* 1988;**20**:289–304.
9. Stebbins RA. Serious Leisure, Volunteerism and Quality of Life. In Haworth JT, Veal AJ (eds), *Work and Leisure.* New York: Routledge, 2004, pp. 200–212.
10. Larson R. Towards a psychology of positive youth development. *Am Psychol* 2000;**55**:170–183.
11. Witt P, Caldwell L (eds). *Recreation and Youth Development.* Venture Publishing, Inc.: State College, PA, 2005.
12. Reid D. *Work and Leisure in the 21st Century.* Toronto, ON: Wall and Emerson, 1995.
13. Kloseck M, Crilly R, Mannell RC. Involving community elderly in the planning and provision of health services: Predictors of volunteerism and leadership. *Can J Aging* 2006;**21**:77–91.
14. Cameron R, Manske SR, Brown KS, Jolin MA, Murnaghan D, Lovato CY. Integrating public health policy, practice, evaluation, surveillance, and research using local data collection and feedback systems: The example of the School Health Action Planning and Evaluation System (SHAPES). *Am J Publ Health* 2007;**97**:648–654.

Chapter 18

Socioeconomic Status, Health, and Leisure

Kathleen Wolin
Geoffrey Godbey

You know about the things you should do to keep yourself in good
health—you've heard it all before. Get plenty of exercise, eat a low-fat
diet with lots of fruits and vegetables, don't smoke, don't drink to excess
or drink and drive, get help if you think about suicide. Health educators
have encouraged you to change your lifestyle to make you healthier and
live longer. You also understand that your genetic predispositions play an
important role. All of these things are important but, as it happens, there
is another stunningly important predictor of your health and how long you
live—your social status.

While much of what health educators have done in the U.S. and elsewhere is to try to change lifestyles in ways that are presumed to be healthy,
where one stands in the social pecking order is often ignored. Medical care,
lifestyle, and one's genes are all critical variables in predicting health, but
a major influence of how we lead our lives is rarely the target of intervention. The higher one's level of education, the longer he/she is likely to live
and the better his/her health. Similarly, the higher the prestige of the job,
the better one's health and the higher the social status of one's parents, the
better the health. With lower incomes, people's health levels decrease and
their lives are shorter.

This isn't to say that people with low education levels can't live a long
time or that those who grew up in poor health circumstances can't improve
them and improve their health. In fact, studies that examine changes in
social class over the life course indicate that those who increase their status
are better off than those who stay at the bottom of the pecking order, but
are worse off than those who were always on top (1).

Let's put this in perspective. As the author of a large study of British
civil servants discovered:

> The evidence shows that, even after adjusting for risk fac-
> tors such as smoking, blood pressure, cholesterol, blood
> sugar, etc., the mortality rate is still 1.5 times higher
> among those lower on the social gradient and less than
> one-third of these difference has been explained by such
> risk factors (2).

> In other words, if you were going to pursue one strategy to
> protect your health and live longer—you would get as
> much education as you could and take a job that paid a lot
> of money and was high status!

Have you been taught this? That the increasing gap in social status is increasingly responsible for a great gap in the health and longevity of individuals? The U.S., of course, has the greatest income gap of any modern nation so the impact of the status syndrome is greater here than elsewhere. From southeast Washington, DC to Montgomery County, Maryland, for instance, for each mile you travel, life expectancy increases one and one-half years. What does this imply for health policy?

These findings appear to hold true regardless of whether the environment is harsh or welcoming. There are, in effect, almost no diseases of the rich, in spite of talk about high-stress jobs of the affluent leading to heart disease. Even heart disease is more common among those lower in the social hierarchy (3).

What is Socioeconomic Status?

Socioeconomic status (SES) can be measured by several different indicators, including income, education, and occupation. Income is the most commonly used measure and is linked to the ability of a person or family to secure quality food, housing, and health care. It also reflects the relative position of an individual within the social hierarchy. However, income fluctuates over time, particularly for those at the lower end of the spectrum who are at increased risk of job loss during economic downturns. Income can also change dramatically in response to health, as when illness leads to job loss. Income information can also be difficult to gather since many individuals are reluctant to report their income on surveys. This can result in a significant portion of individuals being excluded from research. Income is sometimes converted into a poverty indicator, which relates the household or family income to the federal poverty level. Federal poverty data is adjusted each year to account for inflation and also accounts for the size of the household/family.

Education is an alternate approach to measuring SES, although income and education level are closely linked. Research participants are typically willing to report their education and are able to do so with a high degree of accuracy. Education level remains fixed for most adults over age 25 and, unlike income, is unlikely to be influenced by health status. Average educational attainment has changed over time, which can impair comparisons across age demographics. People are getting more formal education than a decade or two ago. Educational attainment in one country often doesn't translate to another country, which can make education level a less meaningful indicator in immigrant groups.

Occupation is often a reflection of both income and education, but may not reflect socioeconomic position well for older persons or individuals not employed outside the home (i.e., a significant number of women during childbearing years) (3).

SES and Health

The relation of SES and health is often an inverse gradient, with those at the low end of the SES spectrum having the worst health outcomes and those at the high end of the SES spectrum having the best health outcomes. This is typically true regardless of race/ethnicity, which has its own health gradient (4, 5). The inverse relation between SES and health was documented in the mid-19th century and has continued since then. The poor have higher death rates and a lower life expectancy. Mortality from heart disease, diabetes, and many cancers increases as household income decreases (3). The poor are also more likely to experience heart disease, cancer, and diabetes (4).

Yet the causes of this disparity have likely changed. In the mid-19th century it was a function of poor sanitation, nutrition, and housing. Despite improvements in all these areas, disparities in mortality between rich and poor have actually increased since 1960. In addition to predicting poor health outcomes, SES is also inversely associated with many of the risk factors for disease and death including smoking, being overweight, and physical inactivity (3). In 1995, those with less than a high school education were two to three times more likely to smoke as those with at least a college degree. Those with a college degree are also less likely to be overweight and are more likely to report participating in the recommended amount of physical activity. While there doesn't appear to be a strong income gradient in hypertension in men, there is a clear gradient in women; poor women are 1.8 times more likely to have uncontrolled hypertension as high-income women (3). High-income women are also more likely to undergo screening procedures; women with high incomes are 60–70% more likely than poor women to have had a recent mammogram. The poor also have diminished access to quality health care, which may explain some of the remaining differences, but there is still a significant portion of the disparity in health between rich and poor that remains unexplained. The U.S., unlike most other modern nations, has no universal health care funded by government, which decreases the access to health care for those in the lower portion of the social gradient.

It isn't just physical health that is adversely affect by SES; individuals of low SES consistently report their "self-rated" health as fair or poor (3). Men and women in poor households are five to seven times more likely to report their health as fair or poor as those in the highest income group. The poor are more likely to report limitations to their normal daily activities, which impair their ability to work, perform household tasks, and other routine activities. The inability to perform activities of daily living such as eating, bathing, dressing, and getting out of bed is a significant issue for the elderly where it may preclude independent living and contribute to substantial health care costs. Poor men and women are 50–80% more likely to report difficulty with these activities as middle and high-income men and women (3).

Jobs and SES and Health

Jobs provide income, but many also provide health insurance and con-tribute to our health by providing a means of social support and positive self-esteem. Jobs can also negatively affect health by increasing stress and exposing workers to dangerous conditions. Workers lower on the totem pole are more likely to be exposed to harmful chemicals and physical hazards. One of the reasons that males constitute 92% of all occupationally related deaths is that they take the most dangerous jobs, from lumberjack to taxicab driver to airline pilot (6). Lower-status workers also are subject to non-physical stressors that are associated with adverse health. Low-wage workers are often in jobs that require shift work which can include working overnight or alternating day and night shifts. These conditions have been associated with numerous health problems including depression, weight gain, and cardiovascular disease (7).

Job stress also contributes to poor health. Jobs with high job strain are characterized by low control over decisions and high demands (and often times conflicting demands). These jobs have been associated with poor health-related quality of life and increased risk of cardiovascular disease and death (8–12). The effects of high job strain are often exacerbated for those of low socioeconomic position (13).

Low-wage workers are also more likely to be in jobs with higher risk of job loss (contributing to job stress). Worry about job loss has been shown to increase risk of heart disease. While the stereotypical example of job stress is the executive working long hours, in reality, those at the top of a company hierarchy often command a high degree of control over their work and their work day, offsetting some of the negative consequences of the high demands placed on them. In contrast, those at the lowest end are subject to high demands and low control. Stress is associated with disruptions to the body's system including immune function and both the cardiovascular and nervous systems. Those who are stressed are also more likely to report depression and sleep problems and are more likely to smoke, abuse alcohol, and eat a poor diet, which all contribute to poor health. Stress increases risk of mortality, heart disease and infection, and reduces recovery time from illness (7).

The way that individuals cope with stress can offset the adverse health effects or it can make them worse. Those who smoke or drink to excess in response to stress are putting additional adverse strain on their physical health. In contrast, those who exercise experience mood improvements as well as physical health improvements, as exercise decreases the risk of many of the conditions to which stress contributes. Those who are higher SES typically have more opportunity and resources available for exercise including access to parks, recreation centers, gyms, and safe physical environments free from crime.

Few studies have examined the link between SES, psychosocial factors, and health in a single analysis. Those that have done so have found that SES is inversely associated with social support, stress, anger, and self-rated health, but the psychosocial factors do not explain all of the SES variation in health (14). Given the paucity of data, the theory that SES acts on health through social and cognitive factors cannot be supported or dismissed. However, indirect evidence gathered by examining pieces of the theory (SES and health, SES and social or cognitive factors) can provide some important clues. Most of the research on depression and SES indicates an inverse association exists (15). Depression is also linked to adverse health outcomes including cardiovascular disease and death. Only two studies have examined the association between anxiety symptoms and SES, but both suggest anxiety is highest in those with the lowest SES (15). More research has studied the association with anxiety disorders and also suggests an inverse association. Anxiety is associated with increased risk of cardiovascular disease and cardiovascular disease mortality to some degree, but is more strongly associated with sudden cardiac death.

It isn't just the perceived control over one's work environment that may influence health. Individuals who report having low levels of personal control also have poorer health (16). This is seen across gradients of socioeconomic status but there is an interaction between the two. In fact, perceived self-control may offset being in the lowest socioeconomic level. For example, Lachman and Weaver found that individuals in the lowest income group who perceived themselves as having high levels of control had health and well-being levels comparable to those in higher income groups (16).

Leisure Differences and SES

It is ironic that leisure, the realm in which it is assumed individuals have the chance to exercise freedom and autonomy, is only beginning to be thought of as a critical variable in the relations described previously. Americans have more free time than is commonly perceived by the public. Time use studies over the last few decades confirm Americans average between thirty-five and forty hours per week of free time (17). The potential for use of leisure to reinforce or change the relationship between social status and health would seem great. Lower SES individuals do not necessarily have less free time. Indeed, some studies find they have more. Many forms of leisure thought of as "healthy" or socially desirable do appear to follow a social gradient. These include physically active forms of leisure, participation in the arts, most forms of outdoor recreation (with a few exceptions, such as hunting and fishing), most forms of sport (perhaps contrary to popular belief), tourism, and social capital activities, such as serving on boards of local government (18).

Some forms of leisure (e.g., television viewing) appear to increase with lower social status. One recent study, for example, found that more than 2 hours of television viewing per day was positively associated with those who had a high school education or less, who lived in low-income households, and who were employed. It was also associated with obesity. High TV viewers were, on average, in poorer health (19).

To the extent the previous is true, improving the health of lower SES people might involve seeking to change their leisure habits—an idea as old as the Industrial Revolution, when various Rational Recreation movements sought to reform the leisure of the emerging urban lower class. While very little can be definitively stated about the potential for leisure to lessen the impact of social status on health, perhaps three ideas need to be considered: leisure constraints, specialization in leisure activity, and preparation for meaningful leisure.

Leisure Constraints

Lower SES individuals appear to have more constraints to leisure. Lower social status is often associated with other variables which create more severe constraints to leisure participation. Such variables include everything from obesity to ethnic status to poor health to lack of transportation to fear of crime. In combination, for instance, being obese, in poor health and African American may mean it is less likely an individual can or will participate in a given leisure activity. As numerous researchers have reported, everyday life is influenced by multiple social statuses, including SES, ethnicity, age, and gender. Leisure lifestyles are influenced by a combination of these multiple statuses. As reported in one study:

> Indeed, th(is) perspective provides a more realistic picture of leisure lifestyles than studies that focused solely on the impact of a single status. The perspective suggests that since elderly, minority women who have a lower socioeconomic status have four disadvantageous statuses, they are likely to occupy the bottom of a multiple hierarchy stratification of outdoor recreation participation (20).

Hierarchical leisure constraints theory assumes that an individual must negotiate three forms of constraints in order to participate in a leisure activity (21). The most profound, but often underrated constraint, intrapersonal constraints, consists of the individual's assessment of whether or not participation is appropriate for him or her. Would they enjoy the activity? Could they succeed? Do people "like them" do the activity? Would their parents, family, or friends approve? If the answer to such questions is "no," the individual may lose interest in participation and no longer look for opportunities. If the desire to participate continues, however, the next level of constraints to be negotiated is interpersonal constraints. Are there people to participate with and are they acceptable? If this constraint level is negotiated, the final constraint level, structural constraints, consists of logistical considerations. Does the individual have the time, money, transportation, equipment, etc. to participate? Low SES people often have more of each type of constraint, but it is intrapersonal constraints, because they often kill off the desire to participate, that may be most important. Minimizing this problem may include showing lower SES people models of other people, like them, who are doing the activity and enjoying it. When kids in low SES schools in Harlem saw others like them becoming expert chess players, for example, participation in the game blossomed (22).

Finding others who are appropriate to participate with may take experimentation. Many older women, particularly those who are lower SES, will not do water exercise until those running the programs segregate the activity by gender—keeping males away from the older women who were, often, in a bathing suit for the first time in decades. Structural constraints can often be changed by social policy—providing transportation, for example, or supplying tennis racquets and balls for an inner-city tennis class. What is necessary to minimize the impact of SES on leisure constraints is the will to do so and social policy which reflects that will.

Minimizing leisure constraints for lower SES students and others would be a very daunting task. According to numerous studies, the United

States has the highest level of income inequality among all modern nations. For example, low-income households, or those at the 10th percentile of the income distribution, spend approximately $8,900 per year per child, while high-income families, or those at the 90th percentile, spend $50,000 per child (21). The same problem exists in public schools. Since real estate taxes and other local revenues provide the bulk of public school funding, public school spending per student varies greatly from school to school, sometimes by a multiple of two.

In terms of social mobility, the likelihood of a child moving up (or down) the socioeconomic ladder compared to their parents, the U.S. ranks close to last among modern nations. Thus, Americans not only have the greatest inequities in SES among modern nations but also very little likelihood that it is easily changeable. Since parental education and occupational class were recently found to be stronger predictors of offspring's educational attainment than parental income (23), investments in public schools which were equal on a per student basis would go a long way toward increasing not only opportunities for upward mobility but also toward teaching leisure skills to students who are lower SES.

It is also important to note that, as we saw in many of the examples above, SES interacts strongly with other sociodemographic factors to constrain leisure pursuits. Thus, strategies that seek to intervene on one, but ignore the other, will have limited success.

A great example of a program that has impacted these levels is the Ed Snider Youth Hockey Foundation in Philadelphia (ESYHF). Concerned with the trajectories of inner-city kids in the greater metro area, Snider, the founder and chairman of the Philadelphia Flyers hockey team, started a foundation to introduce hockey to an area where kids had never been on skates or paid attention to the sport. Ninety-six percent of students in the Foundation's program go on to the next year of school compared to 45% in their peers. The Foundation's program isn't just about learning to skate and shoot a puck, it also teaches communication, study skills, healthy habits, and respect. While the ESYHF believes athletics and team sports help to promote positive development, they believe fostering an atmosphere that encourages academic achievement is just as critical. ESYHF coaches ensure that every player understands that while ESYHF programming (equipment, ice time, coaching, tutoring, etc.) is free of charge, their participation is a privilege earned by doing the right thing in school and in their communities. Players that show effort and improvement in school are praised and rewarded, while players that struggle with school attendance or performance are encouraged to work with tutors and mentors and are told that they may need to take a break from the ice if their approach to school doesn't improve.

Jan Koziara, Director of Hockey Operations at ESYHF, describes the effect of the program on one student athlete:

> Last year at the beginning of the season, a 13-year-old that was new to our program shared his report card with me for the first time. I found him to be a smart kid, and was therefore surprised to see a majority of D's with a smattering of C's on his report card. I talked with him and encouraged him to work harder on his schoolwork, and told him that if he was having difficulties in any subjects that we could have a tutor work with him. Over the course of the winter he came to the rink 4 or 5 days a week, and we made it a point to discuss school at least once a week. In the spring he proudly shared his report card, which contained a number of B's and a few C's. He was selected to join a group of 30 players on a trip to Canada as a reward for his effort. I'm convinced that for him (and for many other players that I see), improvement in school came because he was spending time with a group of coaches and teammates that valued academic success. (personal communication)

Specialization in Leisure Activity

A second line of research, which deals with serious leisure, amateurism, and specialization in leisure activity, is also relevant here. Basically, this body of knowledge indicates that some leisure activities become "serious" as the participant becomes more knowledgeable, more dedicated, and more interested in participating only with those who are similarly specialized in the activity (23). As participation progresses to greater levels of complexity, the individual becomes an amateur, one who loves the activity in question (23). As one specializes in the leisure activity, it begins to provide durable benefits, foremost among them—an attractive identity. The amateur does not make his/her living from the activity in question, be it playing guitar or raising orchids, but does base his/her identity around an activity in which, in most senses, he/she has succeeded (24). Amateurs sometimes cross the line and become professionals, earning some or all of their living from the activity.

The extent to which the individual who has become an amateur in a leisure activity can minimize the negative health impacts of lower social status is largely unknown. What *is* known is that, as a person becomes specialized in a leisure activity, the basis for selecting others with whom to participate is based on their similar specialization, rather than their SES.

Thus, those in the Master Gardeners' Program, for example, may participate with other highly competent gardeners regardless of SES.

Preparation for Meaningful Leisure

Most leisure skills are learned during the first two decades of life. They are
taught by parents, in schools, on television and computer screens, by peers
and by organizations serving youth. The forms of leisure that have been
shown to confer attractive, enduring identities are often skill-challenge
forms of leisure, which require serious involvement and a long learning
curve. Thus, teaching such skills must be thought of in terms of years of
preparation, rather than just exposure to an activity. Preparing for a leisure
"career" in a given activity will require that numerous organizations
coordinate their involvement. Rather than being "well-rounded" in leisure
activities, the goal for lower SES individuals, if leisure is to play a role
in minimizing the health gap, may be to provide an environment for specialization in a skill-challenge form of leisure to take place, providing an
attractive identity in the process. This is exactly what organizations like the
ESYHF aim to do in youth—turn Shawn from another kid at school to the
kid who is the great hockey player. The same can be seen in adults. Dave is
no longer the janitor but the great banjo player in a Dixieland band. Wanda
is not the Walmart clerk but the grower of prize-winning orchids. While
leisure, historically, was often used as diversion by lower SES individuals, often with the support of government and large corporations, serious
leisure might lead to fulfillment and positive self-image, with better health
occurring in the process.

References

1. Bennett GG, Wolin KY, James SA. Lifecourse socioeconomic position and weight change among blacks: The Pitt County study. *Obesity (Silver Spring)* 2007;**15/1**:172–181.
2. Marmot MG. *The Status Syndrome—How Social Standing Affects Our Health and Longevity*. Henry Holt and Company: New York, 2004.
3. National Center for Health Statistics. *Health, United States, 1998 With Socioeconomic Status and Health Chartbook*. Hyattsville, MD, 1998.
4. Adler NE, Boyce T, Chesney MA, Cohen S, Folkman S, Kahn RL, et al. Socioeconomic status and health. The challenge of the gradient. *Am Psychol* 1994;**49/1**:15–24.
5. Marmot MG, Smith GD, Stansfeld S, Patel C, North F, Head J, et al. Health inequalities among British civil servants: the Whitehall II study. *Lancet* 1991;**337/8754**:1387–1393.
6. Farrell W. *Why Men Earn More*. American Management Association: New York, 2005.
7. Adler NE. Health disparities: What's optimism got to do with it? *J Adolesc Health* 2007;**40/2**:106–107.
8. Lerner DJ, Levine S, Malspeis S, D'Agostino RB. Job strain and health-related quality of life in a national sample. *Am J Public Health* 1994;**84/10**:1580–1585.
9. Lynch J, Krause N, Kaplan GA, Salonen R, Salonen JT. Workplace demands, economic reward, and progression of carotid atherosclerosis. *Circulation* 1997;**96/1**:302–307.
10. Van Egeren LF. The relationship between job strain and blood pressure at work, at home, and during sleep. *Psychosom Med* 1992;**54/3**:337–343.
11. Marmot MG, Bosma H, Hemingway H, Brunner E, Stansfeld S. Contribution of job control and other risk factors to social variations in coronary heart disease incidence. *Lancet* 1997;**350/9073**:235–239.
12. Unden AL, Orth-Gomer K, Elofsson S. Cardiovascular effects of social support in the work place: Twenty-four-hour ECG monitoring of men and women. *Psychosom Med* 1991;**53/1**:50–60.
13. Wege N, Dragano N, Erbel R, Jockel KH, Moebus S, Stang A, et al. When does work stress hurt? Testing the interaction with socioeconomic position in the Heinz Nixdorf Recall Study. *J Epidemiol Community Health* 2008;**62/4**:338–341.
14. Cohen S, Kaplan GA, Salonen JT. The role of psychological characteristics in the relation between socioeconomic status and perceived health. *J Applied Social Psychology* 1999;**29/3**:445–468.

15. Gallo LC, Matthews KA. Understanding the association between socioeconomic status and physical health: Do negative emotions play a role? *Psychol Bull* 2003;**129/1**:10–51.
16. Lachman ME, Weaver SL. The sense of control as a moderator of social class differences in health and well-being. *J Pers Soc Psychol* 1998;**74/3**:763–773.
17. Robinson J, Godbey G. *Time for Life: The Surprising Ways American Use Their Time, Revised Edition*. Penn State Press: University Park, PA, 1999.
18. How Americans Spend Their Time - Defining Leisure and Recreation. http://www.libraryindex.com/pages/1944/How-Americans-Spend-Their-Time-DEFINING-LEISURE-RECREATION.html. Accessed June 21, 2010.
19. Bowman SA. Television-viewing characteristics of adults: Correlations to eating practices and overweight and health status. *Prev Chronic Dis* 2006;**3/2**:A38.
20. Dattilo J, Dattilo A, Samdahl D, Kleiber D. Leisure orientations and self-esteem in women with low incomes who are overweight. *J Leisure Research*. 1994;**22**:213–227.
21. Godbey G, Crawford D, Shen S. Assessing hierarchical leisure constraints theory after two decades. *J Leisure Research*. In press.
22. Stewart B. In Harlem, a chess champion passes on his moves and enthusiasm. *N.Y. Times*. December 29, 1999, 1999;B: 2.
23. Kerstetter D, Confer J. An exploration of the specialization concept within the context of heritage tourism. *J Travel Res* 2001;**39/3**:267–274.
24. Stebbins R. *Amateurs, Professionals and Serious Leisure*. McGill-Queens University Press: Montreal, QC, 1992.

Chapter 19

Children's Physical Activity and Healthy Development: Physical, Social, Emotional, and Cognitive Benefits

Maureen R. Weiss
Lynn A. Barnett

"Get up and play an hour a day!" This was the catchphrase in a recent promotion by the Ladies Professional Golf Association. Besides being catchy, the message is an accurate reflection of the *Physical Activity Guidelines* for children (1) that state, "Youth can achieve substantial health benefits by doing moderate- and vigorous-intensity physical activity for periods of time that add up to 60 minutes (1 hour) or more each day" (p. 15). Although the term *health benefits* often conjures up physiological outcomes such as decreased likelihood of cardiovascular disease, diabetes, and overweight/obesity, satisfying adequate levels of daily physical activity also contributes to other health benefits, including physical, social, emotional, and cognitive outcomes. Thus, physical activity is a critical context for promoting child development from a holistic perspective.

The term *physical activity* can be applied to a range of structured and unstructured contexts. Structured activities include organized sport, out-of-school-time programs (e.g., *The Little Gym,* dance classes*)*, and school physical education. Unstructured activities include school-based recess, free play, recreational activities (e.g., family hiking), and active transport (e.g., riding a bike to school). Within these contexts, children have the *potential* to attain a number of developmental health benefits. We say *potential* because mere participation in physical activity does not automatically contribute to healthy outcomes, just as maturation alone does not produce gains in motor, social, and emotional development (2). The purpose of our chapter is to outline children's developmental outcomes attainable from a physically active lifestyle. Our discussion includes theory-driven research on developmental health benefits and take-home messages for adults who work with children in physical activity settings. Table 19.1 displays a sampling of children's and adolescents' physical, social, emotional, and cognitive health benefits as a result of regular physical activity.

Table 19.1 Developmental Health Benefits of Physical Activity (Adapted from Weiss & Wiese-Bjornstal (41))

Physical Benefits
Motor skill and sport-specific competencies Physically active lifestyle Physical fitness Physiological capacities Physical health
Social Benefits
Support from significant adults and peers Feelings of social acceptance Close friendship and friendship quality Leadership, teamwork, cooperation Respect, responsibility, courtesy, and integrity
Emotional Benefits
Positive identity, body image, and self-esteem Perceived physical competence and self-efficacy Positive emotions and management of negative emotions Feelings of self-determination, autonomy, and choice Moral identity, empathy, and social perspective-taking
Cognitive Benefits
Cognitive functioning and intellectual health Knowledge about physical activities, sports, and games Improved executive function Academic achievement (grades, test scores, college entry) Career goal attainment

Contributions of Children's Physical Activity to Their Physical Development

Along with the observation that children are more pressured today to achieve academically, they are also enrolled in more structured out-of-school activities, lessons, and instructional programs. Opportunities for free play are declining, and outdoor play in America has dropped precipitously (3). Modern parents are more reluctant than parents of past generations to let their young children play out-of-doors without supervision, largely based on their concern about safety and crimes against children. Sedentary activities compete for children's attention, such as watching TV and playing computer games, which are fast replacing more vigorous outdoor and indoor play and games. One result of this decline in physical activity, attributed in part to changes in play styles and frequency, has been a child-hood obesity epidemic (1). Unfortunately, physical inactivity in childhood tracks to adolescence (4) and from adolescence into adulthood (5), and has been linked to a number of chronic health conditions, including cardiovas-cular disease, type 2 diabetes, certain cancers, cognitive dysfunction, and depression. Thus, recent position papers (1, 6) advocate that children have regular access to play and other forms of physical activity, in recognition of important short- and long-term benefits.

Children also need to be physically active as a means of developing their motor skills. Fundamental motor abilities (e.g., balance, coordina-tion, control, agility, strength), locomotion skills (e.g., walking, running, jumping, skipping), and object-control skills (e.g., throwing, catching, kicking, striking) are essential prerequisites to mastering sport-specific and movement skills needed for becoming competent at lifetime activities (e.g., softball, skiing, dance, golf) (2, 7). Strong et al. prioritize motor skill and movement activities for preschool and early school age youth (up to about age 10) so that, once these skills are attained, physical activities that emphasize health and fitness outcomes can become the focus for youth ages 10 to 18 years. Opportunities for age-appropriate physical activities in school physical education, motor development programs, and recreational and play contexts contribute to mastering motor abilities and skills. The bottom line is that these skills need to be learned through competent instruction and practiced within environments that encourage curiosity, effort, interest, and improvement (2).

Motor skill development occupies both sides of the physical activ-ity equation. That is, opportunities to be physically active contribute to learning, practice, and mastery of critical motor skills and abilities, and attainment of abilities and skills such as postural control, coordination, run-ning, and throwing enhance children's physical activity competencies as an adolescent and adult. As Clark (2) convincingly articulates, "Children who leave elementary school without a strong foundation of motor skills are 'left behind' in the same way that children are left behind when they leave without the prerequisite language or mathematical skills…Motor literacy is as important as reading literacy. If we want a nation of physically active citizens, then we need to help them acquire the motor skills that will allow them to participate in a wide range of physical activities" (p. 43).

Contributions of Children's Physical Activity to Their Social Development

Several authors hold that active play promotes the development of social competence (8). More playful children are thus more social and cooperative and less withdrawn and aggressive (9), and have age-similar peers as an important source of social support (10). In play, children learn to form friendships, positively interact with peers in mutually beneficial ways, and derive feelings of belongingness to a peer group (11, 12). In addition, playing with peers provides a safe haven, free from adult constraints, in which children can readily share secrets and feelings and achieve a sense of intimacy (13, 14). Play is a context in which children learn cooperation, turn-taking, and the meaning of rules (15).

Social play also provides an important context for developing peer conflict management skills (12). Effectively resolving conflicts involves social perspective-taking—the ability to understand another person's point of view; that is, how they think and feel about an issue. Piaget (16) and others have shown that young children have difficulty with perspective-taking, largely because of their egocentric nature in assuming that their own views are also those held by others. Sociodramatic play has been shown to play an important role in the development of children's perspective-taking ability—children must be able to mentally put themselves in other people's places and experience the world from others' points of view. This act of consciously transforming their own identities promotes perspective-taking skills (17). From an early age, play provides an enjoyable venue in which children find out about themselves and their social world. Through observing, emulating, and playing the roles of important adult figures, children learn social and cultural roles.

In addition to free play, organized sport and physical activities are important contexts for developing social skills, fostering peer relationships, and learning to interact with peers and adults in respectful ways (12, 14). Children are often attracted to and sustain sport and physical activity participation for reasons related to social acceptance, approval, and recognition. Examples include making and affirming friendships, attaining approval from parents and coaches/teachers, and feeling a sense of belonging to one's peer group. Children's perceptions of social acceptance and approval are important factors determining whether they view experiences as positive or negative and, subsequently, influence decisions about continuing involvement.

Children's peer relationships are significant sources of social and moral development (12, 14). Social acceptance, or one's status within one's peer group, is positively associated with being good in sports and a leader of activities. Moreover, greater peer acceptance is associated with positive emotional experiences and greater motivation to participate in physical activities. Close friendship refers to a mutual relationship, one that is characterized by similarity of interests, self-esteem enhancement, emotional support, and loyalty). Children who identify higher friendship quality in physical activity report positive self-perceptions, attraction toward physical activity, and motivation to continue involvement (18). Finally, interacting with peers in organized physical activities provides a level playing field, so to speak, for learning to be a leader and follower, being respectful and responsible to others, and resolving conflicts in mutually satisfying ways (12).

Learning prosocial and antisocial behaviors in youth sport occurs through observational learning of adults' and peers' behaviors, as well as perceived social approval by parents, teammates, friends, and coaches of desirable or undesirable actions (19). Research has focused on social learning of sportsmanlike behaviors and interventions to promote character development in physical activity contexts. For example, Stuart and Ebbeck (20) found that children's perceptions of significant adults' and peers' approval of unsportsmanlike play were related to their beliefs and behaviors related to acting aggressively. If parents, coaches, and teammates were viewed as disapproving of unfair play, this was associated with children's more mature moral functioning—higher moral reasoning and lower incidence of aggressive behaviors.

Intervention studies to promote prosocial and discourage antisocial behaviors among youth in physical activity contexts have shown promising results. The *Fair Play for Kids* program developed in Canada has been effective with fourth through sixth grade children in school physical education (21), and so has the *Teaching Personal and Social Responsibility Model* (22) with youth in school and community programs. These interventions show that when environments are structured to purposefully teach youth positive values and beliefs about sportsmanlike play (e.g., respecting others, controlling negative emotions), and positive role models are available to reinforce such behaviors, effects on character development are meaningful and enduring.

Contributions of Children's Physical Activity to Their Emotional Development

Development of one's self-identity is an important developmental goal that can be fostered through structured physical activities. Self-esteem refers to an individual's global self-evaluation of worthiness, while perceived competence refers to one's beliefs or judgments about abilities in a particular domain (e.g., academics, sports) or subdomain (e.g., math, swimming) (23). When considering the child's self-perceptions in physical activities, it is important to understand *how* perceptions of competence are formed and how these self-appraisals influence motivated behavior such as choosing to continue a physical activity and persisting when learning difficult skills. Children under 10 years of age report greater use of parent feedback, effort, and task mastery to judge physical competence, while older children (ages 10 to 14 years) use peer comparison and evaluation, as well as coach feedback, relatively more than younger children. If young participants interpret these sources of information positively, level of perceived competence (how high or low a child judges her ability) will be positively affected. In turn, belief that one is good at physical activities is associated with greater enjoyment and intrinsic motivation to continue involvement. These trends in sources of competence information help explain changes over time in emotional responses and motivational orientations toward physical activity.

Play has been shown to be an important tool for expressing and managing emotions (24). In imaginative play, children develop more socially acceptable ways to express and control their emotions (25). Children's play occasionally leads to conflict. They must find ways to de-escalate their negative feelings, resolve their disagreements, and reframe their play. Play is an important context for developing conflict management skills and offers unique opportunities to try out strategies that lead to successful conflict resolution. Play has been shown to be a very effective coping strategy in times of trauma or stress (26), and over time, leads to a more resilient child (27).

Lately, much been much written about recent trends in creating the "hurried" child. According to this view, children are growing up too fast—largely the result of pressures exerted on them by parents and other adults to achieve and take on adult roles (28). Play is seen as the antidote for this worrisome condition. The resulting stress from pressures is countered and released through play. Self-directed play is therefore seen as necessary for the child's emotional equilibrium and as an essential and unique remedy to externally imposed pressure and stress.

Contributions of Children's Physical Activity to Their Cognitive Development

Piaget (16) emphasized the role of discovery learning in cognitive development. He emphasized that children must be actively engaged in constructing their experiences to maximize understanding of concepts. Children who have been afforded opportunities to play with materials related to academic subjects they are studying gain an in-depth understanding of the topic (29). These findings are attributed to the child's ability to learn in his or her own way through active play, the perceived safety of the environment where minimal consequences are attached to errors, the accompanying satisfaction in learning about something or figuring out a problem, and the special motivation that is uniquely associated with discovery learning.

Studies of children in many cultures reveal that play helps them discover many ways in which objects can be manipulated and utilized. Through this object-oriented self-directed play, children explore objects and discover myriad possibilities for their use. When later presented with a problem, those that have had play opportunities utilize the objects creatively to form effective tools and successfully solve the problem (30). This has been seen as an important benefit derived from play—acquiring behavioral flexibility in response to a changeable environment (31). Studies linking play with divergent thinking (17) and with creativity (32) support the argument that play affords important cognitive benefits to the developing child.

Play is also an important way in which the child comes to understand symbolism and mental representation (33). Particularly in symbolic, or make-believe, play children pretend to be someone else, allocate and enact role assignments, and come to realize that others may see the world differently and have alternate desires and ideas (34). They act in accord with their own internal ideas and not just in response to external stimuli. Make-believe play facilitates the development of symbolic thought and demonstrates that play provides a window on how children mentally represent their world. Klugman and Smilansky (35) argued that make-believe play facilitates children's cognitive abilities by helping them make connections between seemingly unrelated events and come to a deeper understanding of how things in their world work and are sequenced. In addition, children's ability to use representational skills in pretend play helps them develop mature concepts of space, time, probability, and causality (36). As time and space are altered in pretend play episodes, children revise their conceptions and achieve an understanding of their meaning and significance. Their awareness of the concept of reversibility—that you can change back from your make-believe role to your real identity at any time—also helps children acquire conservation skills (37).

Language is a big part of children's play, from the simple utterances and rhyming of the young to the joking and verbal give-and-take of older children. Play helps children perfect their language skills and increases their conscious awareness and understanding of linguistic rules (38). Through play, children practice and come to understand and appreciate the elements of language; they play with sounds by repeating strings of nonsense syllables, with syntax by systematically substituting words of the same grammatical category, and with semantics by intentionally distorting meaning through nonsense, rhymes and jokes. In this way, play is associated with language development, and carries over into their story comprehension, literacy skills, and reading and arithmetic achievement (29).

Recommendations for Adults Working with Children

Based on the empirical evidence examining structured and unstructured physical activity as a context for children's healthy development, we offer the following take-home messages to parents, educators, and professionals working with children in physical activity contexts (39, 40, 41):

- *Provide optimal challenges.* Ensure children have opportunities for skill building that challenge them at the cutting edge of their abilities—not too easy and not too hard. Success at optimal challenges are most likely to instill positive self-perceptions, emotional responses, and self-determined motivation.
- *Make sure physical activity experiences are fun.* When children enjoy activities, interactions, and overall experiences, they are more likely to develop socially, psychologically, physically, and cognitively. Having fun can be implicit in the physical activities themselves, such has providing choice or variety of activities for children.
- *Create a mastery motivational climate.* When physical activity environments are structured in ways that promote mastery, learning, and effort as the goals, rather than favorable comparison to others or winning, children thrive in their developing physically, socially, cognitively, and psychologically.
- *Maximize social support.* Positive regard by parents, coaches, and peers influences children's self-perceptions, affective responses, and motivated behaviors. Adults should provide appropriate praise and skill-relevant feedback following performance attempts because this communicates positive competence beliefs to children that, in turn, translate to effort and persistence. Parents and adult leaders could promote positive peer relationships and respect and empathy for others by organizing activities that require cooperation to achieve goals and emphasizing group cohesiveness and mutual respect through team building activities.
- *Be a positive role model.* Children look to parents, teachers, coaches, and other important adults to determine the "right thing to do" and how to behave in prosocial ways. When adults demonstrate respect, responsibility, courtesy, and honesty, children's observational learning of these behaviors will be enacted. When children see undesirable or antisocial behaviors, these too will be learned. Thus it is critical that significant adults act appropriately to enhance character development.

- *Help children help themselves:* Mastering skills and achieving personal goals are sources of information children use to judge their physical competence. Competence beliefs, in turn, influence self-esteem, enjoyment, motivation, and physical activity levels. Thus, teaching children self-regulated learning strategies such as goal setting and self-monitoring will allow them to adopt strategies for gauging their own skill progress and influence problem solving and perceived competence.

References

1. United States Department of Health and Human Services (USDHHS). *The Surgeon General's Call to Action to Promote Healthy Homes.* Atlanta, GA, 2008.
2. Clark JE. On the problem of motor skill development. *Journal of Physical Education, Recreation, and Dance* 2007;**78/5**:39–44.
3. Louv R. *Last Child in the Woods.* Algonquin Books: Chapel Hill, NC, 2008.
4. Pate RR, Heath GW, Dowda M, Trost SG. Associations between physical activity and other health behaviors in a representative sample of U.S. adolescents. *Amer J of Public Health* 1996;**86**:1577–1581.
5. Dietz W. Health consequences of obesity in youth: Childhood predictors of adult disease. *Pediatrics* 1998;**101**:518–525.
6. American Academy of Pediatrics. The importance of play in promoting healthy child development and maintaining strong parent-child bonds. *Pediatrics* 2007;**119**:182–191.
7. Strong WB, Malina RM, Blimkie CJ, Daniels SR, Dishman RK, Gutin B, et al. Evidence based physical activity for school-age youth. *J Pediatrics* 2005;**146**:732–737.
8. Parke R, MacDonald K, Beitel K, Bhavnagri N. The Role of Family in the Development of Peer Relationships. In Peters R, McMahon J (eds), *Social Learning Systems Approaches to Marriage and Family.* New York: Brunner/Mazel, 1988, pp. 17–44.
9. Howes C, Matheson C. Sequences in the development of competent play with peers: Social and social pretend play. *Dev Psych* 1992;**28**:961–974.
10. Carver C, Schier M, Weintraub J. Assessing coping strategies: A theoretically based approach. *J Personality and Social Psych* 1989;**56**:267–283.
11. Connolly J, Doyle A. Relation of social fantasy play to social competence in preschoolers. *Dev Psych* 1984;**20**:797–806.
12. Weiss MR, Stuntz CP. A Little Friendly Competition: Peer Relationships and Psychosocial Development in Youth Sport and Physical Activity Contexts. In Weiss MR (ed), *Developmental Sport and Exercise Psychology: A Lifespan Perspective.* Morgantown, WV: Fitness Information Technology, 2004, pp. 165–196.
13. Selman R, Hickey-Schultz L. *Making a Friend in Youth.* University of Chicago Press: Chicago, 1990.
14. Smith AL. Youth Peer Relationships in Sport. In Jowett S, Lavallee D (eds), *Social Psychology in Sport.* Champaign, IL: Human Kinetics, 2007, pp. 41–54.

15. Smith PK, Dalgleish M, Herzmark G. A comparison of the effects of fantasy play tutoring and skills tutoring in nursery classes. *Int J Behav Dev* 1981;**4**:421–441.

16. Piaget J. *Play, Dreams, and Imitation in Childhood.* Routledge: London, 1951.

17. Creasey G, Jarvis P, Berk L. Play and Social Competence. In Saracho O, Spodek B (eds), *Multiple Perspectives on Play in Early Childhood Education.* Albany, NY: Statue University of New York Press, 1998, pp. 116–143.

18. Weiss MR, Smith AL. Friendship quality in youth sport: Relationship to age, gender, and motivation variables. *J Sport Exerc Psychol* 2002;**24**:420–437.

19. Weiss MR, Smith AL, Stuntz CP. Moral Development in Sport and Physical Activity: Theory, Research, and Intervention. In Horn TS (ed), *Advances in Sport Psychology* (3rd ed.). Champaign, IL: Human Kinetics, 2008, pp. 187–210.

20. Stuart ME, Ebbeck V. The influence of perceived social approval on moral development in youth sport. *Ped Exer Sci* 1995;**7**:270–280.

21. Gibbons SL, Ebbeck V, Weiss MR. Fair play for kids: Effects on the moral development of children in physical education. *Res Q Exerc Sport* 1995;**66**:247–255.

22. Hellison D. Teaching Personal and Social Responsibility in Physical Education. In Silverman SJ, Ennis CD (eds), *Students Learning in Physical Education: Applying Research to Enhance Instruction.* Champaign, IL: Human Kinetics, 2003, pp. 241–254

23. Weiss MR, Bhalla JA, Price MS. Developing Positive Self-Perceptions Through Youth Sport Participation. In Hebestreit H, Bar-Or O (eds), *The Encyclopedia of Sports Medicine, Vol. X: The Young Athlete.* Oxford: Blackwell Science, Ltd., 2008, pp. 302–318.

24. Slade A, Wolf D (eds). *Children at Play: Critical and Developmental Approaches to Meaning and Representation.* Oxford University Press: New York, 1994.

25. Singer DG, Singer JL. *The House of Make-Believe: Play and the Developing Imagination.* Harvard University Press: Cambridge, MA, 1990.

26. Barnett LA, Storm B. Play, pleasure and pain: The reduction of anxiety through play. *Leisure Sci* 1981;**4**:161–176

27. Patterson JH. Play and Imagination as Tools for Building Resilience. In Clements RL, Fiorentino L (eds), *The Child's Right to Play: A Global Approach.* Westport, CT: Praeger, 2004, pp. 29–34

28. Elkind D. *The Power of Play*. Da Capo Press: Cambridge, MA, 2008.
29. Roskos K, Neuman S. Play as an Opportunity for Literacy. In Saracho O, Spodek B (eds), *Multiple Perspectives on Play in Early Childhood Education*. Albany, NY: State University of New York Press, 1998, pp. 100–115.
30. Barnett LA. Young children's free play and problem solving ability. *Leisure Sciences* 1986;**7**:25–46.
31. Bjorklund DF. *Why Youth is Not Wasted on the Young*. Blackwell Publishing: Malden, MA, 2007.
32. Lieberman JN. *Playfulness: Its Relationship to Imagination and Creativity*. Academic Press: New York, 1997.
33. Vygotsky LS. *Mind In Society: The Development of Higher Psychological Processes*. Harvard University Press: Cambridge, MA, 1978.
34. Lillard A. Playing With a Theory of the Mind. In Saracho O, Spodek B (eds), *Multiple Perspectives on Play in Early Childhood Education*. Albany, NY: Statue University of New York Press, 1998, pp. 11–33.
35. Klugman E, Smilansky S (eds). *Children's Play and Learning: Perspectives and Policy Implications*. Teachers College Press: New York, 1991.
36. Athey I. The Relation of Play to Cognitive, Language, and Moral Development. In Bergen D (ed), *Play as a Medium for Learning and Development*. Portsmouth, NH: Heinemann, 1988, pp. 81–102.
37. Rubin KH, Fein GC, Vandenberg B. Play. In Mussen PH (ed), *Handbook of Child Psychology: Vol. 4: Socialization, Personality, and Social Development* (4th ed.), 1983, pp. 69–744.
38. Bornstein M, Vibbert M, Tal J, O'Donnell K. Toddler language and play in the second year: Stability, covariation, and influences of parenting. *First Lang* 1992;**12**:323–338.
39. Reeve RE, Weiss MR. Sports and Physical Activities. In Bear GG, Minke KM (eds), *Children's Needs III: Development, Prevention, and Intervention*. Bethesda, MD: National Association of School Psychologists, 2006, pp. 485–498.
40. Stuntz CP, Weiss MR. Motivating children and adolescents to sustain a physically active lifestyle. *American Journal of Lifestyle Medicine*. In press.
41. Weiss MR, Wiese-Bjornstal DM. Promoting positive youth development through physical activity. *President's Council on Physical Fitness and Sports Research Digest* 2009;**10/3**:1–8.

Chapter 20
Leisure, Adolescence, and Health

Clifton E. Watts
Jennifer L. Cremeens

Introduction

Go to any textbook, journal article, or popular press article on the subject of adolescence and it will invariably state that adolescence is a period of life marked by great growth and change. However, when examining the life course, one could make that statement about most stages of life. What makes adolescence unique is that it represents a period of gradual transition from childhood to adulthood. This stage of life is akin to the metamorphosis of a butterfly; boys and girls become men and women over a decade of life. When children age into adolescence they experience well-known changes in biological (e.g., sexual maturation, the development of secondary sex characteristics) and cognitive (e.g., concrete to abstract thinking) processes coupled with shifts in how parents and other adults respond to them as they mature. The transition to adulthood requires adolescents to learn how to effectively function during unsupervised time, manage emerging responsibilities and opportunities, and understand their place in the world and how they fit within it. Maturation into adulthood often depends on how well one negotiates these challenges.

This chapter focuses on the relationship between leisure and health during the developmental period of adolescence. We examine broadly the period of adolescence, health during this period, and leisure's role in adolescent development and its significance in shaping adult behavior. We conclude this chapter by introducing positive youth development as an approach to addressing the needs of adolescents. Our review highlights tenets of positive youth development and gives an example of how to incorporate this approach into practice.

Adolescence

Approximately 14% of the U.S. population is between the ages of 10–19 years old. While three fifths of the adolescent population is categorized as White non-Hispanic; the number of children from other racial and ethnic groups has steadily increased over a 20-year period. It is estimated that by 2050, more than half of the adolescent population will come from families that are Hispanic, Black or African American, American Indian or Alaska Native, Pacific Islander, or a combination of two or more races. Immigration is a significant factor in this change in population, and across the world, many developed nations have experienced similar shifts in population with the expansion of globalization (1).

As populations become increasingly diverse, programs that serve these individuals have sought to become culturally competent in the way they deliver services. Research and the body of knowledge that informs what we know about adolescence needs to be consistent with this trend as well, as it has major implications for how policy is developed. What is gleaned from studies and translated into practice has major implications for developing programs and delivering services. That stated, the overview presented in this chapter represents general knowledge of adolescent development, health behaviors, and leisure behavior. It is not exhaustive, and we recommend that the reader look beyond what is presented here when developing services or performing research with adolescents.

Adolescent Development

Adolescent development consists of the simultaneous biological, cognitive, and psychosocial changes that occur within the second decade of life. Biological changes refer to the hormonal and physical growth occurring during this period. Sexual maturation, the development of secondary sex characteristics (e.g., pubic hair, breasts), and reaching adult height all occur during this period. Cognitive processes within adolescence gradually change as youths' thought processes move from concrete to abstract. Psychosocial development is reflected in the specific developmental tasks associated with adolescence (e.g., identity development, autonomy from parents), and the contexts in which these tasks are performed. Development occurs gradually over the phases of early (11–13 years), middle (14–16), and late adolescence (17–19), and specific developmental outcomes may be achieved within a specific phase or over the course of the entire period.

Biological Development

The biological transformations that occur during adolescence usually start shortly after the second decade of life begins. Girls begin to mature before boys, and may even reach full physical maturity by age 14. Boys often take longer to mature, and may not reach full adult height until late into their teens. Timing of maturation is linked to specific types of behaviors that may have serious long-term consequences for developing adolescents and is linked to very different outcomes for boys and girls (2). Late maturation in boys is linked with lower levels of self-esteem and feelings of inadequacy. Conversely, early maturation in boys is linked to reports of positive self-image and popularity with peers. Early maturing boys are also more prone to delinquency, precocious sex, and substance use when compared to their peers, and these behaviors are linked to time spent with older, deviant peers. Early maturation also plays a role in the health and wellness for girls.

Like boys, early maturing girls may also experience greater popularity, but they also are more likely to have issues with delinquency, problems in school, and experience early sexual initiation when compared to other girls. Beyond these issues, early maturing girls are also prone to having greater emotional problems related to body image, and also experience more problems with depression, anxiety, and eating disorders. These problems are magnified when early maturing girls have lots of older adolescent friends, more opposite sex friends, and when they attend schools that serve both sexes.

Cognitive Development

Cognitive Development Theory states that the primary cognitive transformation occurring within adolescence is the move from concrete to formal operations (3). The concrete operations stage refers to how cognition occurs for children between the ages of six to twelve years. Concrete thinking is often depicted as seeing the world in black and white without understanding that there are shades of gray. Concrete thinkers have a hard time visualizing what might occur and benefit when tasks and learning strategies have clear, step-by-step instructions with a start and end.

Conversely, the formal operations stage is indicative of abstract cognition. Abstract cognition is evident in the learning that typically occurs during adolescence. Schoolwork becomes more abstract for many adolescents as they progress into junior high and high school. For example, math (e.g., algebra, geometry, calculus), literature (e.g., hyperbole, allusion, sarcasm), and history (e.g., political and social ramifications of history) courses all become more abstract in their approach and less structured on the concrete observation of facts and instrumental phases of learning. The formal operations period is one where most adults of normal intelligence operate, and is viewed as necessary to handle the cognitive challenges facing humans in adulthood.

The change in cognition that occurs during adolescence is gradual, and not all adolescents reach the formal operations stage. This has serious implications for how adolescents behave and respond to messages from parents, teachers, and other professionals who are responsible for educating youth about their health. Messages that fail to reach adolescents are often those they cannot understand or appeal to their strengths in cognition.

For this reason, experts in health education advocate that messages to adolescents about health and wellness should be concrete and relevant to adolescents' experience (4). Messages focusing on long-term health and wellness may not be relevant to youth who cannot imagine growing older and having serious health problems in later life. Similarly, messages of the benefits of drinking or smoking developed by advertising campaigns may also connect with youth who desire to look cool, meet members of the opposite sex, and have fun.

Psychosocial Development

As mentioned earlier in this chapter, the period of adolescence is one where youth must learn to balance new roles and responsibilities while managing natural drives for independence and inquiries into who one is and where one fits into the world (i.e., identity development). The term *psychosocial development* describes the psychological and social changes experienced by youth as they mature during adolescence. As alluded to earlier, identity development is a major developmental outcome of adolescence, and it is experienced along with several other developmental outcomes throughout adolescence. From early to late adolescence, youth gradually learn to become independent from parents (autonomy), learn to balance friendships and romantic relationships (intimacy), develop competence in several areas (e.g., work, school, leisure), and learn to internalize the obligatory behaviors of adulthood (5).

Much current literature suggests that identity is not fully formed until late into adolescence or young adulthood (2). Throughout all three phases of adolescence, youth are thought to go through regular instances of moratorium or exploration of identity and then foreclosure where one settles on an identity (6). During this time, a variety of roles are examined and within these roles are associated situational and experiential shifts. It is not uncommon for this period to be one of experimentation. In fact, experimentation is often regarded as a healthy expression during the search for identity. While experimentation is a normal and functional part of the search for identity, it can also lead to the initiation of health-compromising behaviors and the negative effects associated with participation in these activities. Experimentation that leads to long-term patterns of negative behavior is most dangerous to youths' health and wellness, and is often associated with other contextual factors such as time spent with deviant peers and disinterested or uninvolved parents. However, long-term problem behavior is rarely linked to occasional rates of relatively harmless experimentation. Studies show that the majority of youth experiment with alcohol or break the law during adolescence, but very few have serious, long-term problems extending into adulthood (2). That stated, problem drinking and deviance are serious problems for a portion of the adolescent population, and these individuals are at great risk for long-term consequences related to these behaviors into adulthood.

The Interplay of Context and the Developing Self

The developmental literature demonstrates that human development is a complex process that involves negotiating individual level changes while being influenced and acting within different environments. The Bio-Ecological Model provides a framework for understanding how development occurs by examining the interplay between the developing self and several, coexisting environmental contexts (7). According to this model, individuals operate within and are influenced by four environmental systems or settings. The microsystem is the closest and most influential on one's life development. It includes the family, school, and peer group. The mesosystem refers to the interaction between two settings. This could include the interaction of family and school or peers and family. The exosystem is represented by social structures and these are often reflected in government. The exosystem could include school boards, city councils, and coalitions that operate within communities. Finally, the macrosystem is defined by the dominant beliefs and ideologies of a culture, and is often reflected in how government functions (e.g., laws and governance of people), what cultures value, how the economy performs, extant and emerging wars, and other events that broadly impact society. Each level operates within a specific time period or chronosystem. Figure 20.1 illustrates the different systems in a series of concentric circles around the individual with those closest in proximity having the greatest influence.

Within this model, human development is most significantly impacted through reciprocal interactions between the individual and the microsystem, which is the most immediate external environment to the individual. Regular and extended interactions between the individual and the microsystem are known as proximal processes. Proximal processes between the individual and the microsystem can either be developmentally generative or disruptive, and many theories that explain human behavior and development identify the proximal processes that lead to specific outcomes such as academic achievement, regular physical activity, healthy eating, and other behaviors that reflect positive youth development, health, and wellness.

For example, Self-Determination Theory (SDT) explains that humans have *basic needs* for relatedness, competence, and autonomy, and the extent to which these needs are satisfied determines the degree to which one feels self-determined. When these needs are met, one's behavior is often

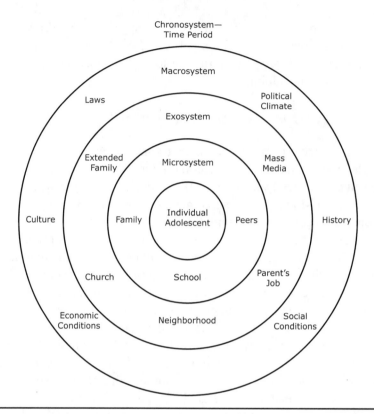

Figure 20.1 Bronfenbrenner's Bio-Ecological Model (Adapted from Bronfenbrenner & Morris, 1998)

intrinsic (i.e., doing something for the sake of doing it) in nature. Having several experiences with intrinsic motivation is beneficial, as these experiences fulfill natural inclinations for perceived freedom and control, mastery, spontaneous interest, and exploration. Furthermore, greater exposure to intrinsically motivated experiences is linked to positive cognitive and social development, and offers the potential for lifelong enjoyment. Supporting the basic needs for autonomy, relatedness, and competence, therefore, are developmentally generative proximal processes. When these basic needs are not supported, individuals feel disconnected from others, controlled, and incompetent, and act based on amotivation. Amotivation indicates that individuals lack intention in their action, and this state is linked to an external locus of control, where they perceive their actions to be regulated by outside forces. Locus of control is an important concept that refers to how a person attributes good and bad events that occur within one's life. Those with an internal locus of control believe that their actions are related to the events they experience. This often facilitates the attitude that a person can correct mistakes and make good things happen through their actions. An external locus of control is undesirable because it suggests that events are beyond one's control (e.g., things happen by chance or are forced upon an individual) (8). Frequent experiences with amotivation may be developmentally disruptive, as it is correlated with low levels of need satisfaction, less perceived control, and negatively associated with overall well-being.

From this example, we can glean that proximal processes relate to the ways in which parents, peers, teachers, recreation leaders, and others interact with and impact youth. Developmentally generative processes are enacted when practices are developmentally appropriate or congruent with the developmental needs of adolescents. Programs and services aimed at improving adolescent health and wellness are unlikely to be successful if their approach to working with youth does not appeal to these needs.

Adolescent Health Behaviors

Adolescents are often faced with negotiating the challenges presented by the increasing amount of freedom afforded to them by parents and social institutions. According to the Youth Risk Behavior Surveillance System (YRBS), a national school-based survey conducted biannually among students in 9th–12th grades, 20% of students had smoked cigarettes in the past 30 days (9). Approximately 45% of adolescents reported consuming alcohol in the past 30 days, with 26% engaging in binge drinking (consuming 5 or more drinks in a row). Almost half of all students reported engaging in sexual intercourse, with only 62% using a condom the last time they had sex. In addition to high risk behaviors, only 35% of adolescents met the physical activity recommendations and only 22% had eaten the recommended servings of fruits and vegetables, lending to almost 30% of students being overweight or obese.

Adolescent patterns of behavior can have major implications for long-term health, wellness, and quality of life in adulthood. Youth who experience good health during adolescence and into young adulthood are likely to have good, long-term health and low risk for chronic disease. While experimentation with negative health behaviors occurs with a significant portion of the adolescent population, many adolescents either mature out of (e.g., delinquency) or learn to regulate these behaviors (e.g., alcohol use). However, those who initiate these behaviors early in adolescence, and sustain prolonged periods of engagement with these behaviors often experience profound long-term consequences related to health such as smoking behavior and alcohol consumption (10, 11). Similarly, developing patterns of positive behaviors (e.g., physical activity, healthy eating) in childhood and through adolescence can lead to prolonged engagement in these types of behavior (12). That stated, behaviors like physical activity participation require adjustment to contextual and sociodemographic differences that emerge naturally as youth age. For example, the numbers of youth sport leagues dwindle and become far more competitive as youth enter their teenage years. Often times, no viable alternative exists, and youth sport participation is significantly reduced as a result in adolescence. This is a critical change in opportunities available in free time for youth of this age, and also eliminates an important path for prolonged physical activity participation, as participation in sport during adolescence is clearly linked with physical activity participation in adulthood. In this case and others, it is not enough to promote health and wellness early, facilitate positive behaviors, and prevent negative behaviors. Policies and programs need to account for the specific challenges facing humans at each stage of life to facilitate lifelong health and wellness.

Leisure and Adolescence

Childhood and adolescence are the periods of life most linked to leisure. During these years, youth spend more time free from the traditional obligations of life (e.g., work, school, family), and are afforded the freedom to explore opportunities and experience enjoyment. In the U.S., adolescents spend nearly half of their waking hours in free time or leisure (13). These estimates represent the mean time spent in free time and vary by race and ethnicity, and also decrease over time as late adolescents begin working. That stated, free time or leisure represents a significant amount of time from which adolescents can work toward the developmental outcomes often associated with this period of life.

Earlier, we mentioned proximal processes that occur between the developing self and the environment. Prolonged exposure to generative (e.g., adults support autonomy and relatedness) and disruptive processes (e.g., adults are highly controlling and uninvolved) can impact long-term development, health, and wellness. Therefore, leisure represents a potentially significant opportunity from which adolescents can address a number of developmental outcomes. Youth exposed to contexts in leisure that support their developmental needs benefit most during adolescence.

Structured activities in free time are often cited as meeting developmental needs and are linked to better academic performance, positive adjustment during adolescence, and lower levels of delinquency. Examples of structured activities are extracurricular activities offered through school or programs supported by youth service agencies (e.g., park and recreation programs, Boys and Girls Clubs), and sports. Structured activity experiences connect adolescents to positive adult role models, and provide a place for adolescents to learn and master experiences. Long-term involvement in structured activities is theorized to aid in the transition to adulthood because adolescents learn to endure in their involvement and assimilate the goals of these activities to form a coherent sense of self. In the U.S., youth spend an average of 40–80 minutes a day in these types of activities (13).

Unstructured activities are those activities where monitoring from parents and other adults is low, and where youth have great autonomy to make choices and decisions. These types of activities can be beneficial when they provide experiences for adolescents to operate and be successful in situations where adult control is low. However, frequent exposure to unstructured activities combined with the influences of a deviant peer group can lead to high-risk behavior (i.e., substance use, early sexual behavior) and peril. However, unstructured activities can be beneficial and developmentally valuable for youth because they promote experiences that can be self-defining in nature, which is critical for identity development. Unstructured experiences also allow adolescents to develop friendships and romantic relationships, as these activities are typically social in nature. Adolescents spend an average of two to three hours a day interacting with their peers in unstructured activities (13).

The most common unstructured activity experience is television viewing. Adolescents spend between one and a half and two hours a day watching television (13). Television viewing and its associated activities represent one of the greatest challenges to those wishing to promote physical activity during this time period, as youth are sedentary during these periods. Developmentally, television is a low-yield activity that offers little benefit to youth's cognitive and psychosocial development.

Many health promotion programs seek to reduce the number of hours youth spend in this behavior to direct youths' attention to activities that offer benefits to their health and well-being. While highly enjoyable and socially rewarding, unstructured activities offer experiences low in challenge and engagement, which are critical to the processes of internalization and initiative development.

Self-Determination Theory (SDT) describes internalization as a process where one learns to value and integrate behaviors into their lives (14). As described earlier, intrinsic motivation reflects behavioral engagement for the sake of itself. Extrinsic motivation refers to behavioral performance to attain some outcome separate from what exists within an activity. The process of internalization explains how individuals learn to find personal meaning for activities that are initially externally regulated (i.e., behavioral performance based on gaining rewards or avoiding punishment).

For example, a teen-aged girl named Terri might start attending a teen center for peer acceptance. As basic needs for relatedness, competence, and autonomy are supported, youth learn to gradually find personal meaning in these activities and exhibit self-determined, internally regulated behavior. Continuing our example, Terri continues to attend the teen center because she feels connected to peers and adults at the center, and is involved in activities like organizing a walk for hunger that allows her to make decisions about organizing the walk and feeling competent as the walk is a success. Going to the teen center is no longer something performed for peer acceptance (i.e., external reasons), but because the activities at the teen center are personally meaningful. The example describes the process of internal regulation. SDT identifies three forms of internal regulation: 1) introjected, 2) identified, and 3) integrated.

Introjected regulation occurs when needs for relatedness exists within behavioral contexts, and connections to others leads to the adoption of social norms and mores. This form of regulated motivation is consider internalized, as the reason for behavioral performance emanates from personal meaning and values, and not for rewards or aversive consequences associated with acting or failing to act in the behavior. As needs for competence and autonomy are supported, internalization of behavior becomes stronger, as individuals feel competence and identify with the behavior (i.e., identified regulation), or learn to integrate (i.e., integrated regulation) the behavior into a broader perspective of the self with the support of all three basic needs.

Self-determined, structured activities are thought to support the development of initiative. Initiative is reflected in the ability to persist through challenges presented within activities or behaviors over an extended period of time. Often, youth are placed in structured activities where a goal is presented. For example, many youth organizations work toward raising money to fund a trip or for charitable purposes. As youth work toward this goal, they may experience setbacks related to interpersonal conflict or challenges inherent in the process of working toward the goal. As youth persist through these challenges, they learn to direct their behavior and see the endpoint to the goal of their actions. This is an important developmental outcome for the transition to adulthood, as sustained behavioral performance in the work place and in social relationships is critical to the quality of life one experiences in adulthood.

A Positive Youth Development Approach to Health

For many years, the characterization of the typical adolescent was that of the angst-filled teenager who possessed the potential to lash out at adults, while being drawn to risky behaviors like a magnet. Over the last two decades, that anachronistic depiction has given way to a view that adolescents have the potential to become highly valued and engaged contributors to society. Proponents of this modern view of adolescence have advocated a *Positive Youth Development* (PYD) framework to describe the shift in emphasizing youth as assets to society rather than society's problems to manage or prevent (15). This view does not deny that the potential for risk and engagement in unhealthy behavior is a major challenge for adolescents. Rather, it emphasizes that all adolescents have the potential to develop and live healthy, fulfilling lives if given the necessary supports and opportunities to prepare adolescents for adulthood.

The PYD framework identifies a common core of sustained supports and opportunities that are thought to promote positive development and inhibit engagement in negative or risky health behaviors. These supports and opportunities include, but are not limited to: positive relationships with adults and peers, physical and psychological safety, skill-building experiences, and leadership opportunities. Youth development theory emphasizes intentionality in the design of programs, which outlines the purpose of providing these types of support. Critical to the PYD approach is that young people learn and develop across a range of developmental areas, taking into account their cognitive, physical, social, moral, civic, and vocational well-being. The PYD approach reflects a long-term vision for personal development, and espouses a philosophy where youth are not only problem free, but fully prepared and engaged in their lives and society for life. These ideas are valuable when considering how health promotion and prevention efforts are implemented, and has implications for how we understand health behaviors, and retool the contexts that support specific health behaviors.

For example, while physical activity and sports participation in adolescence are correlated or linked to physical activity participation in adulthood, sports participation is also linked to the abuse of alcohol and illegal substances such as marijuana (16). These potential threats are partly related to context-environment specific influences (e.g., coaching behavior—that emphasizes the goals of winning at all costs). Advocates of PYD suggest that the goals of sport should emphasize enjoyment, personal fulfillment, skill development, and long-term health benefits (12, 16). These latter goals are often more feasible over the long-term as very few individuals can compete at the highest levels of sport into adulthood. Opportunities that enhance competence and offer personal fulfillment are more likely to yield consistent performance over time, as opposed to a limited period of engagement.

Summary

Adolescence represents a unique period in the life cycle that brings both challenges and opportunities. This period of life is important for developing habits and reinforcing behaviors that lead to long-term health and wellness. Given that adolescents spend nearly half of their time in leisure, this period of time offers great potential for the promotion of goals related to health and wellness. We advocate a PYD framework for developing programs and strategies to attain these goals. The PYD framework moves beyond the traditional risk factor, public health approach by focusing on developing strengths and assets in youth, and realizing that youth function in multiple contexts which support development. Prevention is implied in this approach and oftentimes, the message reflects long-term benefits such as enjoyment and personal fulfillment through leisure. PYD advocates the mobilization of multiple stakeholders such as clinicians, nurses, educators, community groups, elected officials, and youth themselves. PYD principles are based on developmental appropriateness, where strategies appeal to and work toward the developmental needs and outcomes of adolescence. In the previous chapter on Prevention, the Timewise and Healthwise curricula are good examples of how to integrate approaches that appeal to developmental needs while emphasizing values, beliefs, and behaviors that are consistent with long-term health and wellness. These curricula build internal assets while educating youth about the positive uses of free time. Furthermore, these programs are integrative and demonstrate the relationship between one's leisure and one's health. PYD depends on the notion that integrative programs and services create an environment that maximizes external and internal assets for youth, while minimizing threats to health and safety. These types of environments are essential for long-term health and wellness.

References

1. MacKay AP, Duran C. Adolescent Health in the United States, 2007. National Center for Health Statistics, 2007.
2. Steinberg L, Sheffield-Morris A. Adolescent development. *Annu Rev Psychol* 2001;**52**:83–110.
3. Piaget J. *The Psychology of the Child*. Basic Books: New York, 1972.
4. Perry CL. Preadolescent and Adolescent Influences on Health. In Smedley BD, Syme SL (eds), *Promoting Health: Intervention Strategies from Social and Behavioral Research Division of Health Promotion and Disease Prevention*. Washington, DC: National Academy Press; Caldwell, 2000, pp. 217–253.
5. Caldwell LL, Baldwin CK, Walls T, Smith EA. Preliminary effects of a leisure education program to promote healthy use of free time among middle school students. *J Leisure Res* 2004;**36**:310–335
6. Meeus W. Studies on identity development in adolescence: An overview of research and some new data. *J Youth Adolesc* 1996;**25**:569–598.
7. Bronfenbrenner U, Morris PA (1998). The ecology of developmental processes. In the Handbook of Child Psychology. pp. 993–1028.
8. Furnham A, Steele. Measures of locus of control: A critique of children's health, and work-related locus of control questionnaires. *Br J Psychol* 1993;**84**:443–479.
9. Centers for Disease Control and Prevention. YRBSS: 2007 National Youth Risk Behavior Survey overview. http://www.cdc.gov/healthyyouth/yrbs/pdf/yrbs07_us_overview.pdf. Accessed June 8, 2009.
10. Moffitt TE. Adolescence-limited and life-course-persistent antisocial behavior: a developmental taxonomy. *Psychol Rev* 1993;**100**:674–701
11. Maggs JL, Schulenberg JE. Trajectories of alcohol use during the transition to adulthood. *Alcohol Res Health* 2004;**28**:195–201.
12. Le Menestrel S, Perkins DF. An overview of how sports, out-of-school time, and youth well-being can and do intersect. *New Dir Youth Dev* 2007;**115**:13–25.
13. Larson R, Seepersad S. Adolescents' leisure time in the United States: Partying, sports, and the american experiment. *New Dir Child Adolesc Dev* 2003;**99**:53–64.
14. Ryan RM, Deci EL. Self-determination theory and the facilitation of intrinsic motivation, social development, and well-being. *Am Psychol* 2000;**55**:68–78.
15. Pittman KJ, Martin S, Yohalem N. Youth development as a "big picture" public health strategy. *J Publ Health Manag Pract* 2006;November (Supp):s23–s25.

16. Moore MJ, Werch CE (2005). Sport and physical activity participation and substance use among adolescents. *J Adolesc Health* 2005;**36**:486–493.

Chapter 21
Leisure in Family Wellness

Ramon B. Zabriskie
Carl Hanson

What are some of your fondest childhood memories with your family? When asked this question, our thoughts typically race to a time when we gathered together with brothers and sisters around the campfire to hear Dad's new version of his favorite story after a long day of hiking, fishing, and roasting hotdogs. Or to the time when Mom joined the ultimate backyard water fight and drenched us all. Or to the summer vacation that we planned for months and although Dad's shortcut got us lost, it led us to the greatest family adventure ever! Or to the year of the super garden and the great family pumpkin sale. Or to the countless times we gathered in the family room for our regular game of Monopoly, Risk, Pictionary, Sorry, Pit, or Ultimate Uno. Whatever those great family memories are, most of us have them, and they typically revolve around some kind of family leisure. They are defining moments. They are the kinds of experiences that build relationships, develop skills, establish roles, start traditions, and lay a foundation for quality family life. Is that the only thing necessary for healthy families today? Of course not! But, family leisure is definitely one of the essential ingredients to today's recipe for successful families.

Scholars have consistently reported significant relationships between family leisure participation and positive family outcomes related to family wellness since as early as the 1930s. Hawks (1) concluded that six decades of family leisure research had consistently found that "family strength or cohesiveness is related to the family's use of leisure time" (p. 424). Holman and Epperson (2) reported that both families and professional helpers see joint leisure time as an important element in promoting marital and family quality. Shaw and Dawson (3) found that family leisure was often purposive in nature and that parents "consciously and deliberately" planed and facilitated family leisure activities to improve family relationships, enhance family communication, promote health and fitness, teach and instill values, and to create family unity and identity. Parents reported that family leisure was so integral to healthy family life that it was with a "sense of urgency" that they planned to spend time with children participating in family activities.

Although it seems quite clear that involvement in family leisure activities is important and perhaps even essential for healthy family life, it is definitely not a magic pill or panacea that will "fix" all family difficulty.

How then, does it work? Are there different kinds of family leisure activities and experiences that can strengthen different aspects of family life? Can parents intentionally plan and provide better family leisure experiences that will improve family wellness and the quality of our families today? Wouldn't it be great if we understood family leisure well enough to look at our families and know what kind of family leisure activity we should do in order to address a specific problem or weakness? Or better yet, wouldn't it be great to know how to effectively utilize family leisure to help promote family wellness and prevent the problems in the first place? Among the many contributions of researchers in recent years has been the development and testing of a theoretical model of family leisure that does just that. It's a simple practical model of family leisure that explains how different kinds of family leisure involvement contribute to different aspects of family wellness.

Core and Balance Model of Family Leisure Functioning

Leisure theorists have long suggested that individuals tend to meet essential needs for "both stability and change, structure and variety, and familiarity and novelty" through their leisure behavior (4, p. 98). Freeman & Zabriskie (5) explained that the interplay and balance between stability and change plays a much greater role when considering the needs of a family unit. They said "the balance of these needs is one of the underlying concepts of family systems theory that suggests that families seek a dynamic state of homeostasis" (p. 76). In other words, families must continually meet the need for stability in interactions, structure, and relationships, as well as the need for novelty in experience, input, and challenge, in order to develop and function effectively. Furthermore, as with individuals, families also tend to meet these needs through their leisure behavior.

The Core and Balance Model of Family Leisure Functioning indicates that there are two basic categories or patterns of family leisure, core and balance, which families utilize to meet needs for both stability and change, and ultimately facilitate outcomes of family cohesion and adaptability which are primary components of family functioning (see Figure 21.1). Core family leisure is depicted by "common, everyday, low-cost, relatively accessible, often home-based activities that many families do frequently" (6, p. 283). This may include family activities such as playing board games together, making and eating dinner together, watching videos or television, playing Frisbee in the yard, shooting baskets in the driveway, gardening, or simply jumping in the pile of leaves when the raking is done. Such activities often require minimal planning and resources, and can be quite

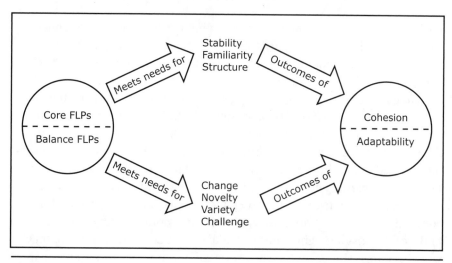

Figure 21.1 The Core and Balance Model of Family Leisure Functioning. FLP = Family Leisure Functioning.

spontaneous or informal. They provide a "consistent, safe and usually positive context in which family relationships can be enhanced and feelings of family closeness increased" (5, p. 77).

Balance family leisure, on the other hand is "depicted by activities that are generally less common, less frequent, more out of the ordinary, and usually not home-based thus providing novel experiences" (6, p. 283). This may include family activities such as vacations, camping, fishing, special events, and trips to sporting events, theme parks, or the bowling alley. Such activities often require more investment of resources such as planning, time, effort, or money, and are, therefore, less spontaneous and more formalized. They tend to be more out of the ordinary and "include elements of unpredictability or novelty, which require family members to negotiate and adapt to new input and experiences that stand apart from everyday life" (5, p. 77).

Overall, the model suggests that core family leisure involvement primarily facilitates feelings of closeness, personal relatedness, family identity, and bonding. Balance family leisure involvement on the other hand, provides the input necessary for families to be challenged, to develop, to adapt, to progress as a working unit, and helps foster the adaptive skills necessary to navigate the challenges of family life in today's society. Family systems theory holds that these two constructs, family cohesion and family adaptability, are both necessary and are the primary components of healthy family functioning and wellness. Similarly, findings (5, 6) related to the Core and Balance Model suggest that involvement in both categories of family leisure is essential, and that families who regularly participate in both core and balance types of family leisure report higher levels of family functioning than those who participate in high or low amounts of either category. Families who primarily participate in one category without the other are likely to experience disarray, frustration, and dysfunction. Let's consider the following examples.

No core. The Anderson family consists of Mom and Dad and their two teenagers, John who is 16, and Amy who is 14. Whether both parents have full-time jobs or not, all four have hectic lives and spend very little time together as a family. They often pass in the night or early in the mornings headed out in different directions for the day. They rarely eat dinner together and participate in very few, if any, core family leisure activities. After hearing rumors about her daughter from a concerned friend, Mom confronted Amy about drug use and other behavioral concerns. In the midst of the ensuing fight, Amy yelled that John does things that are much worse and that Mom should just stay out of her life. Of course, later that night Mom, heartbroken and distraught, begged her husband for answers and a plan to save their family before they lost both kids forever. After a long discussion, they decide that it's time to go on that long overdue family vacation to Disneyland that they've promised the kids for years, so they can get away from the stress of life and bond as a family. Surprised the next morning with the negative reaction and complaints about missing important things with friends, Mom and Dad become that much more determined to get their kids in the car and on the road trip to Disneyland so they could have some "fun" and fix their family. How do you think it went? Without the basic cohesive relationships and the related family skills that are developed during core types of family activities, the flexibility required by such a balance type of family activity is likely to "overwhelm the family system resulting in chaos including arguments, frustration, blaming, and guilt" (7, p. 56). In other words, without some foundation of core family leisure involvement, participation in balance family activities is not only less effective, but may actually be disruptive to the family and lead to more harm than good.

No balance. Let's consider the opposite. The Jenkins family has four kids and the oldest is just about to turn sixteen. They have a very structured and protected home life and have always participated exclusively in large amounts of core types of family activities. In fact, everything is done together and very little if any outside influence or people are allowed in. They have little social interaction with others, little experience in the community, and have never been on a family vacation or outing. What do you think would happen if their sixteen-year-old daughter became enamored with the eighteen-year-old boy next door and he took advantage of her? Or if Mom became very ill and was diagnosed with breast cancer? Would this family have the necessary skills and abilities to handle these unpredictable situations and remain intact? It is likely that they would be ill prepared to effectively adjust or adapt to such circumstances, or many other out of the ordinary stresses and challenges that abound in today's society.

Both core and balance. Now let's consider a family that regularly participates in both core and balance types of family activities. The Johnson family also has four children ages 7, 9, 12, and 15. Although Mom and Dad both work full time, they consciously choose to do things together regularly as a family and plan and adjust their busy schedules accordingly. They have family dinner together most evenings where they talk about their day and what's up. This is typically followed by help with homework, shooting baskets in the driveway, or gathering together to laugh at their favorite show. Often they all go to watch the oldest daughter's play performance, the younger daughter's piano recital, or to cheer at the boys' basketball or soccer games. Occasionally they plan outings such as bowling, going to the local theme park or museum, or attending the fair when it's in town. Sunday afternoons are informally reserved to bake cookies and play games. The kids often bring their best friends who don't seem to mind getting caught up in the family battles of Pictionary, Monopoly, Catch Phrase, Sorry, Pit, or Ultimate Uno.

Let's say that one evening Dad gathered the family together to decide on their next big family outing and after several ideas that they couldn't quite afford, they decided they were going to go camping. They quickly looked on the calendar and finally found a weekend five weeks away where nobody had major conflicts and began to make plans. While they continued to participate in their regular core types of activities over the next several weeks, it was clear that they were preparing and looking forward to the big camping trip. One evening Dad and the boys practiced casting their fishing rods into the splash pool in the back yard until it was too dark to see. Another evening the girls turned the family room into the great outdoors and built the best blanket tent ever made, so they wouldn't have to miss their favorite show. The boys got to fall asleep on the floor in their sleeping bags and the rest of the family got to watch the American Idol finale. Sunday afternoon game time was even postponed once because Mom and Dad were laughing themselves silly for what seemed like hours as they watched their daughters trying to teach their two over excited boys how to put up the family tent in the backyard.

Finally, the big day arrived and everybody helped load the family van. Even though Dad assured them that they could live off the land and the fish they would catch, Mom packed enough food and treats to feed them for a week. They made their way towards the mountains amidst several new songs with goofy words, the never-ending license plate game, and a myriad of "are we there yets?" They finally made it, found the perfect campsite, and got unloaded. After the tent was set up and everything was ready, Dad got them all lined up on the trail, fishing rods in hand, and they started the mile and a half hike up the mountain to the perfect fishing spot to catch dinner. Mom laughed at her determined husband as he blazed the way and the kids meandered back and forth between them picking flowers and swinging their rods at butterflies along the trail. Suddenly the wind began to blow, the clouds rolled in and lightning flashed with a loud crack of thunder right behind. A few sparse drops turned into a downpour in minutes and they were drenched!

What happens next? Do Mom and Dad start yelling or blaming each other or the kids for ruining the entire trip? Typically not, because it's "fun," it's recreation, and they've chosen to be there and looked forward to it for some time. In such a "leisure" context people tend to make external attributions (it's the weather, it's out of our control) and be much more proactive in how they adjust, adapt, or deal with unforeseen circumstances or stress because it's "leisure" or a "step away from real life", and part of the experience. So, let's say that after splashing in the mud for a few minutes they all ran back down the trail to the safety of their tent. Soon, all the wet clothes were off and they were huddled around the lantern in the tent listening to the rain. Mom told a story about when she was young and went camping with her dad and almost broke her leg. Dad told the same spooky stories he told two years ago, but the kids all pretended to be scared again anyway. Pretty soon the oldest daughter reached into her pack and pulled out the Uno cards. With resounding cheers, the game began and they laughed and played deep into the night. It's these types of outings that result from effectively acknowledging and adapting to differences in plans and expectations that often result in experiences families deem most memorable and better than originally planned. These are also the types of experiences that illustrate the interrelationship between or synergistic nature of both core and balance types of family leisure, as well as how families develop and refine appropriate adaptive skills in a leisure context. A family such as this is likely to have the skills, resiliency, and connected-ness to be able to adjust, adapt, or even thrive when faced with the plethora of "real life" stresses and challenges that abound in today's society.

Related Research. Scholars have used the core and balance frame-work to examine family leisure functioning among a variety of different family samples including traditional families, adoptive families, single-parent families, families with a child who has a disability, families with a child in mental health treatment, and Mexican-American families. In general, when examining such families from multiple views including parent, young adult, young adolescent, and family perspectives, family leisure researchers have consistently supported the tenants of the model and reported direct relationships with family cohesion, adaptability, and overall family functioning (8). Furthermore, both core and balance family leisure involvement have been related to a variety of other family constructs such as family communication, family leisure satisfaction, and satisfaction with family life or overall quality of family life. These are the kinds of characteristics that we expect to associate with family health, strength, resiliency, and wellness.

Family Wellness

Whereas the term "health" may be viewed as a passive state and includes the absence of disease, the term "wellness" is defined as an active process of adapting to life challenges and making choices that improve functioning in mind, body, and spirit. Halbert Dunn first defined individual wellness, even high-level wellness, as "an integrated method of functioning which is oriented toward maximizing the potential of which the individual is capable, within the environment he is functioning" (9, p. 9). This view of wellness is holistic in nature and requires a balance in functioning between each of the wellness dimensions. It requires the integration of social, mental, emotional, spiritual, and physical dimensions into one's life with no one dimension improved at the expense of another (10). Achieving a higher level of wellness would require that each of the five dimensions of wellness be balanced. Balancing the five dimensions may be illustrated as a symmetrical circle with each dimension representing equally shaped slices. An asymmetrical circle would mean one dimension is favored above another. For example, a marathon runner who spends an inordinate amount of time training for an event in order to achieve an optimal level of functioning physically may neglect spending time with his family (social dimension). Greenberg (11) suggests that the smoothest ride down the road of life comes when the dimensions are balanced and the wheel of wellness is symmetrical.

Central to the multidimensional nature of wellness is the idea that even a family member who is ill may be well. From a health perspective, a family member who has been diagnosed with cancer using state of the art medical technology would be considered unhealthy. This family member, however, could achieve high-level wellness by integrating and maximizing the five dimensions such that strong social connections are maintained with friends and family, intellectual growth occurs through study, professional growth continues at work, feelings are expressed appropriately, appropriate physical fitness goals are achieved, and meaning or purpose in life is sought through religious belief or belief in laws of nature (10).

High-level wellness also applies to all types of social organizations, particularly the family, in the same way it applies to the individual (9).

Although family wellness may be viewed as a product of the wellness achieved by each individual member of the family, it also goes beyond a simple sum of parts and includes how each member's behavior interrelates with that of one another to contribute to the family's overall sense of identity, and their ability to develop, adjust, grow, and function together as a family unit. Prilleltensky and Nelson (12) expand this thinking to suggest that family wellness is a two-way street and a "state of affairs in which everyone's needs in the family are met" (p. 87). Family wellness is balancing the need to meet personal desires with meeting the needs of other members of the family. Whereas individual wellness may be described as more than the absence of disease, family wellness is described as "more than the absence of discord; it is the presence of supportive, affectionate and gratifying relationships that serve to promote the personal development of family members and the collective wellbeing of the family as a whole" (12, p. 87).

Family Resiliency and Protection

Individuals and families who have achieved high-level wellness tend to be resilient to challenges and trials in life. Prevention researchers seeking a new hope for prevention against the social morbidities that threaten children and families have recognized this fact and have attempted to better understand resilience and what makes a resilient individual/family. The term resilience refers to the way individuals/families adapt to extraordinary circumstances to achieve positive and unexpected outcomes in the face of adversity (13). It is "a class of phenomena characterized by patterns of positive adaptation in the context of significant adversity or risk" (14, p. 75). While reducing risk factors that lead to these morbidities remains important, increasing protective factors within families and other systems that support the resilience of individuals ultimately contributes to family wellness and is important for prevention.

Protective factors are factors that buffer the effect of risk factors and reduce the likelihood of problem behavior. These protective factors, as defined by resiliency researchers, are important for healthy development and family wellness and include opportunities for caring relationships, high-expectation messages, as well as opportunities for participation or contribution to the family as a whole (15). These factors are not to be viewed as mutually exclusive, but should each be considered as dynamic and synergistically working together. For example, families that foster caring relationships without giving attention to creating high expectations or providing opportunities for meaningful participation ultimately foster dependence and codependence that can be quite harmful to family wellness

(15). Families must provide a common context through which protection and resiliency is practiced, developed, and fostered. Family leisure is one of the primary means, methods, and processes through which protection and resiliency can be realized for family members. "Besides family crisis, shared leisure may be one of the few experiences that brings family members together for any significant amount of time today" (6, p. 287). Well families, therefore, tend to use family leisure to strengthen relationships, improve functioning, promote protective factors, and foster resiliency, all of which contribute to family wellness.

Core and Balance Implications for Family Wellness

Family leisure is family wellness! When instituted using core and balance principles, family leisure has the potential to provide an empirically directed mechanism through which protective factors can be developed—thus contributing to a well and resilient family and buffering and protecting against life stresses. Resiliency and thus family wellness is exemplified as strengths, internal assets, or competencies among family members. These characteristics are not antecedents to resiliency but are considered positive outcomes and suggest that something is working correctly within the family system. These outcomes include social competence (i.e., communication, empathy, caring, and compassion), problem solving (i.e., planning, flexibility, critical thinking, and resourcefulness), autonomy (i.e., positive identify, initiative, self-efficacy, and self-awareness), and sense of purpose (i.e., goal direction, creativity, and faith) (14). The likelihood of achieving such outcomes within a family can be increased as parents intentionally plan and facilitate participation in both core and balance types of family activities.

Beyond providing specific direction on the types of family activities that parents should plan that foster family well-being, principles of core and balance family leisure also have significant implications for health and human service professionals that promote family wellness. Parks and recreation professionals should provide more services that cultivate family leisure skills and promote regular participation in core types of family activities along with the balance types of big events and celebrations. Community health educators working in prevention should incorporate principles of family leisure as an essential way to help develop protective factors and promote resiliency. Social service professionals working in the adoptive arena may consider assessing family leisure when screening for prospective parents and/or providing family leisure education prior to placement. Overall, family leisure must be recognized as essential to healthy families and the promotion of core and balance family leisure involvement is likely to provide a valuable, practical, and cost-effective behavioral approach to prevent risk factors and to promote family wellness today.

References

1. Hawks SR. Recreation in the family. In Bahr SJ (eds). *Family Research: A Sixty Year Review, 1930–1990, Vol. 1*. New York: Lexington Books, 1991, pp. 387–433.
2. Holman TB, Epperson A. Family and leisure: A review of the literature with research recommendations. *J Leisure Res* 1984;**16/4**:277–294.
3. Shaw SM, Dawson D. Purposive leisure: Examining parental discourses on family activities. *Leisure Sci* 2001;**23**:217–231.
4. Iso-Ahola SE. Social Psychological Foundations of Leisure and Resultant Implications for Leisure Counseling. In Dowd ET (eds). *Leisure counseling: Concepts and applications*. Springfield, IL: Charles C. Thomas, 1984, pp. 97–125.
5. Freeman P, Zabriskie RB. Leisure and family functioning on adoptive families: Implications for therapeutic recreation. *Ther Rec J* 2003;**37/1**: 73–93.
6. Zabriskie RB, McCormick BP. The influences of family leisure patterns on perceptions of family functioning. *Fam Relat* 2001;**50**:281–289.
7. Zabriskie R, Freeman P. Contributions of family leisure to family functioning among transracial adoptive families. *Adoption Q* 2004;**7/3**:49–77.
8. Agate J, Zabriskie R, Agate S, Poff R. Family Leisure Satisfaction and Satisfaction with Family Life. *J Leisure Res* 2009;**41/2**:205–223.
9. Dunn HL. What high-level wellness means. *Health Val* 1977;**1/1**:9–16.
10. Greenberg JS. Health and wellness: A conceptual differentiation. *J School Health* 1985;55/1:403–406.
11. Greenberg JS. *Health education: Learner-centered instructional strategies*. Madison, WI: Brown and Benchmark Publishers 1995.
12. Prilleltensky I, Nelson G. Promoting child and family wellness: Priorities for psychological and social interventions. *J Comm Appl Soc Psychol* 2000;**10**:85–105.
13. Fraser MW, Richman JM. Risk, production, and resilience: Toward a conceptual framework for social work practice. *Social Work Research* 1999;**23/3**:131–144.
14. Masten A, Reed M. Resilience in Development. In Snyder CR, Lopez SJ (eds). *Handbook of Positive Psychology*. New York: Oxford University Press, 2002, pp. 4–88.
15. Benard B. The Hope of Prevention: Individual, Family and Community Resilience. In Cohen L, Chavez V, Chehimi S (eds). *Prevention is Primary: Strategies for Community Well-being*. San Francisco: Jossey-Bass 2007, pp 63–89.

Chapter 22
Leisure and Health in Middle Age

Gaylene Carpenter
Jean Stockard

Life expectancy has become much greater in recent years, and North Americans can now expect to live well into their late 70s or early 80s (78.2 years in the United States 80.3 years in Canada). Because this increase has occurred relatively recently, it can be said that interest in adult development during middle adulthood is only just now entering "middle age." That is, it was only about thirty or forty years ago that serious research regarding peoples' lives during their middle adult years began to appear. Prior to this time, those interested in human development focused on infancy, childhood, adolescence, and the elderly. They were intrigued by the clear evidence of factors associated with growth early in life and then decline in later life and essentially paid little attention to human development in the middle years.

This lack of interest in middle adulthood began to shift in the 1970s, with the work of developmental theorists like Daniel Levinson, Roger Gould, and George Valliant. Drawing from and building on earlier works by Erik Erickson, Bernice Neugarten, and Robert Havighurst, they shed new and enhanced light upon what happens to people and how they feel about their lives during middle adulthood. Since then, researchers have continued to examine concepts embedded in psychological, biological, personal, and social theories and in doing so, increased our understanding about what many find to be the longest and most dynamic period of time in the life span.

Middle age is said to start around age thirty, after young adulthood. Most scholars today agree that middle age lasts a minimum of thirty to a maximum of forty-five years of a person's life, thus well beyond the age of 60. Yet the span of years has increased as adult health and wellness practices increase longevity. As a cohort, middle adulthood keeps including more years because we live longer, healthier lives.

Contrary to many popular conceptions, middle adulthood is anything but a static period of time. Rather, it appears to be highlighted by many ups and downs and many life changes that can be viewed as both gains and losses. In addition, people who are in middle age have diverse lifestyles. This increases the likelihood that changes experienced during this period of time will take many twists and turns unique to the pattern of an individual's life and social roles. This chapter examines the role of leisure, health, and wellness during this developmental period. We use data from a unique longitudinal study of leisure among middle-aged adults to explore changes and continuities in views regarding leisure and the ways in which health and wellness affect their perceptions.

Leisure During Middle Adulthood

The concept of leisure tended to be overlooked or minimized by adult developmental researchers historically. It was not until the late 1980s and early 1990s that leisure researchers with interests in middle age development began to study and write about general issues related to this age group. Concurrently, by exploring recreation behavior and leisure perceptions from social-psychological perspectives, several leisure researchers were increasingly demonstrating the role of leisure for middle-aged adults (1). More recently, leisure researchers with interests in both adult development and health and well-being are adding to the body of knowledge about leisure during the middle adulthood years (2, 3).

In considering leisure, health, and wellness in this chapter on middle-aged adults, we will focus on one study that was conceptually based in theories associated with adult development and leisure. Called "A Study of Leisure During Adulthood" (ASOLDA), the study collected in-depth information on individuals' lives for ten consecutive years. Researchers were interested in assessing change and continuity of leisure, life perceptions, and values in the lives of middle-aged adults over time. As a result, the information available helps us illustrate how the thread of leisure has been spun into individuals' lives in-depth over a decade of life in middle age.

Eighty-four middle-aged adults participated in ASOLDA by providing their perceptions regarding leisure and life on a 13-page survey sent to them each year from 1987 through 1996. Midway through the study, participants were invited to be included in an interview phase of the study. Sixty-six of the original study participants agreed to be interviewed, demonstrating their commitment to the study and enabling researchers to develop informative case studies.

Those participating in ASOLDA were primarily of Euro-American descent, female (61%), well educated (54% of respondents held post graduate degrees), and geographically distributed throughout North America. Variables investigated included leisure attitude, measured by the Leisure Ethic Scale (LES) (4); perceived freedom of leisure as measured by the Perceived Freedom in Leisure Scale (Short Form) (PFLS) (5); Valuing Leisure, Life Structure (6); List of Values (LOV) (7); and the Life Experiences Survey (8).

Using ASOLDA data, we have a rich reservoir of facts about participants' leisure attitude, perceived freedom in leisure, and the value they place upon leisure in their lives. We also have information about the broad range of life experiences they encountered during the decade, including times of stress and anxiety such as serious illness or injury or the death and illness of loved ones. Study participants provided both an extensive record of their actual life experiences and their thoughts regarding how they felt about these events, so we are able to reflect upon the relation such experiences may have to their values and leisure using longitudinal quantitative and qualitative data. We thus have continuous information from respondents who provided us with insights regarding their leisure, health, and wellness during many years of mid-life adulthood. We can both examine the group as a whole and we can look inside certain individuals' lives for some answers.

By examining leisure, health, and wellness in this way, we have the benefit of exploring these concepts from either an interindividual or intraindividual perspective. That is, we can focus on the group as a whole and note how individuals may perceive or change, or we can focus on one individual in order to note how he or she perceives or change over time. In developing this chapter,we intended to show the benefits of both perspectives as we have examined key concepts related to leisure, health, and wellness for the total group or for selected individuals. If we have been successful, you can *see* a snapshot of factors that relate to the leisure, health, and wellness for the group of adults as a whole and you can *see* several snapshots found a photo album taken over time during a person's middle adulthood that relate to that person's perceptions related to leisure, health, and wellness.

Leisure Continuity

The quantitative data from ASOLDA show that middle-aged adults value leisure and hold very positive attitudes over time. Consistently, the vast majority of the participants indicated that leisure was their most enjoyable time, that they admired people who know how to relax, that they don't feel guilty about enjoying themselves, and that it is good for adults to be playful. Each year, participants were asked to rank how important family, leisure, and work were in their lives. Not surprisingly, people prioritized family as most important, but leisure and work were ranked equally.

Of course, people vary in the views that they hold. For instance, some people prefer to have less free time than others and some value leisure more or less than other people do. At the same time, even those who prefer less free time still place a high value on leisure. In addition, individuals have remarkably consistent views regarding leisure over time. This stability suggests that leisure maintains its importance to individuals during middle adulthood regardless of their life experiences. That is, whether or not individuals have ups and downs, their leisure values and attitudes toward leisure do not appear to be altered greatly. As a result, we can suggest that leisure perceptions maintain their strength and resilience during middle adult years.

Take the cases of Allison, Jeff, Annie, Ed, and Betsy for example. Allison retired early from her professional career at age 54 in order to pursue her interest in art. Over time, Allison held a high regard for leisure evidenced by her positive attitudes and valuing leisure. She perceived freedom in leisure, "I think I'm just very happy to have time when I can really let myself be who I am, which is, of course, perfect freedom, and then to find out who I am...I guess I am letting myself become more of who I am through my experience of leisure." Jeff, who retired at the age of 50, left a constrained work environment that lacked autonomy. Having a positive attitude about and valuing leisure, he saw "work as a way to pay for my toys." He looked forward to a "life of leisure" having indicated his most important want out of life was fun and enjoyment. Annie, following the death of her husband, found herself with way too much free time for leisure, yet she consistently felt positive about and valued leisure and perceived freedom in leisure. Ed and Betsy, married 39 years at the point of retirement, attributed their ease of transition into retirement in part due to their positive feelings toward leisure and perceptions of freedom that they experienced in leisure over time.

Health and Life Experiences

Over the ten years that we followed the people in our sample, almost ten percent experienced a significant health event, such as a serious illness or injury. The vast majority reported that they had little control over the event and perceived it as having a negative impact on their lives. In other words, it was unexpected and traumatic. Nevertheless, those who experienced illness or injury continued to report attitudes toward leisure that were similar to other participants. They continued to place the same value on leisure and to prioritize leisure as others did. These similarities appeared even if the health event was perceived as being negative or positive.

The case of Annie depicts this situation. Though she experienced health-related changes in sleeping and eating habits, sexual difficulties, and bouts with personal illness and injury, she maintained her high regard for leisure. And though Allison expressed frustration about a longer than expected recuperation period following knee surgery when she experienced persistent mobility challenges, she too maintained her high regard for leisure.

The concept of "life structure" was used by Levinson to describe the unique pattern or design of an individual's life at a given point in time, suggesting that adults go through alternative periods of stability and change. In the periods of stability, which he called "structure-building," individuals are generally reaffirming their choices and decisions and maintaining their life structure. In the periods of change, which he called "structure-changing," individuals are in the process of questioning their life structure and reassessing, rather than reaffirming it. The participants were given Levinson's definitions and asked to reflect upon their own lives using these terms. Slightly more than half (58%) said that they were structure-building, while the remainder said that they were in the process of structure-changing and questioning their life structure.

When we compared the leisure-related attitudes and values of the participants in these two groups, we found no differences in their attitudes toward leisure, how much they valued leisure, or in the average hours of leisure that they experienced or wanted. When asked to rank the relative priority that they currently gave family, work, and leisure, there were also no differences in their rankings of family. However, there were slight differences in the average ranking that they gave to leisure and work. Those who saw themselves as structure changing and reassessing their lives gave slightly higher priority to leisure and slightly lower priority to work. The opposite was true for those who were structure building and who gave slightly higher priority to work than to leisure. In general, leisure remained important for participants in various stages of life and appears to become even more important in times of change.

To illustrate, consider Dottie's case. The year that Dottie learned she had lung cancer was also the year she recorded her highest positive and negative impact scores related to her life experiences. She indicated that her life structure was changing in both that year and in the next year, the year she died. She also identified self-fulfillment and fun and enjoyment out of life as her most important values. Her leisure perceptions were always high and were the highest in the year that she died.

Wellness and Life Perceptions

People in middle adulthood often find themselves caring for others, from aging parents to spouses and even siblings. As time goes on it becomes increasingly likely that they will experience serious illness and death of significant others, especially parents, but also spouses. Such caregiving and loss are often seen as a challenge to individuals' well-being. We were able to use data from ASOLDA participants' reports on the Life Experiences

(LE) Survey to see how these difficult experiences might be related to their leisure perceptions.

In any given year of the ASOLDA study, about one-fifth of the participants reported the death of a family member or close friend during the previous year. The data indicate that those who had these experiences valued leisure at least as much, if not more, than those who did not. For instance, those who had experienced a death of a loved one were slightly more likely than other participants to report positive attitudes regarding the role of leisure in their lives. They also tended to rank order family, work, and leisure in different ways. As would perhaps be expected, they gave family a higher priority and work a lower priority. However, reflecting the way in which attitudes toward leisure remain constant, the priority attached to leisure remained the same as for other participants.

To highlight the relation of wellness and leisure in middle adulthood, consider these case study findings for Annie, Ronny, and Connie. When Annie was asked when she sought leisure, it was when she felt stress and wanted relief. As such, leisure provided Annie with an escape from stress, adding to her sense of well-being. And though Ronny reported that the impact of life experiences related to his work were quite negative, he still valued leisure and held it in high regard. Of leisure he said, "It's an escape from the workplace." Connie had to adjust to a major life transition when twins she had given up at birth unexpectedly re-entered her life. She experienced major shifts in her perceptions regarding her life structure, values, and in how she used her leisure. The tendencies observed prior to the epiphany changed and then over time reverted as her life evolved around her new and expanded family role. Throughout the transition, however, her leisure perceptions remained intact.

Each year, the ASOLDA participants were also asked to reflect upon things that they looked for or wanted out of life and indicate which of the following was most important to them in their daily lives: a sense of belonging, warm relationships with others, self-fulfillment, being well-respected, self-respect, a sense of accomplishment, fun and enjoyment in life, excitement, and security. The vast majority of the participants rated relationships with others, self respect, and being respected by others as most important to them and, on average, these participants were very similar in their views toward leisure. In contrast, a few participants (no more than 6% of the total in any one year) said that "fun and enjoyment" was most important. No participant gave this response every year and most of those who reported this value as most important did so only once or twice during the ten years of participation. Yet, during the year when they saw fun and enjoyment as most important, these participants had significantly more positive attitudes toward leisure, valued it more, actually spent more time in leisure activities, and wanted to spend even more times in leisure than the other participants. Thus, while the participants had remarkably similar leisure views over time and in varying circumstances, there were periods when leisure became especially important in the lives of some of the participants.

Looking at important values associated with well-being (i.e., self-fulfillment, warm relationships with others, sense of accomplishment, self-respect, and fun and enjoyment), differences along with consistencies are notable in the case studies for two married couples. The first couple is Rick and Rita, who are in their 40s and 50s and working full time. The second couple is Pete and Laura transitioning into retirement. Values that they singled out most frequently as 'most important' over time included warm relationships with others and self-respect. Their verbal comments illustrate the relevance of these values to their sense of well-being. Rita takes "tremendous pleasure in self-fulfillment out of making something happen out of nothing…things I do in my leisure [are] valuable to me as part of being a human being." Rick feels that self-respect is "something I get from how I behave in all settings." Laura "always appreciated and enjoyed the warm relationships," particularly with her grandchildren. And Pete connected warm relationships with people and almost anything he pursued that he also called leisure in saying "most of the things that I like to do involve people."

Summary

So what might all of this mean in terms of leisure, health, and wellness? Using the brief assemblage of information garnered from grouped and case study data, we can see that a high regard for leisure exists in spite of positively or negatively rated life experiences and life perceptions. The clear pattern of continuity in leisure perceptions across the life span during this period is striking. It should also be apparent that multiple aspects play a role during middle adulthood and contribute to individuals' leisure, health, and wellness perceptions and experiences. It is important acknowledge individual uniqueness, for one size does not fit all. Every adult has and thinks about their unique life experiences in relationship to the unique nature of their life structure.

Though the grouped and case study ASOLDA data clearly show that a high regard for leisure exists, we still cannot say with certainty that leisure behavior, satisfying or not, will follow. Just knowing that adults hold positive attitudes about leisure, value leisure, and perceive freedom in leisure is not enough information for professionals to make prudent decisions about planning and providing recreation opportunities and services.

Leisure behavior is a far more complex phenomenon, one that Mannell and Kleiber (9) remind us involves the interplay of internal psychological dispositions (e.g., perceptions, feelings, emotions, beliefs, attitudes, needs, personality characteristics) and situational influences that are part of an individual's social environment (e.g., other people, group norms, human artifacts, and media).

Within this context then, let us briefly put forward responses professionals may want to consider when thinking about providing leisure, recreation, and physical activity programs designed to encourage adult participation. These include responses directed toward both the facilitation of programs and services made available to middle-aged adults and to ways in which professionals choose to view this demographic. Drawn from ASOLDA findings presented in this chapter, we conclude by offering factors that would likely influence our thinking about providing recreation programs and services designed to encourage adult participation.

- Life experiences will vary for most adults during middle adulthood. Such variances may open or close discretionary time available. Their high regard for leisure alone does not necessarily translate into participation interests or behaviors.

- Constraints resulting from physical health or injury may be temporary or chronic. There are times when adults may not participate in recreation or other forms of activity even though they value leisure highly and may be in good or poor health (or in times of stress).

- Adult participants would be well served if professionals used facilitative practices in designing and delivering programs. Given the varied life experiences adults have, professionals will want to rely upon good needs assessment processes when developing and managing programs. Those professionals who facilitate programs and services in ways that acknowledge and honor adults' tendency for self-determination in making life choices will likely be more successful.

We hope you have enjoyed this leisure journey through middle adulthood. Having taken this journey with us, we hope you can see the relevance of leisure and how it impacts health and well-being of middle-aged adults during this portion of the life span. Considering leisure over time, as we have done using ASOLDA longitudinal data, provides us with both several snapshots of the total group of adults and with a few photo albums for selected individuals. It seems to us that this perspective which emphasizes interindividual and intraindividual concepts is representative of the way professionals are encouraged to design and implement programs and services. Professionals are typically responsible for programs and services designed to meet both the needs and interests of both groups of people and for individuals seeking leisure experiences. In thinking about and programming for adults, prudent professionals should be employing their knowledge associated with this particular age group of middle aged adults, and then using their skills to produce experiences that adults would find attractive.

References

1. Carpenter G, Robertson B. A call for the increased use of longitudinal methods in research on adult leisure. *Leisure/Loisur* 2000;**24**:101–129.
2. Janke MC, Payne LL, Carpenter G, Stockard J. Does the nature of life events affect adults' leisure attitudes and perceptions of leisure freedom? Results from a 10-year longitudinal study. NRPA-SPRE Leisure Research Symposium Abstracts; 2008; Baltimore, MD.
3. Smale B, Morden P, Carpenter G. A Longitudinal Analysis of the Impact of Major Life Events on Perceived Freedom in Leisure, Tenth Canadian Congress on Leisure Research Book of Abstracts, 2002; 311–312.
4. Crandall R, Slivken K. Leisure Attitudes and Their Measurement. In Iso-Ahola SE (ed). *Social Psychological Perspectives on Leisure and Recreation*. Springfield, IL: Charles C. Thomas Publisher, 1980, pp. 261–284.
5. Ellis G, Witt PA. The leisure diagnostic battery: Past, present, and future. *Therapeutic Recreation Journal* 1986;**20**:31–47.
6. Carpenter G. A longitudinal investigation of mid-life men who hold leisure in higher regard than work. *Society & Leisure* 1997;**20**:189–211.
7. Kahle LR (ed). *Social Values and Social Change: Adaptation to Life in America*. New York: Praeger, 1983.
8. Sarason IG, Johnson JH, Siegel JM. Development of the Life Experiences Survey. In Sarason IG, Spielberger CD (eds). *Stress and Anxiety, Volume 6*. Washington: Hemisphere, 1979.
9. Mannell RC, Kleiber DA. *A Social Psychology of Leisure*. State College, PA: Venture Publishing, Inc., 1997.

Chapter 23
Leisure in Later Life
Cheryl Der Ananian
Megan Janke

"Men do not quit playing because they grow old; they grow old because they quit playing." - Oliver Wendell Holmes

At what age do we enter "later life"? Commonly in the United States we perceive older adulthood to begin in an adult's 60s. The average life expectancy for women in the U.S. is approximately 80 years of age, while for men it is slightly less at a little over 75 years. Based on these statistics, older adults spend approximately 15 to 20 years in later life. The aging population is also growing faster than any other age group. The number of older adults in the U.S. is expected to increase from 34.8 million to 77.2 million by 2040 (1). An understanding of "who" older adults are is going to be increasingly important as we try to provide services and programs for this population in the future.

So what are characteristics of older adults? We often have stereotypes of aging in our society. Consider some of the ways that you think about older adults. Common negative stereotypes of older adults in our society are that they are forgetful, slow, frail, disabled, and lonely or socially isolated. In addition, we often attribute positive characteristics to the general aging population such as that they are: caring, wise, patient, and mature. But are these realistic depictions of all older adults? Some of these attributes are based in truth and may result from aging-related changes in physical and cognitive abilities. For example, with the onset of chronic conditions and disability, older individuals may have more difficulties moving quickly and may become frailer. However, only 5% of adults reside in nursing homes or long-term care facilities. Most older adults live in their own homes and are often productive members of their community. In addition, only 800,000 adults aged 65 and older living in the community report difficulties with memory loss (2), and most older adults have established social support systems and do not experience problems with loneliness.

Our perception of older adults often influences our ideas about the leisure activities that they wish to participate in on a regular basis. Bingo, shuffle board, playing bridge, rocking on the porch, these are some of the activities that we associate with aging. It is less common for us to think of older adults as being physically active and mentally engaged in their daily lives. But what activities do adults participate in as they age? How much do our stereotypes of aging reflect the actual experiences and involvement of older adults? And how does participation in leisure activities during later life affect adults' physical health and mental well-being?

Theories of Aging and Activity

A few theories on aging attempt to address the leisure involvement of older adults and how this influences their overall health and well-being. The first theory to really explore this topic was the disengagement theory, proposed by Cumming and Henry (3). The basis of this theory is that during later life adults and social systems mutually withdraw from each other in order to prepare for the eventual death of the aging individual. Its basic premise is that ceasing participation in leisure activities and social roles leads to more life satisfaction and better adjustment in older adulthood. Disengagement theory was controversial from the moment it was introduced as many individuals did not buy into the fact that from withdrawing from activities and roles in society benefits the majority of older adults. However, one of the virtues of this theory was that it advanced the development of alternative theories of aging.

Activity theory (4) was formally introduced in response to the critique of the disengagement theory, although essentially the view of this theory had been the basis of much interactions and work in social gerontology prior to this point. This theory proposes that the way to achieve greater life satisfaction in older adulthood is through one's ability to maintain or increase involvement in social roles and leisure activity. Even today, this theory is the basis for much of the activity programming for older adults in senior centers, long-term care facilities, and retirement communities. We encourage older adults to be "as active as possible", and have the mentality that the more activity the better. However, while there is some support for this theory, there are many individuals for whom this theory just does not fit, who are not interested in maintaining or increasing activity levels during later life, or who find this process stressful rather than rewarding.

Another perspective was proposed around the same time as activity theory called Continuity theory (5). Continuity theory suggests that several patterns of aging could lead to positive development in later life and that adults do not need to withdraw or increase their involvement in activities to age successfully. In addition, this theory suggested that the pattern of involvement that was most appropriate for individuals might be linked to their personality style. In general, there has been much support for this theory as it promotes individualism in the aging process and highlights that individuals' preferences (for activities, social involvement, etc.) do not necessarily change just because they reach older adulthood.

One of the more recent theories to be introduced relating to aging and activity level is Successful Aging (6). While the term successful aging has been used to describe other theories of aging, Rowe and Kahn proposed a model that identified three central components to adults' ability to age successfully based off of the MacArthur Foundation Study. In their model, successful aging is characterized by the ability of adults to: (1) avoid disease, (2) maintain high physical and cognitive function, and (3) continue engagement in life. Engagement with life refers to our leisure activities— the activities that we find meaningful, rewarding, and interesting. This model suggests that leisure activities in later life should provide adults with the opportunity to relate to and socialize with others, to be productive and contribute to society, or just have "value" to the individual, whether they are paid or unpaid.

There is no one "right" theory of aging and it is possible to find support for all of the theories described in the preceding paragraphs in our society. This brief description of these different perspectives provides an introduction to how society and scholars have viewed how leisure and activity involvement are related to health and well-being in later life. A few real-life examples of these theories are provided in the following case studies.

Case Study #1: Disengagement Theory

Mary is 72 years old. She worked as a nurse for 40 years at the local hospital and used to always volunteer her time in the community. Now that she has retired, she is taking the opportunity to gradually cut down her volunteer hours and hopes to soon withdraw from this activity altogether. She is looking forward to spending more time alone and has removed herself some several of the social groups she used to attend. She used to be very involved in her children and grandchildren's lives, and has recently taken on more of a role as a passive observer of their lives, rather than actively being involved in their development and the events going on in their lives.

Case Study #2: Activity Theory

George recently celebrated his 75th birthday. He retired from the local telephone company at the age of 67 and has spent the last several years focusing on family and increasing the amount of time he spends with them. He and his wife travel to Florida every winter for 3 months, where they meet up with friends, play golf, and walk the beach daily. He has discovered an interest in woodworking since he retired, and has started building doll houses and games for his grandchildren. His children and wife often comment that he is busier now in retirement than he ever was when he was working full-time.

Case Study #3: Continuity Theory

Betty retired from teaching on her 65th birthday. In her retirement, she volunteers as a teacher's aide at the elementary school. She has always been a religious person and continues her involvement in her church activities. She and her friends started a monthly women's group when they were in their 30s and they continue to meet—they are now planning an annual trip since they are all retired and have more free time.

Case Study #4: Successful Aging

John is a retired physician and has always strived to be healthy. During the last several years he has started volunteering his time at a local clinic, providing free health care checkups to individuals with low incomes in his community. He goes to the gym three times a week to stay physically fit, and continues reading medical journals to keep his mind engaged. He also realizes that prevention of disease is important, so he takes a daily vitamin and regularly goes to the doctor for checkups to monitor his health.

"The more we do, the more we can do; the more busy we are,
the more leisure we have."

— Dag Hammarskjold

How Do Older Adults Use Their Time?

Understanding time use patterns in older adults is critical for understanding the relationship between leisure, aging, and health outcomes. Older adults are encouraged to "actively age" in order to optimize their health. Studying time use patterns allows us to examine if older adults are actually engaging in different types of leisure activities and helps us to better understand the determinants of leisure pursuits. This information can then be used to more closely examine the relationship between leisure activities, aging, and health, and would better enable practitioners to plan activities and interventions for the aging population to promote better health and well-being.

Examining time use patterns in older adults is even more important given that the life expectancy of older adults has increased dramatically during the 20th century. Furthermore, there is some evidence to suggest that older adults are retiring at earlier ages, resulting in additional years to pursue leisure activity and actively age. Overall, research suggests that adults do not dramatically change their participation in leisure during later life and that activity patterns among adults are diverse. It appears that participation in activities is relatively stable until very late in life, although patterns of continuity may vary based on type of activity and gender. Women appear to be more involved in social and public service activities than men, while men remain more active in physical activities during later life. However, both men and women appear to decrease their participation in active leisure and exercise with age. When adults do experience declines in their leisure participation in later life, these changes generally result more from the onset of disability and change in functional health rather than age per se.

Sedentary or passive leisure pursuits are more common among the older adult population. Socializing with friends and family is common in later life and the amount of time devoted to this activity does not appear to change much with age. Studies have also suggested that the time spent watching television, listening to the radio, and just relaxing increases with age. Older adults appear to allocate most of their active leisure time to socializing and participating in hobbies (7). In fact, the time older individuals spend engaging in hobbies and personal interests generally increases with age for both men and women. The most common physical leisure activities among adults tend to be those that do not require a lot of intensity, such as gardening and walking. Current cohorts of older adults show relatively low levels of participation in active sports. This lack of participation in sports may be related to a lack of opportunity as youth to engage in sports, particularly for current cohorts of older women, or due to a limited availability of community-based group and team sport activities for older adults.

Determinants of Time Use

There are several proposed determinants of time use in older adults including age and health status, gender, education level/socioeconomic status, marital status, and life events such as retirement and caregiving.

Age and Health Status

Age might influence leisure pursuits for several reasons. As people age, they are more likely to develop chronic illnesses and are more likely to experience impaired physical functioning. Currently, at least 80% of older adults over the age of 65 report having one chronic illness and nearly 50% report having 2 conditions. The average 75-year-old has three chronic conditions (8). It has been noted that disability and the onset of chronic conditions is a predictor of declines in some types of leisure activities, particularly physically active pursuits, and that as adults age they spend more time in home-based activities. There is some evidence to suggest that with age, older adults reduce their informal social interaction, membership in voluntary groups, and volunteering habits.

Gender

As indicated earlier, there are a few gender differences in leisure patterns during later life. In particular, women are much more involved in social activities than men across the life course and this does not appear to change in older adulthood. Yet, men tend to engage in physical activities more than women across the life span and motivations for participating in sports and exercise during later life may differ by gender. Older women often indicate that they are more likely to get involved in physical activities such as walking when they are done in a social setting with friends, while these motivations are not necessarily the same for men. Research has also suggested that women engage in more types, or a greater variety, of leisure activities during later life than men, indicating they may have a larger leisure repertoire.

Education and Income Levels

There are several mechanisms through which education might influence leisure pursuits. First, there is a strong linear association between education and income. Individuals with higher levels of education typically earn higher incomes. A higher level of income may be associated with an earlier retirement, and therefore, more opportunity and available time to engage in leisure. Second, a higher level of education is typically associated with better physical health and fewer health limitations which have been related to participation in active leisure pursuits. Third, a higher level of education is associated with greater disposable income that could be used to pay for more expensive leisure activities such as traveling. Finally, higher education levels have been consistently associated with greater participation in leisure time physical activity. The current cohort of baby boomers have much higher education levels than previous generations of older adults and this is expected to influence how they spend their leisure time during retirement.

Race and Ethnicity

Race has also been associated with leisure patterns across the lifespan. However, most studies on leisure patterns of older adults have been conducted using samples of predominately white, middle-class non-Hispanic Americans and thus it is often difficult to determine the exact effect that race and ethnicity has on participation. In addition, in our society race and ethnicity is often confounded with education and income levels. In other words, differences in older adults' participation based on race may actually be related to differences in income, education levels, and available leisure opportunities rather than due to racial differences. A few studies that have explored the leisure activities of older adults with racially diverse samples have suggested that older African Americans are significantly more involved in some types of formal leisure activities, such as church. However, much more research is needed in this area to thoroughly understand the effect of race and ethnicity on older adults' leisure behaviors.

Marital Status

Marital status is another factor that may influence older individuals' participation in leisure activities. One of the common barriers to participation in activities for older adults is the lack of a partner to participate with in the activity. This is often an important factor for older women, as much of their motivation for engaging in leisure activities is for the socialization, yet women tend to outlive their spouses, making them more likely to experience difficulties finding a leisure partner. Being married has been associated with increased participation in some types of leisure activities, particularly physical activities and exercise. As the prevalence of divorce increases in our society, there are increasingly more adults who are single in later life and the effects of marital status on time use will need to be explored further.

Retirement

Retirement may provide older adults with a unique opportunity to transfer the time spent in paid work to active leisure pursuits, although research suggests that retirees typically do not engage in a great number or types of activities than they did when they were working. Rather it appears that retirees are more likely to increase their participation in the same activities they have engaged in throughout adulthood. Retirees may even decrease their overall involvement in leisure activities upon leaving the workforce, as they transition into this new stage of life (9). The question then becomes, how do older adults reallocate the time they spent in paid work during retirement and what types of activities are they engaging in? For example, do they reallocate the time they spent in paid work to unpaid work, volunteer work, or housework? Or, do they reallocate the time they spent in paid work to physically active leisure, social leisure, or passive leisure activities?

The time use studies of international samples of retirees have been conducted to explore these questions. One study found that the time adults spend in active leisure pursuits (e.g., physical activity, social activity, and volunteering) averaged approximately 4 hours per day, increasing after retirement until the age of 75 when participation in these activities appears to decline (10). Overall, time use appears to be reallocated to more passive activities during retirement than active leisure pursuits. Older adults tend to adapt previous leisure patterns from when they were working during their retirement, rather than dramatically change the ways that they use their time. Increases in activity during retirement have also been noted in some studies; however, often much of this increase is devoted to sedentary activities such as watching television.

Caregiving

Caregiving is another potential determinant of leisure pursuits in later life. Taking on the role of caregiver for an ailing spouse or parent can greatly limit the caregiver's free time. Leisure time activities are often restricted or limited for the caregivers, yet once the obligations of care giving are removed, social activities and other leisure activities are often restored. Given the large percentage of older adults who are informal caregivers in society, and the strain that caregiving can place on an individual's physical and mental health, finding ways to help these individuals remain involved in leisure activities may have significant implications.

"Of all the self-fulfilling prophecies in our culture, the assumption that
aging means decline and poor health is probably the deadliest."
— Marilyn Ferguson

How Are Leisure Activity and Health Related in Older Age?

Research has demonstrated a strong relationship between remaining
"actively engaged with life" during one's later years and positive health
outcomes (6). Several studies have examined the relationship between
participation in different types of leisure activities and health (11, 12). The
most commonly studied leisure activities in regards to health have been
physically active leisure pursuits such as physical activity, exercise or
sports participation, volunteerism, participation in social and cultural activities, and passive or sedentary leisure pursuits such as television watching, reading, and listening to the radio. The most commonly studied health
outcomes in later life have include risk of mortality, cardiovascular health,
functional status and/or disability, psychological health (e.g., depression,
anxiety), and cognitive functioning.

Physical Activity and Exercise

Overall, the research suggests a strong, positive relationship between active
leisure pursuits and health outcomes in later life (13). The physical activity literature is replete with studies supporting the relationship between
participation in regular physical activity and improved health. Participation
in regular physical activity is associated with a reduced risk of overall
mortality as well as a reduced risk of mortality from cardiovascular disease.
Involvement in physical activity is also associated with a reduced risk
of several chronic illnesses known to impact older adults including heart
disease, stroke, hypertension, high cholesterol, diabetes, overweight and
obesity, osteoporosis, and certain cancers including colorectal and breast
cancer. There is also evidence to suggest that physical activity and exercise
is associated with delayed onset of disability.

Additionally, participation in regular physical activity has mental
health benefits. There is emerging evidence that regular participation may
delay the onset of or reduce the likelihood of developing impaired cognitive functioning, including the development of dementia and Alzheimer's
disease (14). It is also associated with improved quality of life, health-related quality of life, reduced likelihood of depression and may be associated
with improvements in sleep and reduced anxiety. Because of the numerous
health benefits of physical activity, recent physical activity guidelines

encourage all older adults to obtain at least 30 minutes of moderate intensity activity on 5 or more days per week or to obtain at least 20 minutes
of vigorous activity on 3 days per week; to participate in strength training
exercises that target all the major muscle groups on at least 2 days per week
and to participate in exercises that improve balance and flexibility (15).

Social and Other Types of Leisure Activities

Participation in other types of leisure pursuits is also associated with
improved health outcomes for older adults. The relationships between
participation in social activities, social networks, and health have long been
established. Having a strong social network is associated with reduced
mortality; it has been hypothesized that emotional support is central to
reduced cardiovascular disease mortality. Research has also suggested that
participating in social activities is also associated with improved cognitive
functioning and reduced likelihood of dementia. Volunteerism has been
associated with improved cognitive functioning, a greater sense of well-
being and self-reported health, decreases in depression, improved mood,
and delayed onset of mortality. There is even evidence that participation in
cultural activities such as going to the theater, the movies, or the cinema is
associated with increased longevity.

Understanding the ways that participation in leisure activities affects
health outcomes is critically important. Both physiological and psychosocial mechanisms have been suggested for improving the health of older
individuals and they may work in concert with one another. Proposed
physiological effects include improved cardiovascular health, improved
physical functioning, and improved immune function. Active participation
in leisure activities may have psychological benefits such as improved
mood, decreased anxiety or stress levels, and greater social involvement
which, in turn, might influence physiological pathways. A better understanding of the physiological and psychological pathways through which
participation in leisure activities exert their effects will enhance our ability
to understand how leisure involvement influences our health.

Summary

There are many ways to view the relationship between leisure and health
during later life and several theories have addressed this topic. Overall, participation in leisure activities appears to be stable across older adulthood,
although declines are evident during very old age, particularly as adults
begin to experience more chronic conditions and disability. Yet, maintaining or increasing involvement during older adulthood may have significant

implications for older adults' health. Research has suggested that participation in several types of leisure activities (e.g., physical, social, cognitive) can delay the onset of disability and chronic conditions, decrease mortality, increase overall life satisfaction, and decrease depressive symptoms in later life. Thus, finding ways to keep older adults actively engaged during their later years and determining how to best meet the leisure needs of older adults is important.

References

1. U.S. Bureau of the Census. *65+ in the United States: 2005 current population reports*. http://www.census.gov/prod/2006pubs/p23-209.pdf. Accessed March 20, 2009.
2. Bernstein AB, Remsburg RE. Estimated prevalence of people with cognitive impairment: Results from the nationally representative community and institutional surveys. *Gerontologist* 2007;**47/3**:350–354.
3. Cumming E, Henry WE. (1961). *Growing Old: The Process of Disengagement.* New York: Basic Books.
4. Lemon BW, Bengston VL, Peterson JA. An exploration of the activity theory of aging: Activity types and life satisfaction among inmovers to a retirement community. *Journal of Gerontology* 1972;**27**:511–523.
5. Neugarten BL, Havighurst RJ, Tobin SS. Personality and Patterns of Aging. In Neugarten BL (ed). *Middle Age and Aging*. Chicago: University of Chicago, 1968, pp. 77–102.
6. Rowe JW, Kahn RL. *Successful aging*. New York: Random House, 1998.
7. Gauthier AH, Smeeding TM. Time use at older ages cross-national differences. *Res Aging* 2003;**25**:247–74.
8. Centers for Disease Control and Prevention. Public health and aging: trends in aging—United States and worldwide. *Morbidity and Mortality Weekly Report* 2003;**52**:101–106.
9. Nimrod G, Janke MC, Kleiber DA (2009). Expanding, reducing, concentrating and diffusing: Activity patterns of recent retirees in the U.S. *Leisure Sci* 2009;**31**:1–17.
10. Gauthier AH, Smeeding TM. Patterns of time use of people age 55–64 years old: some cross-national comparisons. *Center for retirement research working papers, Boston College.* http://escholarship.bc.edu/retirement papers/31. Accessed December 20, 2008.
11. Janke MC, Davey A, Kleiber D. Modeling change in older adults' leisure activities. *Leisure Sci* 2006;**28/3**:285–303.
12. Menec, VH. The relation between everyday activities and successful aging: A 6-year longitudinal study. *Journal of Gerontology* 2003;**58**:74–82.
13. DiPietro L. Physical activity in aging: Changes in patterns and their relationship to health and function. *Journals of Gerontology* 2001;**56A**:13–22.
14. Scarmeus N, Luchsinger JA, Schupf N, Brickman AM, Cosentino S, Tang MX, Stern Y. Physical activity, diet, and risk of Alzheimer's disease. *J Am Med Assoc* 2009;**302/6**:627–637.

15. Nelson ME, Rejeski WJ, Blair SN, Duncan PW, Judge JO, King AC, et al. Physical activity and public health in older adults: Recommendation from the American College of Sports Medicine and the American Heart Association. *Med Sci Sports Exerc* 2007;**39**:1435–45.

Chapter 24
Leisure and Rehabilitation

Catherine P. Coyle
John W. Shank
Nannette M. Vliet

Introduction

Individuals involved in rehabilitation are experiencing a significant challenge to their health due to a loss in their functional ability as a result of a health crisis/condition. These health conditions/crises arise from a wide variety of events including trauma (e.g., motor vehicle accidents, gunshot wounds), infection (e.g., frostbite, viruses, cancer), surgery (e.g., joint replacement), progressive disorders (e.g., multiple sclerosis), neurological or cardiac malfunctions (e.g., stroke, heart attack, brain tumor), behavioral/ mental health episodes (e.g., depression, schizophrenia), or existing, on-going but poorly managed health conditions (e.g., diabetes, asthma). Functioning may be lost in the physical, social, cognitive, or emotional domains and may be permanent or temporary. Regardless of etiology or prognosis, the loss presents a serious challenge to the person's health, sense of self, and life quality.

Purpose of Rehabilitation

The primary mission of rehabilitation is to help individuals recover functioning and maintain their health. Rehabilitation, while often identified by a setting, can also be understood as a process in which individuals, in collaboration with a rehabilitation team comprised of a variety of professionals including physicians, nurses, therapists, social workers, psychologists, and family members, learn how to recover/maintain and live healthy lives while managing a health condition that has resulted in a change in functioning. The ultimate aim of rehabilitation is to assist the individual who has experienced an injury, illness, or disease to return to as normal a condition as possible or as the word's Latin root suggests, "to make able again."

Much of the rehabilitation process is guided by the latest social model of disability proposed by the World Health Organization—the International Classification of Functioning, Disability, and Health (ICF). This model illustrates health and disability as a complex and dynamic interplay between and among body structure and function, activities and participation, and environmental factors that support or impede health and life quality. Within this conceptualization, rehabilitation is no longer driven by a disease model of health; rather, it embraces a holistic model of health, which includes health promotion and wellness. This newer model presents health as more than the absence of disease; it is a dynamic process aimed at achieving a sense of balance and integration between body, mind, and spirit. The holistic conceptualization of health found in the ICF model (often referred to as "wellness") places particular emphasis on the physical, psychological, social, and environmental determinants of health and the capacity of the individual, in concert with his/her community and culture, to define, determine, and manage personal health and well-being. The application of the ICF to therapeutic recreation practice has been detailed by Porter and Van Puymbroeck (1).

While the main goal of rehabilitation is to maximize health and to restore independence, the journey through rehabilitation must be individualized, with the person served being the most important member of the team. The importance of individuals being active participants in decision-making about the management of their care and the establishment of therapeutic objectives cannot be underestimated and is consistent with a wellness approach to rehabilitation. Any health crisis results in a disruption of life goals; therefore rehabilitation in any setting must include the individual in the decision-making processes as well as give consideration to the valued life roles of the individual, in addition to the impact that the health condition has on successful functioning within these roles (2).

Rehabilitation Services and Settings

The intensity, duration, and type of rehabilitative services that individuals receive will vary based on their age as well as the severity and complexity of the health care issue and comorbidities they are experiencing. There are a variety of agencies and facilities that provide rehabilitative services to individuals. Common settings for rehabilitative services include specialty units in acute care hospitals (e.g., physical, psychiatric, cardiac, oncology), rehabilitation hospitals (e.g., in-patient physical rehabilitation facilities [IRFs]), in-patient psychiatric rehabilitation facilities (IPFs), transitional care facilities (e.g., skilled nursing units [SNFs]), intermediate care facilities (e.g., group homes), long-term care facilities (e.g., nursing homes, assisted living facilities), or outpatient centers/clinics. These facilities may be for-profit entities or nonprofit organizations.

Most have some type of accreditation, typically from the Council on Accreditation of Rehabilitation Facilities, an independent, nonprofit accrediting body with established customer-focused standards to help organizations measure and improve the quality of their programs and services, and the Joint Commission, a voluntary accrediting organization whose mission is "…to continuously improve the safety and quality of care provided to the public through the provision of health care accreditation and related services that support performance improvement in health care organizations" (3). In 2008, the Joint Commission accredited 4,250 general, children's, long term acute, psychiatric, rehabilitation and surgical specialty hospitals, 358 critical access hospitals, more than 1,800 behavioral health care organizations, and over 1,100 organizations offering long-term care and skilled nursing services in the United States.

Illnesses and Disabilities Seen in Rehabilitation Settings

The individuals treated in rehabilitation settings and the health problems they are experiencing are diverse. They include individuals from all age ranges (e.g., children to elderly) who are experiencing a "health crisis" that results in either a chronic or temporary period of disablement. The number of individuals that fall into this category is astounding. For instance, an estimated 2.2 million Medicare beneficiaries live in long-term care facilities and about 350,000 of this population are adults under age 65 (4). Additionally, about 38 million people living in the community report a disability (4.1 million people between 5 and 20 years of age, 20.2 million people between the ages of 21 and 64, and 13.5 million people ages 65 and older) (5) and it is likely that these individuals have or will be involved in the rehabilitation process.

The type of disability experienced by these individuals is equally diverse. According to U.S. Census data, the leading chronic health conditions reported for children and youth 17 years of age and under were learning disabilities, attention deficit/hyperactivity disorders, speech impairments, mental, emotional and behavioral problems, mental retardation, and other developmental delays; while, for those between the ages of 18 and 65, arthritis or musculoskeletal disorders, mental illness, heart or circulatory disorders, fractures or joint injuries, and lung diseases were most prevalent. Among the 65 and older group, heart and circulatory disorders, arthritis or musculoskeletal disorders, senility/dementia, vision/hearing disorders, diabetes and lung disorders were the most prevalent health conditions leading to disability (5). Regardless of the diversity in terms of health conditions and age, the process of rehabilitation, across disability types, is proactive and forward thinking with a focus on assisting individuals to understand and engage in the steps necessary to make informed decisions and to take action that promotes their recovery and maintains their health. Table 24.1 details the various foci for therapeutic recreation interventions across these settings, diagnoses, and impairments.

Table 24.1 A Rehabilitation Focus for Persons with an Acquired Disability

Degree of Impairment in Body, Structure, Function	Sample Diagnosis	Typical Treatment Settings	Focus of Therapeutic Recreation Interventions*
Decline in functioning of permanent nature	Spinal cord injury, acquired brain injury, cerebrovascular accidents, amputations, neurological and autoimmune disorders (e.g., transverse myelitis, Guillain Barre syndrome)	Specialty units IRF	• diversion and distraction to buffer stress • functional skill remediation or acquisition • leisure skill remediation or acquisition • psychosocial adaptation through leisure involvement • goal planning and self-regulation • community reintegration • assistive technology/device training • social support development/enhancement • environmental modification
Decline in functioning of intermittent and/or progressive nature	Multiple sclerosis, Parkinson's disease, Amyotrophic Lateral Sclerosis, asthma, diabetes, mental health disorders (e.g., depressive episodes, psychosis, schizophrenia), dementia	Specialty units IPF IRF Outpatient/clinics	
Decline in functioning of temporary nature	Hip/knee replacement, transplant, cardiac surgery	Specialty units IRF Outpatient/clinics	

* Therapeutic recreation interventions may be used across settings, diagnoses, level of impairment

Rehabilitation Focus for Individuals Acquiring a Decline in Functioning of Permanent Nature

Probably the most common association made to rehabilitation is that of individuals who have acquired a permanent disability through a traumatic event or the initial onset of a severe disease process. The process of recovery for those who have acquired a disability (see Table 24.1 for sample diagnoses) begins with acute care where the focus is on achieving medical stability of the individual through the initial stages of the health crisis. Once stabilized, the rehabilitation process is initiated through transfer to a specialty unit or an IRF. Maintaining medical stability while maximizing physical, cognitive, and/or emotional functioning are the primary foci of the rehabilitation team, and are essential to regaining functional independence.

Rehabilitation Focus for Individuals Experiencing a Decline in Functioning of Intermittent and/or Progressive Nature

The rehabilitation process with individuals with a chronic illness/disease (See Table 24.1 for sample diagnoses) also begins with medical management by the physician typically in outpatient/clinic settings and includes educating the individual on the basics of the disease/diagnosis and lifestyle changes that must be made. While many individuals with chronic illnesses/diseases succeed without further health care services, others often require admission to an IPF, IRF, or specialty unit. Admission may be the result of illness/disease exacerbations, medical complications, and/or changes in functional status due to disease progression or as a result of poor compliance with management of a medical regime. Achieving medical stability to thwart a downward spiral of functional loss is the major focus of rehabilitation, along with educating the individual about the disease progression and self-management techniques.

Rehabilitation Focus for Individuals Experiencing Decline in Functioning of Temporary Nature

The rehabilitation experience of individuals who are experiencing a temporary disability is often quite short. These individuals generally undergo a standard surgical procedure requiring a brief rehabilitation stay. Table 24.1 details sample diagnoses that individuals in this category may have. Because the presurgery symptoms that provide the impetus for surgical intervention often negatively impact the individual's health patterns, including decreased physical and social activity, the focus of the rehabilitation process may involve achieving a level of functioning better than the individual had immediately prior to admission.

Shared Foci and Approaches in Rehabilitation Regardless of Setting and Diagnosis

Clearly, the rehabilitation process spans a broad variety of disabilities/ diagnoses and settings. As individuals work with their treatment teams, there are key factors associated with the process that are common across disabilities/diagnoses and settings including a focus on (a) recovery of as much independent functioning as possible; (b) education about the health condition and mechanisms to prevent/minimize complications; and (c) active involvement of the individual and his/her support system. However, in keeping with the ICF model, approaches and interventions used in the rehabilitation process ought to be individualized and contextualized so that they are cognizant of the person's circumstances (e.g., living environment, social support network), values, and preferences. Therefore, the rehabilitation process is highly unique to each person, their health condition, and their life circumstances.

Health Promotion and Rehabilitation

Traditionally, rehabilitation has focused on medical management and restoration of functioning. However, the importance of health promotion and theories of health behavior change for individuals undergoing rehabilitation and/or living with a disability is gaining momentum. The recent Surgeon General's Call to Action on Promoting Health in Persons with Disabilities (6) as well as the health promotion goals identified for persons with disabilities in Healthy People 2010 (7) underscore the growing recognition of the role of health promotion for persons with disabilities. Research repeatedly shows health disparities between persons with disabilities and those without disablement (8). Persons with disabilities face a greater risk for developing complex health care needs due to (a) the number of associated conditions—conditions that are expected as a result of the primary disability, although their actual occurrence varies (e.g., dsyphagia [swallowing difficulties] and Parkinson's disease) (9), (b) secondary conditions—additional physical or mental health condition that occur as a result of having a primary disabling condition (5, 7) (e.g., decubiti ulcers, depression, obesity), and (c) general health conditions that are likely to occur with increased age (i.e., hypertension) (5–7, 9–11). Because of this, some researchers (12, 13) propose a number of reasons for moving health promotion and, in particular, health behavior change theories to the forefront of rehabilitation research and practice. The reasons drawn from health behavior change theories include, but are not limited to:

- the recognition within of the preventive aspects of positive health behaviors (e.g., regular physical activity, healthy nutrition, smoking cessation, mental engagement, social contact can lead to optimal health and well-being);

- the incorporation of self-management techniques (including self-regulation and self-monitoring) that can be used as a form of tertiary prevention for minimizing the impact of long-term disease by reducing opportunities for increased impairment;

- the recognition of the role of treatment adherence as a necessary link between effective treatments and treatment effectiveness—individuals need to comply with intervention regimens in order for them to be effective; and,

- the recognition that knowledge/information alone is insufficient to instill behavior change and that healthcare providers need to be facilitators of behavior change by actively promoting clients' confidence in their skills, enhancing clients' self-efficacy, and increasing clients' awareness and avoidance of potential risk factors that will compromise their health and well-being.

By incorporating these tenets, rehabilitation providers and researchers are more likely to identify, develop, and apply interventions that successfully achieve the desired outcomes from rehabilitation (12). These tenets are consistent with the philosophy of therapeutic recreation and lend support to recreation therapists who advocate for and incorporate health promotion interventions within their rehabilitation practice.

Leisure and Recreation's Contribution to the Rehabilitation Process

Leisure and recreation involvement are aspects of human functioning that provide an important context within which individuals can work towards achieving and maintaining health. If the aim of rehabilitation, as established earlier in this chapter, is to assist a person in regaining functioning in order to resume active involvement in all aspects of life and to learn ways to maintain their health and current level of functioning, then leisure is certainly a major life domain that has relevance to the rehabilitation process. Numerous authors have discussed the potential roles of leisure in the rehabilitation process (14–19) and there is a growing body of evidence that suggests involvement in leisure pursuits, whether they are physical, social, or cognitive activities, can promote and contribute to maintaining health and current levels of functioning (cf., Chapters 7–17 this text). Additionally, since leisure and recreation are by definition pleasurable and enjoyable activities, they can represent a unique intervention focus for which treatment adherence may be less of a problem.

Caldwell (15) provided a succinct review of the empirical evidence that leisure can be therapeutic and contribute to health and well-being through prevention, coping, and transcendence. When this evidence is applied to rehabilitation settings, recreation and leisure can assist in preventing secondary health conditions, and can aid in coping and adjustment to sudden and chronic disabling conditions. Indeed, these are pertinent rehabilitation goals and germane outcomes of the rehabilitation process.

As it is beyond the intent of this chapter to provide a comprehensive review of the evidence-based research supporting the health outcomes that can be achieved through recreation interventions within rehabilitation, we have chosen to highlight the inherent aspects within recreation activities that allow them to be used to achieve three broad rehabilitation goals: (a) functional outcomes, (b) psychosocial adaptation, and (c) wellness.

Recreation as a Mechanism for Achieving Functional Outcomes

Any recreation activity requires a varied mix of physical (e.g., strength, mobility, coordination), cognitive (e.g., memory, planning, comprehension), affective (e.g., emotional control and expression), and social skills (e.g., conversation, cooperation). Because of this, participation in most recreation activities, provided it is suitably structured, can enable clients to develop, improve, or adapt functional skills needed to increase independent functioning and improve their health. Additionally, recreation activities are also a valuable mechanism for functional improvement because of the "process" inherent in them. This process involves the sequence of (a) planning the activity, (b) taking action to follow through with the plans, (c) making adjustments as needed in response to one's action, and finally (d) completing the activity with appropriate ending and closure. This sequence encompasses the task skills Mosey (20) considered to be essential to all human action. Task skills include the ability to organize materials needed for an activity, the ability to follow oral, written, or demonstrated directions, and the ability to solve problems as they arise. These task skills are inherent in the process of selecting and engaging in recreation activities, thus making recreation activities an appropriate venue for achieving rehabilitation outcomes related to functional independence.

Recreation as a Mechanism for Achieving Psychosocial Adaptation

Adaptation to disability is a primary focus of the rehabilitation process for individuals with chronic illnesses and acquired disabilities. Facing the sudden and dramatic challenges to one's sense of self is the essence of psychosocial adaptation. Bishop (21) described psychosocial adaptation as a multidimensional process of responding to the functional, psychological, and social changes that occur with the onset and experience of living with a disability, chronic illness, or associated treatments. It is also a highly subjective process in that the individual's perspective and subjective assessment of the overall situation are the most important factors guiding his/her response. Bishop (21) has posited that psychosocial adaptation is inextricably linked to quality of life in that both are largely regulated by internal mechanisms that assess overall well-being based on important core domains of life.

During psychosocial adaptation, the importance or "centrality" of core and peripheral domains may become reaffirmed or altered, depending in large measure on one's perceptions of control in these areas. When recreation therapists assist clients with the simple task of making choices about what they may do during non-treatment time, they have been instrumental in helping clients regain perceptions of control and when these choices reaffirm "core" life domains or roles, the recreation involvement can assist with the process of psychosocial adaptation. Take for instance the research of Reynolds and Lim (22) with cancer patients. These researchers found that by giving cancer patients an opportunity to produce artwork that could be shared and offered as gifts to others, the patients were able "to retain a view of themselves as wife, mother, or friend who continued to reciprocate care, rather than being defined solely as a care-recipient" (p. 69).

Likewise, when recreation therapists assist clients with resuming preferred leisure pursuits, even if they are in an 'adapted' manner, the therapist is providing a foundation for psychosocial adaptation. This is particularly important when the preferred leisure activities are central to the individual's self-identity and roles. Take, for example, a business executive who routinely plays competitive golf with colleagues and friends. After being hospitalized for a cerebral vascular accident (CVA), his recreation therapist introduces the idea of adapted golf as a way of assisting this individual with regaining control in one aspect of his life that was part of his self-identity. However, the introduction of adapted or modified versions of preferred leisure activities will not always lay the foundation for psychosocial adaptation, as sometimes the context or the adaptations needed for resuming these preferred activities are so different that it makes them unappealing to the individual.

Accordingly, the focus of rehabilitation professionals in assisting individuals through this adaptation is to examine the importance placed on all domains of life (i.e., employment, family and social relations, leisure activity, community involvement, spirituality) and the impact illness or disability has or will have on these domains. This is particularly relevant in those instances when the illness/disability challenges the individual's ability to return to work, especially if the individual believes that "work/ employment" defines them as contributing member of society. In these instances, the recreation therapist needs to assist clients with exploring leisure involvement as a mechanism for redefining the way they can contribute to society (e.g., volunteering).

Recent leisure research on the transformative nature of leisure is consistent with Bishop's (21) view of centrality in psychosocial adaptation. This line of inquiry has described (a) how individuals who were adjusting to a traumatic life event ended up "transforming" themselves and their perspective on the future by finding new meaning in life through leisure engagement (23), and (b) how individuals with multiple sclerosis adapted to their chronic disabling condition by reprioritizing and finding ways to compensate for intrusions from their illness so that could remain engaged in personally meaningful activities (24). This line of leisure research illustrates the relevance of recreation and leisure to psychosocial adaptation in particular for redefining one's identity and sense of self through meaningful leisure. Personal identity is often inextricably linked to an individual's leisure attitudes, values, and behavior. Such is the case for the avid golfer, hunter, or skier. While these examples emphasize action, other forms of identity can be manifested in one's leisure behavior and pursuits. For instance, the role of parent or civic volunteer is often expressed in leisure; consider the time and energy some parents devote to being faithful spectators at their children's sporting and performing arts events. Kelly's (25) typology of leisure would label these actions as "relational" leisure or "role-determined" leisure. The degree of freedom/choice ascribed to these events determines which type of leisure it is. Likewise, civic activity is also a common discretionary behavior in adulthood. In fact, each developmental period contains preoccupations that are germane to identity and are often the basis for determining discretionary behavior. The point of this is that the process of psychosocial adaptation ought to include an examination of preferred leisure pursuits and the concomitant skills and environmental supports necessary to resume and maintain these preferred actions or the development of new pursuits that allow for expression of self-identity should a person experience a significant health crisis. Thus, leisure interests and preferences are a relevant context for not only functional goals associated with rehabilitation, but also for supporting the psychosocial adaptation of individuals going through the rehabilitation process.

Recreation as a Mechanism for Health Promotion/Wellness: The Special Role of Leisure Education

Leisure education provides a unique context for recreation therapists working within rehabilitation settings to promote health and wellness, primarily as it utilizes an educational process to effect change in person's knowledge, skills, and attitudes. A schematic model has been proposed by leisure researchers that could be used to design leisure education programs that integrate the concepts of health, wellness, and leisure (26). This model, entitled "The Healthy Living through Leisure Model," is grounded in health promotion and health behavior change theories and is focused on assisting individuals to use leisure as a mechanism for health behavior change which can be defined as "…the shift from risky behaviors to the initiation and maintenance of healthy behaviors and functional activities, and the self-management of chronic health conditions" (12). As such, health behavior change and the focus of leisure education within this perspective would include planning, initiating, acting upon, and engaging in recreation and leisure activities as a form of primary and secondary prevention of health conditions, as well as the promotion of health and wellness within one's environment.

In "The Healthy Living through Leisure Model," there are four areas of focus that a recreation therapist would use to design a leisure education program, each grounded in health behavior change and leisure theory (see Figure 24.1). In the first focus area, becoming informed, recreation therapists assist clients with knowledge acquisition by focusing on activities and information that raises their awareness about health and wellness and the current role of leisure in their life. This exploration includes environmental factors as well as personal information, and should culminate in a lifestyle self-assessment that allows individuals to determine their current level of wellness and how their leisure involvement promotes/hinders their health and well-being. The next area of focus is an examination of the client's motivation and readiness to make lifestyle changes. At this point, recreation therapists would design activities/sessions that allow clients to establish goals or outcomes related to promoting wellness through leisure activities that are meaningful and realistic for their situation. The third part begins the "activation" stage, which focuses on decision making and skill development. Clients rework their goals by creating action plans for

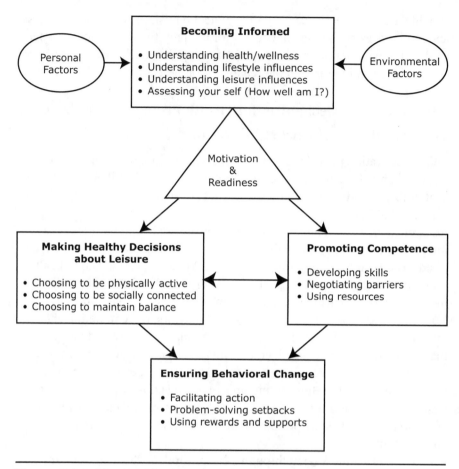

Figure 24.1 The Healthy Living through Leisure Model

behavior change. These action plans are focused on lifestyle changes that promote health through recreation involvement — with an emphasis on using leisure in one's life to be physically active, socially connected and emotionally balanced. Once decisions in these areas are made, the focus of the leisure education program shifts to assuring that individuals have a sense of competence to achieve these goals and engage in these health-promoting leisure activities. Content and learning activities that focus on developing the prerequisite skills or assisting clients with negotiating barriers in the environment are introduced. The final part of this model focuses on ensuring behavioral change. Support is rendered for implementing the action plan, problem-solving setbacks, and using rewards regularly.

The "Healthy Living through Leisure" model is simply a framework. Therapists must select the specific content, learning activities, and facilitation techniques that will be used in each of the four stages to promote the outcomes identified. In this way, the framework can be individualized to help create specific programs for unique groups of clients or unique client needs. An example of how the "Healthy Living through Leisure" model was used to design a specific leisure wellness program protocol for women with physical disabilities appears in the text Therapeutic Recreation in Health Promotion and Rehabiliation (26).

Summary

Given the research evidence suggesting health disparities among those with and without disabilities, as well as the compelling evidence suggesting an increased lifespan among individuals with disabilities, it is clear that rehabilitation needs to embrace a lifestyle management approach to assist those with disabilities to manage the complexities of their conditions. Throughout this chapter, cited research has repeatedly shown that involvement in leisure activities is explicitly linked to health and life quality; therefore, recreation therapists and health and wellness professionals are uniquely positioned to embrace a health promotion agenda within rehabilitation. By doing so within their practice, recreation therapists may find themselves at the forefront of advancing a new era of healthy living for persons with disabilities.

References

1. Porter H, Van Puymbroeck M. Utilization of the ICF within therapeutic recreation practice, *Ther Rec J* 2007;**41/1**:47–60.
2. Lawson S, Delamere F, Hutchinson S. A personal narrative of involvement in post-traumatic brain injury rehabilitation: What can we learn for therapeutic recreation practice? *Ther Rec J* 2008;**42/4**:236–250.
3. The Joint Commission. Accreditation Programs. http://www.jointcommission.org/AccreditationPrograms. Accessed June 8, 2009.
4. Centers for Medicare and Medicaid Services. *The Characteristics and Perceptions of the Medicare Population Series: Data from the 2003 Medicare Current Beneficiary Survey* 2005. http://198.232.249.10/mcbs/PubCNP03.asp. Accessed June 8, 2009.
5. Institute of Medicine. *The Future of Disability in America*, National Academies Press: Washington, DC, 2007.
6. U.S. Department Health and Human Services. The Surgeon General's Call to Action to Improve the Health and Wellness of Persons with Disabilities 2005. http://www.surgeongeneral.gov/library/disabilities/calltoaction/index.html. Accessed June 8, 2009.
7. U.S. Department Health and Human Services. Disability and Secondary Conditions. In *Healthy People 2010: Understanding and Improving Health*, 2nd ed. Washington, DC: U.S. Government Printing Office: 2005. http://www.healthypeople.gov/document/HTML/Volume1/06Disability.htm. Accessed June 8, 2009.
8. Centers for Disease Control and Prevention. Office of Minority Health and Health Disparities. Racial and Ethnic Minority Populations – Disability 2009. http://www.cdc.gov/omhd/Populations/Disability/Disability.htm. Accessed June 8, 2009.
9. Turk MA. Secondary Conditions and Disability. In Field MJ, Jette AM, Martin L (eds). *Workshop on Disability in America: A New Look*. Washington, DC: The National Academies Press, 2006, pp. 185–193.
10. Coyle CP, Santiago MC. Healthcare utilization among women with physical disabilities. *Medscape Women's Health eJournal* 2000;**7/4**. http://www.medscape.com/viewarticle/433156. Accessed June 8, 2009.
11. Rimmer JH, Braddock D, Pitetti KH. Research on physical activity and disability: An emerging national priority. *Med Sci Sports Exerc* 1996;**28/11**:1366–1372.
12. Nieuwenhuijsen ER, Zemper E, Miner K, Epstein, M. Health behavior change models and theories: contributions to rehabilitation. *Disabil Rehabil* 2006;**28/5**:245–256.

13. Landry MD, Jaglal S, Wodchis WP, Raman J, Cott CA. Analysis of factors affecting demand for rehabilitation services in Ontario, Canada: A health-policy perspective. *Disability & Rehabilitation* 2008;**30/24**,1837–1847
14. Beuttner L. Gerontological recreation therapy: Examining the trends and making a forecast. *Ann Ther Rec* 2000;**9**:35–46.
15. Caldwell L. Leisure and health: Why is leisure therapeutic? *Bri J Guid Counsl* 2005;**33/1**:7–26.
16. Coyle CP, Kinney WB, Riley B, Shank JW (eds). *Benefits of Therapeutic Recreation: A Consensus View*. Idyll Arbor: Ravensdale, WA, 1991.
17. Dattillo J. *Facilitation Techniques in Therapeutic Recreation*, Venture Publishing, Inc.: State College, PA, 2000.
18. Lee Y, Yang H. A review of therapeutic recreation outcomes in physical medicine and rehabilitation between 1991–2000. *Ann Ther Rec* 2000;**9**:21–34.
19. McCormick B, Funderburk J. Therapeutic recreation outcomes in mental health practice. *Ann Ther Rec* 2000;**9**:9–19.
20. Mosey A. *Activities Therapy*. Raven Press: New York, 2000.
21. Bishop M. Quality of life and psychosocial adaptation to chronic illness and acquired disability: a conceptual and theoretical synthesis. *J Rehab* 2005;**71/2**: 5–13.
22. Reynolds F, Lim KH. Turning to art as a positive way of living with cancer: A qualitative study of personal motives and contextual influences, *J Positive Psych* 2007;**2**:66–75.
23. Kleiber D, Hutchinson S, Williams R. Leisure as a resource in transcending negative life events: Self-protection and personal transformation. *Leisure Sci* 2002;**24**:219–235.
24. Wilhite B, Keller J, Hodges J, Caldwell L. Enhancing human development and optimizing lifelong health and well being in person with Multiple Sclerosis. *Ther Rec J* 2004;**38/2**:167–187.
25. Kelly J. *Leisure*. Allyn & Bacon: Boston, 1996.
26. Shank J, Coyle C. *Therapeutic Recreation in Health Promotion and Rehabilitation.* Venture Publishing, Inc.: State College, PA, 2002

Chapter 25

Work, Leisure, and Health: Revisioning Retirement in the 21st Century

Barbara A. Hawkins
Harry R. Moody

Introduction

Everywhere one reads about population aging, the text typically begins with dire warnings about the aging of the Baby Boomers. "The sky is falling, the sky is falling..." The threat implied is that clear, drastic changes *must* be made or everything will combust, go up in smoke—the economy, our way of life, and everything else. Consider the typical metaphors used to depict population aging: "train wreck," "iceberg," or "tsunami." It seems that only catastrophic things can happen as Boomers enter the *Third Age*. The Third Age reflects a period of middle age and the transition from being in the workforce to retirement and is sometimes called young old. The authors of this chapter disagree and we hope that readers will find fresh hope with some of the ideas presented in this chapter.

This chapter focuses on the changing the nature of work, leisure, and health in the context of retirement. The Baby Boomers, hereafter referred to as the Boomers, will undoubtedly shape these changes, much as they did other social institutions throughout their lives. Any discussion of retirement as a social institution needs to consider key social policies and programs that also *must* and *will* change, such as Social Security, Medicare, and Medicaid. The problems and issues associated with Social Security, Medicare, and Medicaid are complex and extend far beyond the scope of this chapter. Thus, we focus more narrowly on how the nature of work and leisure may be changing as the result of many societal forces, including the characteristics and expectations of the aging Boomers themselves. The key question is this: Will changes in the nature of work and leisure redefine what retirement is in the 21st century, or are other change forces causing retirement to become obsolete in American life (1)? Retirement as we have known it in the past as the complete cessation of work *will* change. It is likely that retirement will be redefined by aging Boomers to mean less about the cessation of work and more about the kinds of activities that Boomers choose to pursue in their older adult years. These activities may well include work. Retirement is likely to be replaced by notions of a *third age* and *fourth age*, a transition into physical, cognitive, and psychological aging and is sometimes called oldest old, wherein what one does is more important than old notions associated with classic retirement.

The Boomers and Change

Boomers comprise 76 million Americans now beginning to enter older adulthood. They were born during a time of great optimism and represented a 44% increase in the size of the population (2). Ever since their birth, the boomers have been challenging society's institutions to change (e.g., new schools, 34 million new jobs, more housing, explosive expansion in the economy). Now they are beginning to challenge Social Security and Medicare, necessitating long-overdue reform and restructuring of these programs. These institutions of social insurance are products of the Great Depression of the 1930s. These programs will inevitably change, in part because we no longer live with the economy or family structures prevailing at the time when these programs originated. In the high tech, knowledge-based economy of today, many of society's institutions are changing, not just because there is huge Baby Boom generation but also because the very nature of work, the population, and contemporary society are fundamentally different.

During the 20th century, the U.S. evolved from an agrarian and industrial economy to a post-industrial economy in which services and information are the dominant productive factors. During the post-WWII period, suburbanization and the dominance of the automobile decisively reshaped American life. Since the 1960s, social life in America changed further as a consequence of the sexual revolution, single parent and blended families, explosive technology, women's liberation, drugs, rising crime rates, and political activism (2). Today, in addition to the coming of labor shortages for knowledge workers and an inadequately prepared millennial generation, there is growing doubt about whether mass retirement for aging Boomers will be feasible or desirable. For example, surveys have suggested that large majorities of Boomers expect to work at least part-time during the traditional retirement years. The economic downturn beginning in 2008 has reinforced that expectation. With the coming of a "risk society" the forces of instability in today's society are so complex that there is less and less stability or predictability for those entering later adulthood.

It is especially important to recognize that not all Boomers are the same. They are a highly heterogeneous group and it would be incorrect to depict a uniform future for Boomers as they enter older adulthood. First of all, compared with previous generations, they are better educated. Second, they may have longer life expectancy, but their health status is uncertain because of high rates of chronic disease and obesity. Until recently they might have expected to exceed their parent's wealth (2), but recent economic circumstances now put that expectation at risk. How to maintain income security, positive health status, housing, and a lifestyle to which they have become accustomed will be part of the challenge that lies ahead. While "Social Security and Medicare, along with private pensions, have decisively improved the economic well being of older Americans" in the 20th century, many analysts doubt whether they can continue to do so for the Boomers without drastic reform (1, p. 133). According to the most recent Retirement Confidence Survey conducted by the Employee Benefit Research Institute, "American's confidence in their ability to afford a comfortable retirement has dropped to its lowest level" ever, down from 41% in 2007 to 20% in 2009 (3, p. 4). The ability of Boomers to retire and maintain a lifestyle that they have cultivated will vary across Boomers based upon financial well-being, economic capacity, and overall health status. Social Security benefits alone will not allow Boomers to maintain their standard of living without additional income (4).

Boomers can be segmented into three broad groups: the *Set for Life* group, the *Might be OK* group, and the *Struggling and Anxious* group (2, 5). These groups each roughly comprise one-third of the population of Boomers. The *Set for Life* Boomers are generally financially well off, in good health, and are high in intellectual capital. These Boomers should be encouraged to continue to lead vibrant, active lifestyles, especially in terms of continuing to contribute to the economy as well as taking personal responsibility for maintaining a high level of health. Many of these Boomers are able to maintain independent health care insurance, could continue to add to Social Security, and could work a variable amount of time, thus balancing work and leisure in a highly satisfying way. This group is generally very healthy and has access to good health care that they can afford. Because this group is financially comfortable, many may wish to work as free agents setting up new enterprises (6).

According to Goldsmith, the *Might be OK* group represents a very different story, one that can go either way due, in part, to their own making and in part, to what happens in the economy including major reform to Social Security, Medicare, and the general health care system (2). Some in this group have not saved enough or their savings are vulnerable to economic conditions such that they could become financially unstable after retirement. Others in this group cannot afford health insurance outside of employer-provided benefit programs. Some *Might be OK* Boomers could see their health deteriorate and slide quickly into the *Struggling and Anxious* group. Still others will want to continue to work and will need employee benefits, but might prefer to be more independent in their work. These individuals could become frustrated by their inability to provide themselves with adequate health insurance coupled with the growing funding instability of the Medicare program.

Some Boomers in this group will be forced out of work either by social norms and ageist attitudes, or because it simply doesn't pay to work. Older highly skilled and experienced workers are needed in light of growing labor shortages coupled with mounting problems associated with poorly prepared younger people entering the workforce. Many companies and organizations are instituting phased retirement in order to maintain a qualified workforce. The idea that older workers cost more is erroneous, especially given what the older experienced worker can produce over the younger inexperienced and ill-prepared worker. While there is increasing agreement that healthy older people are a potentially valuable resource, negative attitudes continue to fortify both skepticism and a lack of preference for hiring people who are 50 and older (7, p. 142). In addition, a close look at Social Security as presently administered reveals that some younger beneficiaries who work and draw Social Security are penalized through higher tax payments on their benefits than if they did not work (8). It is clear that Social Security and Medicare reform could greatly benefit this group and make their sustained participation in the workforce viable. Many in this group would choose to work either part time or full time, and often they would choose to be free agents if they could have their health care costs contained or assured.

Finally, the *Struggling and Anxious* group are less healthy, are unable to independently take care of their health expenses and needs, and do not have adequate financial resources for old age income security (2). Because this group contains Boomers who have not taken good care of their health throughout life, many of them suffer from obesity, poverty, alcoholism, depression, physical impairment, and chronic disease. Their capability for working is severely limited or nonexistent. Under the present system, Social Security will not adequately provide for this group's needs and they can be expected to be heavy users of Medicare and Medicaid when they reach older adulthood. This is the group of Boomers who are in the greatest need of social policies and programs in order to meet basic financial and health needs. This group must be considered first and foremost in any reform and restructuring of Social Security, Medicare, and Medicaid.

Leading specialists in the economics of aging put the problem this way: "Thus, the biggest retirement issue of this century is likely to be whether workers and employers see the need and are willing to modify the "retirement right." Will work and retirement options be changed or replaced to include what each group sees as viable work opportunities in later life, options that would complement the retirement life everyone now expects and almost all would like to enjoy later in life?" (7, p. 156). One reality is for certain, "[f]or tens of millions of baby boomers, retiring will mean 'rewiring' rather than ceasing to work" (2, p. 55). All

Americans will need to answer the question as to whether or not the mass retirement of the Boomers is economically feasible and viable from a social policy perspective (1).

The Social Security system, by itself, cannot sustain Boomers retiring en masse with the expectation of maintaining the standard of living to which they are accustomed. At present, 64% of retirees depend upon Social Security for half or more of their income. For people receiving Social Security benefits, one-third rely on it for 90% of their income and one in five depend on it for 100% of their income (4). According to AARP, around 80% of Boomers expect and plan to work in retirement. However, the motivation to work for enjoyment vs. for needed income is shifting away from working for enjoyment (5). Boomers (70%) report having special interests or hobbies that they look forward to doing more of in retirement and 68% believe that they will have enough time for recreation. Overall, only 7% of Boomers see retirement as meaning "not working." Many will work full or part time and many more want to start second careers and new enterprises (6). Coupled with the desire to work comes a growing need for skilled workers that is bound to increase. Therefore, a large number of fully retired Boomers seems both unlikely and unrealistic for many reasons. This scenario of work-life extension for aging Boomers should be approached as an opportunity rather than as a sign of doom. Economic and labor force trends could serve to redefine retirement fundamentally, if not remove it from the everyday language and experience of Boomers as they move into later life. *The Economist* magazine editorializes that "it is up to [future] individuals to make the most essential change of all: to accept that early retirement was an historical aberration and to prepare for longer working lives. Their priority must be to remain employable. This will mean a greater willingness to invest in themselves, ensuring that they keep their expertise and skills up to scratch. It will also often mean accepting lower wages if their productivity does decline" (7, p. 138).

One big problem, however, is that most adults avoid planning for retirement or taking much action ahead of time about their retirement, especially in terms of health, wealth, and time use (7). For example, the Employee Benefit Research Institute's 2009 survey revealed that only 44% of the workers surveyed have tried to calculate what they need to save for retirement. Only 25% of workers felt very confident that they would have the ability to manage basic expenses and a meager 13% indicated that they would have enough to pay for medical expenses (3). Among current retirees, only 25% are very confident about meeting their health expenses. Clearly, there is a disturbing pattern of neglect regarding individuals planning for retirement.

The Changing Nature of Work and Leisure

What will leisure mean to the Boomer entering older adulthood? We need to recognize that old age and leisure are social constructions (1), not simple facts about the world. We live in a "symbolic world of shared meaning" (1, p. 109). For many, older adulthood is a time for reflecting on the meaning of life and it also is a time for bringing new meaning into their lives. Leisure is one venue through which the older adult can experiment with and experience meaning through activities that are pursued on the basis of being freely chosen (not obligatory) and intrinsically satisfying. The question is, what symbolic meaning will leisure reflect in a world in which the nature of work is fundamentally changing and retirement is becoming obsolete?

Leisure brings out a variety of reactions in people, including the perception of wasting time to the frenzied pursuit of activities during free time (9). Most people recognize leisure as characterized by the absence of obligation and a sense of satisfaction or pleasure. Having free time, in and of itself, however, does not equate with leisure, it's how the individual defines the activity as fulfilling, satisfying, or pleasurable that is important. For many, leisure is a pathway to finding deeper meaning in life (1). Will Boomers seek work activities as leisure in older adulthood? For some Boomers, the opportunity to engage as "free agents" in entrepreneurial activity could be thought of as a form of leisure. For example, consider the Boomer who has always wanted to try her hand at art and seeks to open a studio, or the Boomer who always dreamed of taking a biking passion to the next level by opening a bike shop. Do these new pathways symbolize leisure or work, or the blending of work and leisure? In these examples, work could be leisure for the *Set for Life* Boomers. While maintaining an active contribution in the economic health of the nation, the *Set for Life* group could experience deeper meaning in their lives through the blending of work and leisure into a pattern of life that only remotely resembles traditional retirement.

The flip side of the coin also applies: if the individual does not experience feelings of satisfaction and freedom, then whatever they are doing can hardly be called leisure. Among the *Might be OK* Boomers, traditional retirement meant a time for experiencing leisure that was independent of work, a set aside time to experience personal development through activities that were distinctly not associated with work. For this group, issues of income security and the costs associated with protecting their health are threats to any potential for blending work and leisure, symbolically and in reality. For many in this group, working as a free agent is not possible primarily because of dependence upon benefit packages that include health insurance. In addition, many Boomers in this group have inadequate retirement savings, which necessitates staying within jobs that provide regular income.

What about the more vulnerable group of *Struggling and Anxious* Boomers? Restructuring life and their lifestyles may require learning to live on extremely meager finances under conditions that hardly accommodate a sense of meaning to life that comes from either leisure or work. These aging Boomers will be neither consumers of leisure services and products nor contributors to the economic foundation of American society. They clearly must be the focus of social policy and program reform of Social Security, Medicare, and Medicaid.

Keeping busy during retirement has been seen as normative but the nature of retirement activities have not been well distinguished as either work or leisure for many older adults. For example, even though many retirees freely engage with great satisfaction in part time work and volunteering, are these activities considered to be leisure or work? As Boomers age, will the division between work and leisure blur, or will it become more defined? As forces related with labor shortages, social security financing shortfalls, and escalating health care expenditures impact the choice to retire or not, can we expect to see the meaning of work and leisure perhaps merge into some new context rather than the old framework associated with traditional retirement? With these changes, some of the long-held benefits associated with leisure may need to be reconsidered carefully (e.g., companionship, compensatory activity engagement, disengagement through passive solo activities, comfortable solitude, expressive solitude, and civic engagement). Of particular interest will be how work may be sought by Boomers for many of the same benefits as did traditional leisure in retirement.

Leisure for aging Boomers, by itself, may not relate as strongly to positive identity and life satisfaction as does work (9). Will this relationship provide an incentive for Boomers to continue to choose work over traditional retirement? Based on research, it is known that higher health status and positive sense of well-being are correlated with leisure among older people who have higher socioeconomic status, which would seem to be applicable to the *Set for Life* Boomers and variously among the *Might be OK* group. Clearly, a retirement filled with leisure is unlikely to fulfill Boomers in the *Struggling and Anxious* group. What, then, is the outlook for this latter group, Boomers who are not capable of working but also may not have the resources to engage in meaningful and satisfying leisure? Further, how do Medicare, Medicaid, and Social Security provide for income security, health protection, and well-being for these Boomers?

While these ideas can be seen as culture bound, they do illustrate the fluid nature of how people perceive and experience leisure and work.

Historically, work has held a dominantly high positive value during early to middle adulthood and leisure in later life has been largely equated with retirement as its source of legitimization for how time is used. Based on the partitioning of Boomers into three segments, we may see new ways in which work/leisure may be manifested in later life. For example, the *Set for Life* Boomers may wish to seize the day for free agency and entrepreneurship (6). The *Might be OK* Boomers, those who do not slide into the *Anxious and Struggling* group, may need to continue to be engaged in traditional jobs with benefit packages or seek retraining for new jobs in technology or health care. For these Boomers, leisure may continue to symbolize what they do when they are not working. It is the third group, the *Anxious and Struggling* Boomers, that is the most worrisome. They are unlikely to have a traditional retirement with income security, high quality leisure, or adequate health coverage.

These scenarios point to the fluid and variable future for Boomers as they enter older adulthood. Several factors will affect lifestyle redefinition. These factors include (a) having an adequate income; (b) securing good health; (c) having work options that match individual interests and needs; (d) assuring adequate health care insurance and service access; (e) diffusing the impact of factors related with gender, racial/ethnic background, and educational attainment; and (f) having supportive family and gender roles and expectations (9).

In the long run, it is unlikely that retirement to a life of complete leisure can continue to define a third or more of life, regardless of which Boomer group is referenced. It is more likely that many Boomers will experience one or some combination of the following scenarios:

1. A shift away from full-time career job toward new work-related opportunities either full or part time, and leisure will become part of the meaning of work. Work and leisure will blend to support an active, healthy, engaged lifestyle.
2. For those unable to work, who are low-income and in poor health, retirement will be a struggle involving increasing health problems and decreasing economic stability. The possibility for leisure as defined by freedom and satisfaction is highly unlikely (9).

The Wild Card—Health

While Social Security reform is necessary, dealing with health care spending far outpaces any problems predicted for future financial gaps within Social Security (7). The root of the problem lies not with Medicare or Medicaid but with health care expenditures in general. These expenditures are escalating and could reach 19% of GDP by 2014 (7). Securing the health of aging Boomers is both a public problem and the private responsibility of every individual. Many observers agree that the American health care system and social contract to ensure access to health care for older adults is need of overhaul. This complex problem and its solution are well beyond the scope of the present chapter. It is relevant, however, to note that Boomers come to older adulthood in uncertain health prospects: better in some respects, worse in others. Longevity, for example, poses new risks of paying for long-term care. The bottom third, the *Struggling and Anxious* Boomers, have clear health problems with a high health care consumption price tag. How should costly health care and drug therapies be provided in a system that has more specialists than family practice physicians, and a financing system that is broken? What is the best approach for supporting the *Struggling and Anxious* Boomers who are likely not to be in the labor force and at risk of increasing dependence due to very poor health status?

Further, how will *Might be OK* Boomers fair if individual health insurance is out of financial reach coupled with a health system that is unwieldy and further, if Medicare becomes narrowed to serve only the most poor and disabled Americans? Will many *Might be OK* Boomers be at risk of slipping into the *Struggling and Anxious* group? An older adulthood that comes with incentives to maintain labor force participation with benefit packages is likely to be very important for the *Might be OK* Boomers. Maintaining a high health status might mean more blending of work and leisure into an active, engaged lifestyle that reflects a health promotion model rather than retirement within the traditional medical model for health care.

Over the years "older workers have been seen by most employers as lacking in physical vigor, being 'tradition bound,' less willing to adjust to technological change, less appropriate for retraining, less productive, and more costly" (7, p. 144). Yet Boomers are highly unlikely to tolerate this negative stereotype. Boomers are anything but frail and they constitute a valuable resource given the outlook of shortages for high skilled, experienced workers and a financial security model that can no longer rely on the Social Security system alone.

A big question is: How will Boomers want to use their time? Health and vigor are keys to answering this question. Will Boomers actually prefer to blend work and leisure, or will they want more work and less leisure? Will work-life extension be driven by a need to replace income or to pay for health care expenses? How will these choices be affected by individual health status? We can agree that the *Struggling and Anxious* Boomers are likely to be consumed by their health concerns. We can hope that false beliefs about older people lacking vigor do not impede the *Might be OK* Boomers from an active blend of work and leisure in older adulthood.

Finally, we will be vigorously persuaded by the *Set for Life* Boomers that old stereotypes "do not apply" and we can expect to see these people continue to push away old ideas about retirement. Finally, we need to remember that "health" and "health care" are not at all the same thing. In all cases, health status remains an individual responsibility, a social necessity, and a critical component of any option that promotes a high quality of life in old age.

One thing is clear: unbridled consumption across the board, including health care, is not a trajectory that can be maintained by Boomers as they reach 65 and older. Recent surveys suggest that the economic downturn that began in 2008 has promoted a shift away from consumerism toward concern for sustainability, at both the individual and societal scale. Aging Boomers may shy away from working themselves to death at some point in their entry into the *Third Age*, as consumerism declines. Yet managing their own health status and health care remains both the wild card and lynchpin in any future lifestyle in old age that blurs the lines between work and leisure.

Closing Questions

The future of aging Boomers opens up questions that demand our attention. For example, was mass retirement merely a phenomenon of the industrial age when work and leisure were more clearly separated in the American way of life? Or, will retirement take on new meaning or become obsolete in a high-tech, knowledge-based society where an increasing number of Boomers are likely to be in good health into and throughout old age? We may be at the edge of the deinstitutionalization of retirement, which is being accompanied by radical change in the nature of work and leisure wherein health status plays a pivotal role. While past research suggests that most people prefer to retire as soon as it is financially feasible, Boomers may or may not follow this pattern. They may seek new opportunities to engage in economically productive roles, especially if it is seen as a financial exigency or it is viewed as an opportunity to be an entrepreneurial free agent.

In this chapter, we have provided no final or definitive answer about work, leisure, health, and retirement during the years that have been labeled as "the long Baby Boom" (2, 8). What we have attempted to do is to focus the reader's attention on the open-ended character of the questions themselves. This analysis suggests that all is not gloom and doom, but rather demands a dialogue to insure that social change is creative and that demography does not become destiny (2, 7, 8). We are clearly at the cusp of change. With eyes wide open, it is a time for revisioning what the future can be and directing our energy toward opportunities for a more balanced blending work and leisure in support of an active, healthy, engaged older adulthood. It is not inevitable, but there is no reason to doubt that is possible.

References

1. Moody HR. *Aging: Concepts and Controversies* (5th ed.). Pine Forge Press: Thousand Oaks, CA, 2006.
2. Goldsmith J. *The Long Baby Boom: An Optimistic Vision for a Graying Generation*. The Johns Hopkins University Press: Baltimore, MD, 2008.
3. Helman R, Copeland C, VanDerhei J. *The 2009 retirement confidence economy drives confidence to record lows; Many looking to work longer*. EBRI Issue Brief, no. 328. http://www.ebri.org/publications/ib/index.cfm?fa=ibdisp&content_id=4226. Accessed April 6, 2009.
4. Villarreal P. Ten ways to wreck your retirement. Policy Report No. 320. http://www.ncpa.org/pub/st320. Accessed July 6, 2010.
5. Roper ASW. Baby Boomers envision retirement II: Survey of Baby Boomers' expectations for retirement. http://assets.aarp.org/rgcenter/econ/boomers_envision.pdf. Accessed July 6, 2010.
6. Rogoff EG. *The Issues and Opportunities of Entrepreneurship After Age 50*. Occasional Papers, Number 5. AARP, Office of Academic Affairs: Washington, DC, 2008.
7. Schultz JH, Binstock RH. *Aging Nation: The Economics and Politics of Growing Older in America*. The Johns Hopkins University Press: Baltimore, MD, 2006.
8. Kotlikoff LJ, Burns S. *The Coming Generational Storm: What You Need to Know about America's Economic Future*. The MIT Press: Cambridge, MA, 2004.
9. Hooyman NR, Kiyak HA. *Social Gerontology: A Multidisciplinary Perspective* (8th ed.). Boston, MA: Allyn & Bacon, 2008.

Chapter 26
Leisure, Health, and Assisted Living

Sarah Burnett-Wolle
Dana Brooks Hart

Assisted living refers to a broad category of supportive housing that spans the gap between independent living and nursing home care. The physical environment, care and amenities, as well as resident autonomy, vary widely. Assisted living enables some people to age in place but it generally serves as a stopgap measure for people who, ultimately, relocate to a nursing home. Residents tend to be homogeneous; most are in their mid-80s, white, educated, female, widowed, and have moderate to high incomes. Nearly all have physical (e.g., difficulty walking, visual impairments), cognitive (e.g., dementia, stroke), or affective (e.g., depression, anxiety) limitations. Assisted living currently fills a small niche in senior housing but its use is likely to expand as the proportion of older adults in the U.S. grows. As people grow older, they tend to develop chronic health conditions. The majority of disability and death in this country is related to these conditions and effective management will be essential to maintain the economic viability of the health care system. While residents spend more than half their lives on leisure, recreation services are minimal and often provided by untrained personnel. To reduce health care costs and extend resident tenure, facilities should offer recreation services that are based on wellness principles including nutrition, physical activity, cognitive maintenance, and psychosocial well-being. Specific programming recommendations regarding these aspects of health promotion and creating meaningful change are provided.

Assisted Living

A menu of supportive housing options is available to people who require some form of assistance. Individually they are called "retirement communities or apartments, senior citizen housing, continuing care retirement facilities (CCRCs), assisted living facilities, staged living communities, and board and care facilities/homes" (1), but collectively they are referred to as assisted living. Assisted living emerged in the late 1970s when some forms of supportive housing could not or did not want to adhere to an extensive set of regulations enacted to improve care in nursing homes (2). Among the characteristics that differentiated assisted living from nursing homes, which increasingly resembled hospitals, was a home-like environment in which residents, sometimes referred to as tenants, had a high degree of freedom. Following a period of slow growth, assisted living expanded rapidly in the 1990s. Today, approximately one million older adults live in over 1100 facilities across the country (2).

The physical environment, care, amenities, and resident autonomy vary widely. Structures range from large single family houses to apartment buildings to purpose-built facilities; ones that are designed to provide assisted living services and often look and function like "nursing home[s] on training wheels" (4, 5). The scope of care and amenities may only include limited supervision by untrained staff, two meals per day, and a common room for socializing (4). However, some facilities offer three meals per day, cleaning/housekeeping, laundry, medication monitoring, limited nursing care, social work, recreation, transportation, dedicated space for crafts and music, walking trails, and pools. Lastly, residents at some facilities have complete autonomy while others are carefully supervised. In sum, it is easier to describe what assisted living is not; the residents are unable to live without support but do not require more than two weeks of 24-hour nursing care. Additionally, physical, occupational, and speech therapy, as well as therapeutic diets are rarely used and generally not available in assisted living (3, 6).

The median length of stay is 20 months (3). However, the median tenure of residents in dementia care units is only 14 months. While 30% of residents live out their lives in assisted living, up to 40% relocate to a nursing home. Most of the residents who move to nursing homes (34%) do so to receive additional care. The remainder do so because assisted living becomes unaffordable. In 2006, the cost was between $26,000 and $42,500 per year and nearly 85% was assumed by residents or their family members. While nursing home care is much more expensive, it cost $53,000 per year in 2004 (1), when residents have few assets these services are paid for by Medicaid (a program supported by taxes).

Assisted Living Consumers

The mean age of assisted living residents is 85 (3). Nearly all, up to 99%, are non-Hispanic white, which is considerably higher than the national average for that age group (6). Residents also tend to have more education than the national average; approximately 48% graduated from high school and 9% earned a Bachelor's degree or more. Three quarters of residents are women and slightly more than 70% are widowed (3). However, these characteristics are far from universal. Among the diverse groups who use assisted living are young and middle age adults with developmental disabilities or mental illness. In some regions of the country, facilities are primarily occupied by people of color (7). Regardless of the demographic characteristics, all assisted living facilities provide support to people with disabilities. Most have mobility impairments; only 23% walk unassisted (3). Many have affective disorders; the incidence ranges between 33% and 38% (3,6). The most common forms are depression and anxiety and more than half take psychotropic medications (6). The affective disorders, as well as aggression, are often associated with dementia. The incidence of dementia ranges widely, between 33% and 67% (3, 6). Similarly, estimates of its severity range widely; 28% to 73% have mild, 18% to 46% have moderate, and 9% to 63% have severe dementia.

The degree of impairment is typically measured by noting impairment in activities of daily living (ADLs) and instrumental activities of daily living (IADLs). ADLs are tasks which are required to maintain health and include bathing, dressing, eating, walking, and transfers (going to and from a chair, bed, and toilet) (1). IADLs are tasks required for independence and include using the telephone, light and heavy housework, meal preparation, shopping, and money management. On average, assisted living residents have two ADL impairments; most need assistance with bathing (68%) and least need assistance with eating (22%) (3). On average they have four IADL impairments; most need assistance with transportation (92%) and least need assistance with the telephone (28%).

Future of Assisted Living

Currently, assisted living fills a small niche in senior housing. Approximately 10% of Medicare recipients (which includes most people in the U.S. over the age of 65) use it; 3% are between the ages of 75 and 84, 7% are age 85 and older (1). However, it has become an important component within the continuum of care and its use is likely to grow in response to population shifts, the cost of medical care, and a disdain for nursing home life. The US population is growing older and the segment that is growing fastest is the 85 and over age group. In 2006, 5.3 million people were in this age group. In 2030, the large group of children born as World War II drew to a close will begin to turn 85. This baby boom is expected to reach its zenith in 2050 when 21 million people will be age 85 and over; nearly four times the figure in 2006. Medical innovations and an emphasis on health promotion may drive the numbers even higher. As people grow older, chronic conditions exert their influence on health and independence. While only 3% of Americans age 65 to 74 have one or more ADL limitation, 23% of those ages 85 and over do (8). A corresponding increase in the number of people who require supportive housing is expected. Currently, the majority of people who are unable to live in their own homes relocate to nursing homes (1). If the move can be postponed, it is an important cost-saving measure since assisted living ($26,000 per year) (3) is half the cost of nursing home care ($53,000 per year) (1). Additionally, taxpayers are responsible for one half the cost of nursing home care (1) while assisted living is primarily paid for by residents and their families (3). Despite the cost, many older adults are willing to spend their own assets on assisted living because nursing home life is so distasteful. To extend tenure in assisted living, many states have created Medicaid waivers to enable some people to remain in place. In 2006, only 8% of these costs were paid for by Medicaid (3) but, in response to the current recession, such programs are being expanded in some states (9).

Public Health and Assisted Living

The development of effective medical treatments for acute illness and infectious disease has altered the leading causes of death in the U.S.; chronic health conditions now top the list (10). More than 60% of deaths are due to three chronic conditions: heart disease, cancer, and stroke. They, along with asthma, chronic bronchitis, diabetes, and arthritis, are the leading causes of disability in this country. To prevent disability and death associated with these conditions, health promotion campaigns and programs often target children and middle age adults. They emphasize smoking cessation, nutritionally balanced diets, adequate exercise, preventative medical care, health education, and stress management. The impact of wellness on public health is remarkable. Changing just three behaviors—smoking, diet, and exercise—can reduce disability and death from chronic conditions by a staggering 35%. While prevention early in life is ideal, even the very old can benefit from a lifestyle based on wellness principles. Although many chronic health conditions may be present, their impact can be reduced and functional independence improved.

In addition to improving the quality of older adults' lives, wellness approaches are necessary for the economic viability of the U.S. health care system. Nearly one third of all health care resources are spent on older adults (11) and 95% are used to treat chronic conditions (10). On average, older adults with no chronic conditions require $4,718 in health care annually while those with five or more require approximately four times as much, $20,334 (1). Given the growth in age-related disabilities, health care spending is expected to grow to 125% of the present level in 2030 (11). This estimate is conservative; it does not take inflation or the cost of new treatments into account. Paying for older adults' care is compounded by a second trend related to age, the number of young people entering the workforce. The ratio of working age people to retirees is likely to decrease from 3:1 today to 2:1 in 2035 (12). Therefore, there will be fewer workers to pay for public health care programs including Medicare and Medicaid. In addition to age-related changes in the population, the U.S. is experiencing unprecedented growth in rates of obesity. Obesity is linked with the presence of diabetes, various cancers, asthma, and osteoarthritis (11). Thus, obesity exacerbates the impact of age-related chronic conditions. In addition to lowering people's quality of life and hastening their deaths, obesity is thought to raise health care costs by 10%. Combined, trends in aging and obesity are likely to have catastrophic effects on the fiscal viability of the U.S. health care system. There will be fewer workers paying the taxes needed to support public health care programs but there will be many more people participating in them and they will be much sicker.

Recreation in Assisted Living

A primary avenue for addressing public health concerns in assisted living is recreation programming. While recreation programs are not mandatory, 92% to 99% of assisted living facilities include wellness activities, social activities, and group outings in the room rate (up to 6% charge an additional fee for them) (11). However, these programs are typically provided by untrained personnel and the quality of programming appears to be poor. One study evaluated recreation programs in 10 assisted living facilities in Wisconsin (13). The authors concluded that, aside from eating and drinking, relatively few structured recreation activities took place and there was little variation among them. Passive activities or sleeping accounted for nearly 33% of daytime hours. In general, "the psychological and social needs of residents were generally not given high priority" by the staff. However, quality recreation programs are commonplace in purpose-built facilities and CCRCs and all should address four aspects of wellness; (a) nutrition, (b) physical activity, (c) cognitive maintenance and (d) psychosocial well-being.

Nutrition

While most nutrition services are outside the realm of recreation, many activities include food and drink, such that the quantity and quality of calories consumed during leisure can play an important role in the lives of residents. Fortunately, the quantity of calories consumed by older adults is less of a concern than it is for other age groups, but rates of obesity are rising among the very old (1). Between 1988 to 1994, only 13% of men and 19% of women were obese, but in 2005 to 2006 the rates were 24% and 25% respectively. It is a risk factor which needs to be addressed. The Center for Disease Control measures diet quality using a composite index which takes fruits, vegetables, grains, protein, and oils into account. Higher scores represent better diets. On average, people age 75 and older score a 68 of 100 possible points indicating that their diets are two thirds of the ideal. Like most younger people, those over the age of 74 need to increase consumption of whole grains, vegetables, legumes, fruits, low fat milk products, and oils from fish, nuts, and seeds while decreasing the consumption of solid fats, saturated fat, sodium, added sugar, and alcohol. Unlike in nursing homes, state regulation of nutrition in assisted living is limited (14). Some facilities take a traditional approach, emphasizing taste, flavor, and appearance of food, and others adhere to wellness principles (15). Food and drinks provided during recreation events are commonly sugar- and salt-laden. Clinicians must consider the degree to which these treats contribute to the quantity and quality of calories consumed as well as hydration. This is especially true for residents whose ability to make sound choices are compromised by cognitive or affective impairments. During recreation, it is difficult to strike a balance between healthful behavior and residents' autonomy regarding nutrition, but, a balanced diet and appropriate hydration can minimize the impact of chronic conditions.

Physical Activity

The very old are unique among adults; they have the largest proportion of discretionary time. Unfortunately, most spend a remarkable amount of time being sedentary. One study suggested that assisted living residents spend 55% of their waking hours on discretionary activities and most, if not all, were sedentary (16). The most common use of discretionary time was watching TV (13%), followed by resting (12%), reading (9%), family interaction (9%), recreation/leisure (6%), friend interaction (5%), radio (1%), and religious activities (0.1%).

The federal government defines adequate exercise as light to moderate activity for 30 or more minutes five or more times a week or vigorous activity for 20 minutes or more three or more times a week (1). The degree to which assisted living residents meet this standard is unknown but less than 10% of people age 85 and over living in the community have adequate leisure-time physical activity. Rates of physical activity among assisted living residents are likely to be even lower due to functional impairments.

While the rates of physical activity among the very old are dismal, nearly all can participate in some form of exercise and even small amounts are very beneficial (10, 11). It helps manage blood pressure, diabetes, obesity, cholesterol, and arthritis pain. Exercise also helps relieve depression, minimize bone loss (thereby reducing fractures), and it appears to reduce falls by 19%. The latter is of particular concern; falls are most common among people age 85 and over and the leading cause of disability and unintentional death, as well as a significant predictor of nursing home admission (8, 10).

Recommendations include obtaining a physician's permission to begin an exercise regimen (10, 11). Traditional activities commonly include walking, Yoga, Tai Chi, and swimming. They are gentle yet effective forms of movement which can easily be adapted to a range of abilities. Participants who are sedentary may begin with brief sessions lasting 10 minutes but should repeat them often. Gradually, duration and intensity should be increased to recommended levels. Sessions should include daily stretching and balance activities. Strength and endurance activities should occur at least two days per week. In addition to providing such programs, clinicians should structure traditional exercise programs by asking residents about their physical activity, helping them to establish specific goals, and following up on the goals. The more effective programs take place in facilities that foster a culture of physical activity by running community-wide campaigns (which may involve residents and staff or, better yet, residents and their families) and improving access. Factors which hinder physical activity and should be addressed include crime, crumbling sidewalks, traffic, potholes, transportation, and caregiving responsibilities.

While traditional exercise may be an efficient method for improving physical activity, a growing body of literature suggests that commitment to such programs is short-lived. To motivate disengaged residents there should be emphasis on desirable social contacts and enjoyable activities, not the number of calories burned in an hour (17). For example, many older adults enjoy gardening and being outdoors. Working on an enjoyable project with a close friend is more likely to result in sustained physical activity than a traditional workout. Physical activity need not be strenuous, but it should take place each day. "Encourage leisure-time" physical activity, it is "an investment with documented cost savings" (10).

Cognitive Maintenance

Cognitive loss was once considered an unavoidable part of old age but a growing body of literature suggests that this assumption is untrue. Some aspects of intellectual development don't peak until people are in their 50s (e.g., acquired knowledge) (18). Furthermore, with practice or remediation, older adults' performance on intellectual tasks can be maintained or improved very late in life. Leisure is the arena of life from which the very old derive cognitive stimulation so the intellectual demands of activities are essential to minimizing the effects of dementia. Specifically, recreation activities that appear to promote cognitive well-being include music, cooking, taking walks, gardening, painting, hand massages, and sensory stimulation (6, 19). An interesting trend in health promotion for seniors is the use of highly structured and sequential programs similar to college courses. The Health and Disability Research Institute and Boston University created a nine-session course to reduce falls (20). In addition to physical activity, the comprehensive program utilized cognitive and affective restructuring techniques to teach participants to manage their fear of falling and correct bad habits. A similar format was used by the Center for Positive Aging at Gulf Coast University. The 10-week course took place in an assisted living facility and included information on dementia and strategies seniors could use to minimize its effects (21).

Psychosocial Well-being

While residents in assisted living may find joy in socializing with one another, the likelihood that these relationships will be emotionally meaningful is remote since there is little time to develop close bonds. Furthermore, residents may actively avoid one another in an attempt to conserve what time and energy they have for the most meaningful relationships, those with close family and old friends. While such behavior was once considered detrimental, a growing body of research suggests the contrary is true (22). Residents' affective well-being appears to be highest if relationships with close family and friends are cultivated, rather than those with other residents. The former are most likely to provide social support and their maintenance is more realistic. Families willingly engage residents via weekly telephone calls and visits (6, 23). While they provide some instrumental and informational support (monitoring care, advocacy, laundry, shopping, maintaining finances, bathing, and dressing), families primarily attend to residents' psychosocial needs "including talking with the resident, holding hands with the resident, reminiscing, and engaging in social activities." To optimize residents' psychosocial well-being, clinicians should foster relationships between residents and their close family members and old friends rather than among one another.

Creating Change

The most difficult part of implementing the preceding wellness principles is creating individual and organizational change. A behavioral systems approach is recommended to bridge this gap. It integrates human interaction, external relationships, and the organizational milieu to make sense of cause and effect relationships (24). The key presuppositions are: (a) organizations are like living things, there is a defined system of input, processes, and output; (b) all people, regardless of age, seek a journey of learning and connectedness; and (c) the context of interactions and activities must be individually meaningful to enhance life's purpose and direction.

Typically, discrepancies among staff, residents, and families emerge in regard to vision, structures, and processes resulting in unmet needs. For example, an assisted living facility may recognize that residents' tenure can be extended if physical fitness is addressed, provide exercise programs, but attract and retain few residents in them. To resolve such conflicts, a simple mental model may be used as a guide to create positive change in behaviors. A unifying premise is that personal behavior change arises from tension between current and ideal states. Successful change occurs when people honestly explore the positive and negative attributes of the current state. As behavioral factors of the current and ideal states are contemplated, a tension develops that intrinsically motivates the person to create desired paths to reach the ideal. The model:

Current State------------------------Ideal State

The purpose of the model is to frame individual or organizational change through three steps (25). First, the conversation begins by asking the following questions: "What is really desired?" and "What could be better?" Second, the conversation converts these vague responses into behavioral statements that the resident and staff can use to establish clear outcomes. Common themes may be similar to wellness principles (e.g., nutrition, physical activity, cognitive maintenance, and psychosocial well-being), however, older adults are more likely to frame them in terms of realizing one's potential, seeking knowledge and wisdom, living a caring and responsible life, attaining spiritual enlightenment, and caring for self and others (26). To gain momentum, the statements must possess two qualities: clarity and meaningfulness. Statements about the ideal state must include language that is honest, clear, tangible, and specific enough so all understand.

Example of refining individual's statements:

- The resident wants to spend time with her family. (vague)
  The resident and her daughter like to garden. When the daughter visits on Saturdays in the spring and summer, they will work in their plot together. (clear)

Example of refining organizational statements:

- Fostering a culture of physical activity is beneficial to the residents. (vague)
- In good weather, residents and staff will participate in a series of local fundraisers that include physical activity such as the American Cancer Society's Walk for Life and the Alzheimer Association's Memory Walk. (clear)

In addition to clarity, it is essential that the statements are compelling and meaningful to the stakeholders. This may be elusive as individuals make meaning for themselves from past and current beliefs, experiences, and perceptions (24). A caretaker seeking to understand and support an individual's ideal state would seek to explore the meaning in more specific terms including the following six modalities:

1. Symbols: Exploring with residents the meaning of language, gestures, and behaviors they use to communicate.
2. Empirical data: Understanding the key foundational facts and theories individuals hold as truths in analyzing their world.
3. Aesthetics: Learning what expressions of caring, beauty, and interests an individual finds attractive and stimulating.
4. Knowledge: Understanding an individual's perception of past experiences and how the individual interprets new information based on past experiences and beliefs.
5. Ethics: Exploring the individual's standards and beliefs of moral and ethical behavior.
6. Spiritual: Understanding the individual's holistic beliefs and philosophy of life, mental and physical and spiritual wellness.

Periodic assessment and understanding of these modalities can reveal the importance of previous hobbies, relationships, significant emotional events, and the value of memories and meaning to rewarding futures. Third, once meaningful ideal states are clearly identified, the team can readily craft strategies to guide change accordingly. This systems approach integrates stakeholders so that they have a clear direction, uniform applied practice, and a system of improvement to achieve desired states.

Summary

Assisted living refers to a broad category of supportive housing that spans the gap between independent living and nursing home care. It enables some people to age in place, but often serves as a stop-gap measure for people who ultimately relocate to a nursing home. Most residents are in their mid 80s, white, educated, female, widowed, or have moderate to high incomes but all have functional limitations. While assisted living is currently used by a small portion of older adults, its use is likely to expand as the proportion of older adults with disabilities grows. The majority of disability in the U.S. is due to chronic health conditions and effective management of these conditions by employing wellness principles will be essential to minimizing the use of expensive and undesirable nursing homes. While recreation is a primary vehicle for instituting wellness principles, the quantity and quality of recreation services in assisting living is poor. To extend resident tenure and decrease health care costs, facilities should offer recreation services that are based on wellness principles including nutrition, physical activity, and cognitive and psychosocial well-being. To create individual and organizational change a behavioral systems approach is recommended.

References

1. Federal Interagency Forum on Aging-Related Statistics. *Older Americans 2008: Key Indicators of Well-Being*. U.S. Government Printing Office: Washington DC, 2008.
2. Wilson KB. Historical evolution of assisted living in the United States, 1979 to the present. *Gerontologist* 2007;**47**:8–22.
3. Assisted Living Federation of America. *Overview of the Assisted Living Industry*. Assisted Living Federation of America: Alexandria, VA, 2006.
4. Stone RI, Reinhard SC. The place of assisted living in long-term care and related service systems. *Gerontologist* 2007;**47**:23–32.
5. Kafka B. *Priority components for inclusion in an integrated managed care system*. CMS New Freedom Initiative Conference: Access to Community Living: Promoting Independence and Choice, Baltimore MD, 2007.
6. Hyde J, Perez R, Forester, B. Dementia and assisted living. *Gerontologist* 2007;**47**:51–67.
7. Hernandez M, Newcomer R. Assisted living and special populations: What do we know about differences in use and potential access barriers? *Gerontologist* 2007;**47**:110–117.
8. Centers for Disease Control and Prevention and National Center for Health Statistics. *NCHS data on older adult health* 2005. http://www.cdc.gov/nchs/data/factsheets/olderadulthlth.pdf. Accessed January 3, 2009.
9. New York State Governor's Office. *Governor Patterson announces $175 million in heal NY grants to support long-term care reform* 2009. http://www.state.ny.us/governor/press/press_0513091.html. Accessed August 8, 2009.
10. Centers for Disease Control and Prevention and The Merck Company Foundation. *The State of Aging and Health in America 2007*. http://www.cdc.gov/aging/saha.htm. Accessed January 3, 2009.
11. Agency for Healthcare Research and Quality and the Centers for Disease Control. *Physical Activity and Older Americans: Benefits and Strategies* 2002. http://www.ahrq.gov/ppip/activity.htm. Accessed February 10, 2009.
12. Social Security Administration. *The future of social security* 2009. http://www.ssa.gov/pubs/10055.pdf. Accessed July 30, 2009.
13. Kuhn D, Kasayka RE, Lechner C. Behavioral observations and quality of life among persons with dementia in 10 assisted living facilities. *Am J Alzheimers Dis Other Demen* 2002;**17**:291–298.

14. Chao SY, Hagisavas V, Mollica R, Dwyer J. Time for assessment of nutrition services in assisted living facilities. *J Nutr Elder* 2003;**23**:41–55.
15. Chao SY, Dwyer JT, Houser RF, Jacques P, Tennstedt S. Experts stress both wellness and amenity aspects of food and nutrition services in assisted living facilities for older adults. *J Am Diet Assoc* 2008;**108**:1654–1661.
16. Pruchno RA, Rose MS. Time use by frail older people in different care settings. *Journal of Applied Gerontology* 2002;**21**:5–23.
17. Godbey G, Burnett-Wolle S, Chow H-W. New ideas for promoting physical activity among middle age and older adults. *Journal of Physical Education, Recreation, & Dance* 2007;**78**:22–26.
18. Schaie KW. *Intellectual development in adulthood: The Seattle longitudinal study*. Cambridge University Press: New York, 1996.
19. Alzheimer's Association. *Dementia care practice recommendations for assisted living residences and nursing homes* 2006. Retrieved April 5, 2009 from http://www.iahsa.com/Content/PDFs/2007/2_AlzAssnRecEndOfLifeCare.pdf
20. Health & Disability Research Institute of Boston University. *A matter of balance* 2007. Retrieved April 5, 2009 from http://www.bu.edu/hdr/products/balance/manual.html
21. Fitzsimmons S, Buettner LL. Health promotion for the mind, body, and spirit: A college course for older adults with dementia. *Am J Alzheimers Dis Other Demen* 2003;**18**:282–290.
22. Burnett-Wolle S, Godbey G. Refining research on older adults' leisure: Implications of selection, optimization, and compensation and socioemotional selectivity theories. *J Leisure Res* 2007;**39**:498–514.
23. Gaugler JE, Kane RL. Families and assisted living. *Gerontologist* 2007;**47**:83–99.
24. Fritz R. *Your Life as Art*. Newfane Press: Newfane, VT, 2003.
25. Senge, PM. *The Fifth Discipline: The Art and Practice of the Learning Organization*. Random House: London, 2006.
26. Prochaska JO, Norcross JC. *Systems of Psychotherapy: A Transtheoretical Analysis 6th ed.* Thomson/Brooks/Cole: Australia, 2007.

Chapter 27

Women, Health, and Leisure: A Lot like Music-Making

Karla A. Henderson
Wendy J. Brown

Examining leisure, health, and women is a lot like making music. Each of the individual musicians plays her or his part, but the music is held together by the relationship of the sounds to one another. Some of the instruments that musicians play, like violins, are central to the orchestra and affect the music in a dominant way. Other instruments, like bassoons and oboes, provide elements that make the music interesting and unique. Brass instruments provide flash and color, while the percussion impart the pulse that holds the orchestra together. When an orchestra plays a symphony, just as when issues about health, leisure, and women are examined, different instruments (i.e., aspects of lived everyday lives of women) take the dominant role at different times. Individual factors might represent the stringed instruments that often lead the way, with varying influences of social (e.g., woodwinds) and physical (i.e., brass) environments providing aspects that make music and women's lives whole. The percussion provides the foundation for the common musical experience just as the foundation for examining women's lives is the experiences of women in a gendered world. No one instrument can make the quality of music that all instruments taken together can. Similarly, in examining health and leisure for women, many contributions must be considered.

Evidence is clear that leisure influences health by providing stress reduction and coping mechanisms that result in outcomes such as positive self-constructs, elevated moods, reduced anxiety, increased happiness and life satisfaction, lower rates of depression, and less loneliness. In relation to physical health, although most of the earlier studies of the benefits of physical activity came from studies of men, compelling evidence from large cohort studies shows that regular physical activity also reduces the risk of heart attack, stroke, diabetes, falls and fractures, and some cancers in women (1).

However, women's access to opportunities for engaging in active leisure has been historically different from that of men (2). The purpose of this chapter is to explore the music making that describes girls' and women's leisure and health.

Music from the Past

History provides a context for understanding more about where women have been and where they are going. Women have been perceived throughout most of Western history as the weaker sex (2). The irony of this perception is that today women on average have a longer life expectancy than men. Nevertheless, this historical perception was based on biological structure, since most women had narrower and smaller shoulders as well as broader pelvic girdles than most men. The Victorian image of womanhood included passiveness, obedience to husband, and attractiveness. Although this ideal was central for upper-class women, even working-class women were expected to maintain gentility outside the physical work that was the only source of income for many women. Avoiding exercise, maintaining a pale complexion, and hiding any type of muscular strength fitted the idealized woman of the Victorian era regardless of class. Physical activity was something to be avoided at all costs. Medical researchers at this time also suggested that physical activities were not good for women because they increased the possibilities of *pelvic disturbances*. Because women were perceived as mentally inferior, physical activity was also thought to create emotional strain. Although many of the restrictions on women's leisure were lifted in the latter half of the 20th century, some of these belief systems linger. Thus, many women today still have obstacles to overcome in their efforts to pursue healthy leisure options.

One common way to examine models of health behaviors is to use social ecological models. These models are particularly useful for examining health behaviors and their health outcomes because women's lives are influenced by individual or personal factors as well as by social and environmental factors (e.g., home situation, community opportunities, gender stereotypes, and policies) that facilitate or constrain women's physical activity experiences. Ecological models take into account the aspects outside the individual girl or woman that influence behavior. They negate the idea that, "If a person wants to be healthy, all she needs to do is motivate herself." For most girls and women, behavior is far more complex, just as making music in a symphony orchestra requires more than just the violins.

Playing in Tune and in Time

Musicians have the same purpose in interpreting the music for a symphony. Describing the relationships among the players, similar to examining health and leisure for particular groups of women, may be one way to better understand how music is made. In the following sections, we describe salient issues regarding health and leisure for girls and young women, adult women, older women, and women with differing cultural and religious backgrounds. We use several sources, but many examples come from the Australian Longitudinal Study of Women's Health, also known as *Women's Health Australia* (3, 4), to illustrate the relationships between physical activity and health. This longitudinal study began in 1996 and is one of few studies around the world that includes three distinct life-stage cohorts of women:18–23 years, 24–50 years, and 70–75 years at the start of the study in 1996. First, however, we describe the physical activity of girls.

Girls and Young Women

Girls and young women have more opportunities today than ever before to be physically active and thus, healthier. However, a study by the University of Minnesota's Tucker Center for Research on Girls and Women in Sport (5) showed that although girls in the U.S. are participating in sports in record numbers, their participation in physical activity outside organized sports is declining, especially as they move from childhood into adolescence. Despite the breadth of knowledge specific to girls' physical activity and the variety of positive outcomes that can accrue through participation, many barriers, stereotypes, and gender inequities remain in place that limit girls' involvement. Many girls, especially in lower socioeconomic situations, fail to meet minimal standards of physical activity needed to accrue developmental as well as health benefits. Many young women are completely sedentary. The Tucker report suggested that outdated stereotypical standards of femininity and masculinity seem to continue to influence how activity is perceived, even though the Victorian era ended decades ago.

Another source of positive news is a study conducted in the UK (6) with adolescent girls. The researchers found that many active young women saw physical activity as a space for leisure and that being active, albeit not necessarily in sports, was a way to enhance their well-being. These findings are important because not all girls have the opportunity, nor do they desire, to participate in elite sport. Having a range of opportunities was important to these girls and they indicated that physical activity had multidimensional meanings. Involvement in activities that were challenging was more important than competition. The "fun" factor was required, and being physically active could be seen as a solo experience or an opportunity for social leisure time. In some ways, these girls redefined physical activity for themselves by resisting competitive performance in exchange for developing a more proactive sense of self. The information about girls is important since these young women will likely carry the experiences and attitudes of their youth into adulthood.

Adult Women

Over the last fifty years, adult women have made numerous gains in leisure opportunities (2). Yet they continue to experience many traditional constraints to participation. In the U.S., women consistently have lower rates of leisure time physical activity than men (7). However, the situation in some countries may be changing. For example, data from *Women's Health Australia* show that physical activity levels in middle-age women have increased steadily since the beginning of the 21st century. The gap between women and men's physical activity may be closing especially in middle- and older-age women. Although the disparities may be changing, however, the prevalence of sedentary living for all adults remains high.

Researchers (8) have concluded that for women in general, several sociodemographic factors seem to influence physical activity. Definitions of physical activity, however, sometimes make it difficult to describe these relationships. For example, education level is usually positively associated with physical activity since women with more education are more likely to be physically active. However, since walking is now regarded as a legitimate form of activity in terms of gaining health benefits, women with lower levels of education may gain these benefits by relying more on active transport in the absence of ownership or access to motor vehicles. Concomitantly, while being employed has generally been associated with more sport and exercise involvement, employment creates salient time pressures for many women. Juggling roles in paid and unpaid work often allows less time for active leisure.

Women's marital status has been inconsistently associated with physical activity. Sometimes marriage and family responsibilities constrain women's leisure opportunities, but in other cases these social relationships with family facilitate these opportunities (2). Data from *Women's Health Australia* indicated that young adult women (i.e., women in their 20s) who got married or started to live with someone in a *de facto* relationship, were more likely to experience declines in physical activity over time than women who remained single (4). Similarly, women who had their first or second baby were more likely to report declining levels of physical activity than women who did not have children. These prospective data add strength to the earlier cross-sectional reports that women with young children are less active than women who do not have children.

Great variation, however, exists among women with young children. One of the critiques of the "prescriptions" offered for girls and women to be physically active is the assumption that in addition to being a good spouse/partner, mother, community contributor, or employed worker, a *good woman* must be physically fit and active. For some women, this expectation may become an additional stressor to an already overstressed life. Thus, promoting physically active lifestyles for some women may simply add to their feelings of guilt and inadequacy, which further raises stress levels and does not necessarily contribute to positive mental health. The irony is that stress is often indicated as a reason not to be physically active and yet, physical activity has a positive relationship to stress reduction (8). Data from the young cohort from *Women's Health Australia,* however, showed that women who experienced distressing harassment at work were more likely to also report increasing levels of physical activity. They seemed to be using activity as a coping strategy for stressful life events (4).

Perceived health and health status have some relationship to physical activity. Unfortunately, women who are not in the best health generally are less physically active, and yet being physically active promotes better health. Data from *Women's Health Australia* corroborate this idea with clear relationships found between current, previous, and habitual physical activity and indicators of depressive symptoms. In prospective analyses, women who were in the lowest physical activity category at baseline, but who then increased their activity levels to meet current guidelines, were less likely to report depressive symptoms five years later than women whose activity levels remained very low (9).

Adult women may face other personal issues related to positive health behaviors. Research has shown a consistent positive relationship between self-efficacy (i.e., confidence in one's abilities to do specific activities) and physical activity levels (8). As expected, women who perceive greater benefits and fewer barriers or constraints are more likely to be physically active. Lack of time is one example of a barrier that is often universally described among women (2). However, this perception of lack of time is often related to other constraints such as household duties, not feeling entitled to prioritize physical activity, or environmental constraints.

Social support and environments are key for adult women and their involvement in physical activity. Social support can come from friends, family, or other peers. All individual and social behaviors, however, occur in physical environments that influence women's lives in both direct and indirect ways. Examples of these environments include transportation availability, safety in neighborhoods, weather conditions, and access to opportunities to be active. Policy issues that impact women include legislation such as Title IX in the U.S. that provided numerous sport equity programs for girls, although equity has not yet been achieved. Even issues such as wages impact women. If women do not have earning power, they may not have the time or the resources to be as physically active as they might desire. Many of these issues influencing adult women also impact older women.

Older Women

Researchers have found that age is negatively related to physical activity (8). Lack of social support, poor facilities, and concerns about safety have been identified as key constraints to physical activity among older women. Many older women who did not grow up in a era of equal opportunity for sports participation and who were impacted by the Victorian ideal that strenuous activity was not good for women may be less physically active. The older women (i.e., women who were 70–75 at baseline and are now 83–88 years) in *Women's Health Australia* have, however, provided data that challenge the negative stereotypes of declining well-being at this life-stage despite declines in their own and family members' health. As expected, their physical activity levels were lower than the young and middle-age women, but 89% of the women reported gardening and 17% reported belonging to a sporting club at age 70–75 years (10). Although past activity may be a predictor of future behavior, and girls who do not get an opportunity to be physically active in their younger days may be less likely to be active later in life, examples do exist of older women becoming and/or remaining active in later life in competitive sports. Dionigi (11) found that older adults, including both men and women, can use sport as not only a way to be physically active, but also as a way to resist contradictory messages about what it means to get older and be physically unhealthy.

Culture and Religion

In addition to life stage, women around the world are influenced in their activity by a variety of cultural implications related to race, ethnicity, and religion. These influences may be reflected cross-culturally or intraculturally. In the U.S., for example, white women are generally more active than women of color (8). In Australia, women born in Asia and the Middle East are less active than their Australian-born counterparts (12).

Cultural expectations and familial roles can reduce the sense of entitlement to leisure and physical activity. For example, religion and culture sometimes dictate what women are "allowed" to do in their societies (13). Family expectations are greater in some cultures than others. Women may also be influenced by the lack of access to opportunities outside the home. Since low socioeconomic status is often a characteristic of some minority groups, issues of access regarding time and money may be limiting.

Although the prevalence of physical activity among some minority groups is generally low, examples of high-level sporting success among women from indigenous or traditionally disadvantaged backgrounds is evident. For example, Cathy Freeman is an Australian indigenous woman who was victorious in the 400m in the 2000 Sydney Olympics. The African-American sisters, Venus and Serena Williams, have both won the U.S. Open Tennis Championship as well as numerous other competitions and their power and finesse have redefined women's tennis in the 21st century. These successes illustrate that with access to appropriate training, "minority" women can achieve at high levels of competitive sport.

We cannot go into great detail about the influence of culture worldwide related to women, leisure, and health, but the unique and important constraints that exist for some women outside the dominant Western culture must be acknowledged. Further, we recognize that many other issues such as disability may influence women's health.

The Final Movement of the Symphony

The previous section of this chapter has provided a summary of some of the antecedent and intervening issues that impact women, health, and leisure. Everyone agrees that being physically active for women is important and beneficial. We would be remiss, however, if we did not present some additional thoughts about the complexity of examining women and health.

Physical activity is sometimes associated directly with being a "normal" weight or having an idealized body image, which usually means being smaller rather than bigger. This issue is complex. On one hand, definitions of beauty as they pertain to weight may be misleading for some women, and the assumption that being physically active is related mainly to beauty may be counterproductive. On the other hand, maintaining a healthy body weight (i.e., defined by Body Mass Index within a certain range) is generally associated with health benefits. Although avoiding weight gain has aesthetic value in most Western societies, the health benefits must be kept at the forefront even though girls and women may be motivated to be physically active for many reasons.

Regardless of the limitations, physical activity has the potential to enhance health for women at all life stages and in social and cultural contexts. In addition, leisure experiences that are physically active may be empowering for women and provide a site of resistance to dominant ideologies that subordinate women. The contributions that active leisure can make to individual health as well as to the public health of all women are many. Almost all women know that physical activity can be beneficial, but challenges exist. Just as making the most beautiful music requires musicians to play together, providing an ecological environment where girls' and women's physical activity can flourish will lead to healthier lives and improved quality of life for women, their families, and the greater community.

References

1. Brown WJ, Burton NW, Rowan PJ. Updating the evidence on physical activity and health in women. *Am J Prev Med* 2007;**33/5**:404–411.
2. Henderson KA, Bialeschki MD, Shaw SM, Freysinger VJ. *Both Gains and Gaps: Feminist Perspectives on Women's Leisure.* Venture Publishing, Inc.: State College, PA, 1996.
3. Australian Longitudinal Study of Women's Health. http://www.alswh.org.au. Accessed March 14, 2009.
4. Brown WJ, Heesch KC, Miller YD (2009). Life-events and changing physical activity patterns in women at different life stages. *Annals of Behavioral Medicine* 2009. DOI 1007/512160-009-9099-2.
5. Tucker Center for Research on Girls and Women in Sport. *The 2007 Tucker Center Research Report developing physically active girls: An evidence-based multidisciplinary approach.* http://cehd.umn.edu/tuckercenter/projects/TCRR/default.html. Accessed December 9, 2008.
6. Brooks F, Magnusson J. Physical activity as leisure: The meaning of physical activity for the health and well-being of adolescent women. *Health Care Women Int* 2007;**28**:69–87.
7. Brownson RC, Boehmer TK, Luke DA. Declining rates of physical activity in the United States: What are the contributors? *Annu Rev Publ Health* 2004;**26/4**:421–443.
8. Eyler AE, Wilcox S, Matson-Koffman D, Evenson KR, Sanderson B, Thompson J, et al. Correlates of physical activity among women from diverse racial/ethnic groups. *J Womens Health Gend Based Med* 2002;**11/3**:239–251.
9. Brown WJ, Ford J, Burton NW, Marshall AL, Dobson A. Prospective study of physical activity and depressive symptoms in mid age women. *Am J Prev Med* 2005;**29/4**:265–72.
10. Feldman S, Byles J, Mishra G, Powers J. The health and social needs of recently widowed older women in Australia. *Australas J Ageing* 2002;**21/3**:135–140.
11. Dionigi R. Competitive sport as leisure in later life: Negotiation, discourse, and aging. *Leisure Sci* 2006;**28**:181–196.
12. Brown WJ, Mishra G, Lee C, Bauman A. Leisure time physical activity in Australian women: relationship with well-being and symptoms. *Res Q Exerc Sport* 2000;**71/3**:206–216.
13. Arab-Moghaddam N, Henderson KA, Sheikholeslami R. Women's leisure and constraints to participation: Iranian perspectives. *J Leisure Res* 2007;**39/1**:109–126.

Chapter 28
Leisure, Health, and Males

Judy Kruger
Geoffrey Godbey

Overview

A number of both evolutionary and cultural factors must be considered
when examining the relationship between health and leisure among males.
While many health issues are similar regardless of gender, males have
several unique advantages and liabilities, and these differences have only
recently been considered. Because gender may explain some of the predict-
able differences in leisure behavior, a little grounding in both the biological
and social characteristics is necessary. In this chapter, we will discuss the
relationship between health and leisure among males, and the factors that
influence their patterns of leisure.

Evolutionary Heritage

Many of the differences between males and females are the products of
evolutionary heritage—traits carried in the genes rather than created by
the ways they are raised. Human male fetuses, for example, are much
more physically active prenatally than females (1). This greater need for
physical activity continues throughout life. Studies show that, universally,
young girls and boys prefer different toys—boys choose trains, cars, guns,
and girls choose dolls. The same holds true when baby vervet monkeys
are given their choice of playthings—male monkeys choose trucks and
other action toys and females choose dolls (2). Many researchers conclude, "There's plenty of evidence over the whole life that males have a
more vulnerable biology. They succumb to all sorts of things faster than
females" (3). Similarly, male babies seem to be less empathetic than
female babies, and males have been found to respond less intensely to the
sound of another human in distress than females. Since females have been
the primary caregivers for eons, they appear to be more sensitive to the
environment and to others around them. In fact, females have a stronger
sense of smell, can hear high-pitched sounds better, and are more sensitive
to touch than males.

Males are on average 17% larger and have more physical strength
than females. The influence of physical size and strength has been associated with perceived control. However, physical power may be overrated

in terms of control. According to Pulitzer Prize winning science writer Diane Blum, "Women seem to have developed a powerful emotional advantage over men. They use emotional response to control relations and the use of language and withdrawal of affection or silence to out manipulate men" (4). Archeologist Donald Grason says men are simply more naturally inclined than females to gamble with their lives (5). Traditionally, males were the providers for their families. They were the nomads who ventured off into the unknown and hunted wild animals; and females were the one's who stayed close to home, tended to the children, cooked food, and gathered firewood.

While culture plays a role in shaping the masculinization of male leisure, so, too, does the genetic endowment of males and females. We need to also consider historical role of man, and the numerous forms of power that males have wielded as a result of genetic endowment. Historically, and in many developing nations, males dominate—often by physical force. One must ask what constitutes dominance if the denominators do not live as long as those dominated, are disproportionately the victims of violent crime, take the most dangerous jobs, are more likely to engage in risky behavior, participate in violent crime, consume higher quantities of unhealthy food and drink, and have less social support. Today, however, in modern nations, the question of domination seems much more complex, because males remain dominant in the political arena and, in the workplace, yet still have more "freedom" during leisure.

Hormones, Sex, and Marriage

Lots of male-female difference may be explained by testosterone levels. Although both genders have some of this hormone, males have about 10 times more than females. High levels of testosterone often are characterized by large body size, lots of facial and body hair, and the tendency to engage in rule-breaking behavior. Low levels of testosterone have been characterized by smaller body frame, more refined facial features, and a passive attitude. "There's a solid consensus among scientists that, in humans, this is the hormone which, at least in the beginning, separates the boys from the girls" (6). A male's level of testosterone is extraordinarily sensitive to the environment, rising when challenged or filled with sexual desire and lowering when defeated. Testosterone not only increases aggressive and competitive behavior in men, it increases levels of "LDL" harmful cholesterol, raising a male's chances of getting heart disease or stroke. Females, up until menopause, are protected by high levels of estrogen and progesterone from heart disease, stroke, and lower levels of LDL (7). However, with increasing age, the gender difference is reduced as this female sex hormones decrease.

Life situations also influence hormone levels. Testosterone tends to decrease with increasing age, but fluctuates depending on certain life stresses such as an argument or dispute. If tension rises in marriage, so does testosterone; and in a stable and happy marriage, testosterone decreases. Over time, research has shown that in monogamous cultures, the evolutionary difference in hormone levels decrease in males and this is reflected in the normalization of relative size of males and females 98). Females on average are taller in the 21st century compared to females born in the 20th century.

In terms of marriage, males with high testosterone levels are less likely to marry, or stay married. Moreover, males and females tend to have a different focus in terms of what is desirable in a mate. In a 33-country study, both males and females stated that they wanted kindness and intelligence first in an ideal mate. Men rated youth and beauty next, while women rated wealth, strength, and stability, often showing up with a preference for older men (9).

Life Expectancy and Illness

Males live for significantly shorter period than females, although the gap in life expectancy is declining somewhat. In 2003, the life expectancy gap was 5.3 years in the U.S. and 3.3 years for the world (10).

In modern society, women tend to outlive men and the leading cause of death is no longer infectious disease or acute illness, but chronic disease. Among men, the top 5 health concerns are heart disease, cancer (prostate and lung), cardiovascular disease, stroke, and depression. Overall, males have 5 times the risk of heart disease as women.

Although access to medical care has improved over the years, males are less likely than females to visit a physician or to participate in recommended health behaviors. Taking immediate action can reduce a person's risk for most chronic diseases. Overall, females are more cautious and proactive about their health, and make more use of health care services, perhaps because they have been regarded as the custodian of health for their families, as well as themselves.

Males are also less careful about what they eat, and when selecting foods for themselves, they eat more fatty red meats, eat more take-out and convenience foods, desserts, and drink more alcohol. The food choices selected by men have contributed to problems, like heart disease, stroke, diabetes, and some types of cancer. High-fat, high-carbohydrate foods also contribute to overweight and obesity–in addition to many other problems such as back pain, arthritis pain, and gall stones (11).

Males are generally less cautious and proactive on almost every health issue including preventing skin cancer by protecting their skin from the sun. They also have injury rates three times higher than females. Males are more likely to pursue risk-taking behaviors, such as taking illegal drugs, engaging in dangerous forms of leisure such as driving fast and recklessly, and committing violent acts (12). These liabilities may shorten their life, as does taking on dangerous and dirty jobs, exploring the world, and going to war.

> "For every age group, male mortality is higher than that
> for females, life expectancy is lower for men, men tend to
> use primary health services less than women, are more
> likely to delay help-seeking when ill and are more likely to
> adopt health damaging or "risky" behaviors, for example
> smoking, drinking, violence, fast driving" (13).

Data from the National Center for Health Statistics (10) suggest that males under 65 are 4 times more likely to commit suicide than women, and are systematically more likely to be the victims of violence than females. Males are, for example, almost 4 times more likely to be murdered, and more than 3 times more likely to be the victims of homicide than females.

Males and Labor (Paid and Unpaid)

Many of the health problems males experience can be traced back to the type of occupation men typically engage in. Males continue to be the main breadwinners in the North American households. Males continue to earn more money than females; sometimes because the pay offsets the health risk consequences on the job. For example, coal miners, lumberjacks, skyscraper window washers are high risk occupations often filled primarily by males and are responsible for the high injury and death statistics. Since one-third of married females now earn more than their husbands, in the future, male expectations about being the principal breadwinner may change.

The selection of one's occupational role influences the amount of time one has for leisure. Historically, both males and females worked on farms doing various chores from sunrise to sunset. Both sexes worked long hours. During the Industrial Revolution, however, males left their farms to work in factories. Factory life replaced land ownership, with money as the basis of wealth. Because men received the money, this gave them a kind of control over women they had not had previously. In terms of unpaid work, males spent less time less in housework and child-rearing than women. To date, this division of labor is slowly changing, particularly with the equal rights movement which lobbies for equality in terms of occupational role and pay for women. However, females still tend to do more housework than men, but the difference minimizes as women work longer hours and earn greater pay.

Male Leisure Patterns and Motives

The term "leisure" has historically been used as a concept to describe the way of life in a minority of privileged males in ancient Athens. It was a concept applied to the elite, and not possible in a democracy. During the Industrial Revolution, leisure was redefined by the factory time clock, each blowing of the factory whistle indicated the start and end of the work day. Once the work day was over, males had more "free time" to engage in drinking, which often included gambling, sports, and prostitution. In general, because females didn't work for pay or, more often, worked part-time or temporarily in low paying servant-type jobs, there was less distinction between work and non-work time. Also, females typically engaged in most unpaid work. Females therefore had fewer leisure options—although socializing at church, reading, home crafts, and shopping were common ways they spent free time (14).

Today, the differentiation between male and female leisure is not as great and we can see this by examining time use surveys, in which individuals record the beginning and end time of all daily activities incurred over a 24-hour day. Three studies done at ten-year intervals show that the way that males and females spent their time has become more similar (see Table 28.1). This trend is likely to continue as more females spend time in traditionally male activities, such as paid work, sport, and travel (15).

Males are generally more competitive and achievement oriented in their leisure behavior. Part of this reflects their evolutionary heritage, and reinforcement of the need for competition by society. Males are encouraged to engage in risk-taking during leisure, to win and to achieve, often regardless of personal cost. Thus, the fact that more than one-third of high school football players are hurt sufficiently so they have to sit out one or more games during the season seems "normal."

> "Our unconscious investment in men's disposability is reflected in our institutions' absence of educating men about their personal safety needs. Thus men die sooner of all 10 leading causes of death" (16).

Perhaps the flip side of this problem is that males have had more freedom to travel, to explore multiple occupations, engage in high-risk behaviors, and ignore problems in family or household responsibilities. Because their role and responsibilities impact their leisure options, they have been raised to think that to achieve and succeed, they need to be recognized, and that this recognition will earn them love and praise.

Table 28.1 Time Diary Data Showing How Males and Females Spend Their Time Over a 30-Year Period

	1965	1975	1985	1995	30-year summary 1995–1965*
Activity					
Total Free	1.04	1.01	1.03	1.09	Same ⇔
Travel	1.36	1.27	1.13	1.08	More ⇑
Contracted Time					
Work	2.50	2.10	1.70	1.40	More ⇑
Commute	2.60	2.30	1.70	1.45	More ⇑
Committed Time					
Housework	0.18	0.31	0.50	0.56	More ⇑
Child care	0.27	0.31	0.29	0.32	Same ⇔
Shopping	0.73	0.65	0.67	0.61	Less ⇓
Personal Time					
Sleep	0.98	0.96	0.99	0.97	Same ⇔
Meals	1.21	1.18	1.08	1.05	More ⇑
Groom	0.78	0.88	0.87	0.85	More ⇑
Free Time					
Education	2.70	1.50	1.30	1.39	More ⇑
Religion	0.67	0.63	0.57	0.62	Same ⇔
Organizations	0.79	0.66	0.75	1.04	More ⇑
Events	1.50	1.00	1.00	1.16	More ⇑
Visiting	0.82	0.96	1.06	0.97	More ⇑
Sports	2.60	2.90	1.90	1.70	More ⇑
Hobbies	0.58	0.57	0.85	1.11	More ⇑
Communication	0.56	0.78	0.78	0.78	More ⇑
TV	1.28	1.12	1.09	1.11	More ⇑
Read	1.24	0.91	0.90	0.95	More ⇑
Stereo	1.45	1.19	1.66	1.76	Less ⇓

* Indicator of gender homogeneity.

International Comparison of Leisure

Patterns of leisure have been studied from an international perspective and it seems clear that participation in nature-based recreation, sports, and cultural activities generally have a positive impact on males in terms of mental and physical health.

International comparisons are useful to illustrate different leisure patterns. One study by Gauthier and Smeeding found that America ranked third highest in terms of the number of hours engaged in passive leisure activities (watching television, reading) after Japan and Finland (17). They also examined active leisure activities and found that in the Netherlands, men devote the largest amount of time to unpaid work, hobbies, and sports—but American men ranked almost last. Using data from the Behavioral Risk Factor Surveillance System from 1988 to 2007, national U.S. trends show the pattern of physical inactivity among males has declined gradually over time. Although it is not clear if American men pursue leisure activities at a lesser rate than other nationalities, it is common for the amount of time spent in active leisure to decrease, and for physical inactivity rates to increase within increasing age. Traditionally, however, the prevalence of physical inactivity is lowest among young men (aged 18–24 years) and highest among older men (aged 65 years).

Social Behavior

Socializing plays a huge role in most forms of leisure. In terms of relationships, males are more likely to be socially isolated than females, which can have several negative health consequences. It is well documented that women, regardless of marital status, are more likely to have wider connections to friends and family than men. Women are more likely to seek relationship when problem solving and develop stable supportive friendships across the lifespan. For instance, playing cards, for females, may be more about being with friends than winning the game, whereas for males, socialization may be secondary to the activity at hand. See Table 28.2, which describes friendship patterns in males and females. Males often seek out relationships at work, in social settings such as bars, coffee shops, and sporting organizations. These relationships develop over time and provide social support, but are often less stable and enduring. Through the commitment of marriage or a life partner, males often experience their deepest relationship, and married men benefit from their social arrangement, especial with increased age. Upon the dissolution of their marriage, whether from death or divorce, men often are faced with developing new, or maintaining existing social networks (18).

Table 28.2 Friendship Patterns in Males and Females

Female friendships are characterized by:	Male friendships are characterized by:
• "connectedness" • Intimacy—face to face • Mutual disclosure, openness • Focus on talk • Context—home	• "separateness" • Sociability—side by side • Self-disclosure is rare • Focus on activity • Context—workplace, coffee shop/pub, sports center or religious institution

Certainly, these characteristics reflect traditional male values of control, achievement, independence, and task-orientation rather than social values. Socialization also clearly is important to the ways in which males and females learn to play. Parents and school teachers reinforce male and female differences. For example, in the school band, there are instruments that seem socially prescribed for girls (e.g., the flute) and those for boys (e.g., drums). Our culture continues to teach males during leisure and elsewhere, that being in control, always having an answer to problems, never needing help, and accomplishing tasks individually, using violence when necessary, is desirable. The violence observed on television, in video games and at the movies may contribute to this, although the amount of impact is still uncertain.

"In summary, these longitudinal studies show a small, but often statistically significant, long-term relationship between viewing television violence in childhood and later aggression, especially in late adolescence and early adulthood. Some evidence suggests that more aggressive children watch more violence, but the evidence is stronger that watching media violence is a precursor of increased aggression" (19).

Physical Activity During Leisure

Activity pattern choices help us understand leisure patterns among males. Results from the 2003–2005 American Time Use Survey finds only 21.4% of males and 15.7% of females participated in sports, exercise or active recreation on a given day. Of those who do, males participate for 1.96 hours on average and females for 1.39 hours. One study examined participation in specific leisure activities among men and found the most common types of recreation activities were: fishing, camping, and hiking (20). They also found that the most common type of sports activities were basketball, baseball, and soccer; and for exercise, the most common activities were running, cycling, and swimming.

Leisure activities should be encouraged because it makes an important contribution to health. The type of leisure activity males select may be based on a combination of factors such as time, access to equipment, access to a fitness facility, open spaces (e.g., basketball court), or outdoor wilderness. In addition, the amount of time males spend in leisure may be affected by their life stage (e.g., energy levels), and responsibilities (e.g., work, family). Regardless of the leisure activity selected, some activity is better than none. However, to impact health, males should engage in a total weekly amount of at least 150 minutes of moderate-intensity physical activity.

Conclusion

Males differ from females in their leisure behavior and attitudes but such differences are like a Venn diagram in which there is a significant area in common, and part of the area which is unique. Although an overlap between two symmetrical circles exists, they never overlap, and perhaps this is what nature had in mind—the distinction based on gender. In summary, the leisure patterns of males are distinctly different from females—partly due to genetic endowment and society's reinforcement, and accentuation of such differences. However, the way males and females spend their time is becoming more similar in today's society.

A critical question concerning the differences between males and females in terms of health, is how much are simply a matter of genetic predisposition and how much is socially induced and capable of being changed? Perhaps in time, science will be able to identify the extent to which differences are innate or a product of society. Because we can't extend the number of hours in a 24-hour day, or change our genetic identity, examining the factors that influence male patterns of leisure are necessary.

References

1. Blum D. *Sex on the Brain: The Biological Differences Between Men and Women*. Penguin Books: New York, 1997.
2. Blum, Ibid, p. 145.
3. Belsky J, Rovine M. Nonmaternal care in the first year of life and security of infant-parent attachment. *Child Dev* 1988;**59**:157–167.
4. Blum, Ibid, p. 80.
5. Blum, Ibid, p. xvi.
6. Blum, Ibid, p. 25.
7. Cromie J. Why women live longer than men. *Harvard University Gazette* 1998. http://www.news.harvard.edu/gazette/1998/10.01/WhyWomenLiveLon.html. Accessed July 12, 2010.
8. Blum, Ibid, p. 96.
9. Blum, Ibid, p. 122.
10. National Center for Health Statistics - 2005 Fact Sheet - Life Expectancy Hits Record High. http://www.cdc.gov/nchs/pressroom/05facts/lifeexpectancy.htm. Accessed July 12, 2010.
11. Davidson K. Why can't a man be more like a woman?: Marital status and social networking of older men. *The Journal of Men's Studies* 2004;**13/1**.
12. Cameron E, Bernades J. Gender and disadvantage in health: Men's health for change. *Sociol Health Illness* 1998;**20/5**:673–693.
13. Blum, Ibid, p. 169.
14. Godbey G. *Leisure in Your Life: New Perspectives*. Venture Publishing, Inc.: State College, PA, 2006.
15. Robinson J, Godbey G. *Time for Life: The Surprising Ways Americans Spend Their Time (revised edition)*. Penn State Press: University Park, PA, 1999.
16. Farrell W. *Why Men Earn More*. American Management Association: New York, 2005.
17. Gauthier AH, Smeeding TM. Time use at older ages: cross-national differences. *Res Aging* 2003;**25**:247–274.
18. Davidson, Ibid, p. 123.
19. Youth Violence: A Report of the Surgeon General. http://mentalhealth.samhsa.gov/youthviolence/surgeongeneral/sg_site/toc.asp. Accessed July 12, 2010.
20. Ham SA, Kruger J, Tudor-Locke C. Participation by US adults in sports, exercise, and recreational physical activities. *J Phys Activ Health* 2009;**6**:6–14.

Chapter 29
Promoting Health and Wellness With Persons With Disabilities: The Role of Recreation and Leisure

Mary Ann Devine
Lynne Cory
Amy Rauworth

Introduction

Individuals with disabilities have historically been portrayed as *victims* of their limitations, *afflicted* with their disability, *confined* or *bound* to apparatus such as wheelchairs, and *stricken* with their condition. None of these descriptions conjures an image of a healthy, active person. Yet, in recent years, individual with disabilities, advocates for those with disabilities, professionals in disability-related fields, and world health bodies have made strides to not only change the image of someone with a disability as one who is not always sick and in constant need of medical attention, but to change the ways in which societies behave toward these people. The goal of this chapter is to create a portrait of a healthy active person with a disability, discuss ways in which health can be promoted for these individuals, and demonstrate the benefits of healthy active living for those living with a disability.

Who are People with Disabilities?

Disability can be defined in several ways. It can be defined according to limitations (i.e., physical, cognitive, sensory) or medical condition, known as the *medical model.* The medical model of disability views disability as a variation from the norm that can disadvantage the person physically, cognitively, socially, emotionally, sensor-wise, or in mental health (1). Unfortunately, when the definition of disability is aligned with this model, conditions are viewed as undesirable, unhealthy, limiting, abnormal, and in need of being cured (2, 3, 4). Disability can also be defined using the *social model,* which views the limitations experienced by individuals with disabilities as a result of social expectations of how people should and should not function. In other words, inaccessibility of a park for a person who uses a wheelchair would not be a direct result of the wheelchair, but be the result of how the park is designed. The assumption is that people who use wheelchairs are not going to use the park and that there is only one way to enjoy a park, as an ambulatory person. The social model of disability does not ignore limitations some experience in functioning, but places responsibility of addressing limitation on society rather than the individual. This model is reflected in The World Health Organization's (WHO) definition of health, which is "a state of physical, mental, and social well-being, not merely the absence of disease of infirmity." (5, p. 1). However, WHO's approach to defining disability is an integrative model that entails considering all factors that interact to influence a person's health, including etiological causes of limitations and the context in which people live. For the purposes of this chapter, we will use the WHO framework to discuss disability and health.

Healthy Individuals with Disabilities

The concept that people with disabilities can be healthy is supported by good intentions; however, existing writings, terminology, images, and definitions from commonly accessed sources provide little documentation that supports this concept (6, 7). Some define "health" as "freedom from physical disease or pain" (6). The WHO's definition of "health," as previously stated, is much more comprehensive and encompassing as it includes mental and social well-being as well as physical aspects (7).

One definition of "disability" is "the condition of being disabled; inability to pursue an occupation because of a physical or mental impairment" (6); and although WHO does not provide a specific definition of disability, it does describe "disabilities" and "impairments" as:

> an umbrella term, covering impairments, activity limita-
> tions, and participation restrictions. An impairment is a
> problem in body function or structure; an activity limita-
> tion is a difficulty encountered by an individual in execut-
> ing a task or action; while a participation restriction is a
> problem experienced by an individual in involvement in
> life situations. Thus, disability is a complex phenomenon,
> reflecting an interaction between features of a person's body
> and features of the society in which he or she lives (5).

None of these definitions provides an option for "health" and "disability" to appear together, nor is there a commonly-accepted conceptual framework for existence of an individual who has a disability to also be healthy. Thus, the challenge for health promotion professionals is to create a perspective of one who has a disability as a person who is also healthy and vibrant. Recent research suggests robust coexistence between disability and health. Thus, this section addresses aspects of individuals with disabilities relative to: (a) psychosocial, (b) cultural, and (c) physical health.

Psychosocial

Coexistence of disability and health has been associated with psychosocial domains such as quality of life, general satisfaction, perception of body image, and management of disability through these mechanisms (8, 9, 10, 11). Research has provided insight into roles of psychosocial processes to support the concept that one can experience a healthy existence and live with a disabling condition.

Positive Attitude, Engagement with Life, Coping, and Independence

Whether living with a newly acquired disability or living with a lifelong condition, studies have found that attitude and outlook have a great deal to do with psychological health. For instance, men who experienced upper limb amputation reported that while it took time to adjust to their lives following their injuries, they were able to "positively reframe problems and ultimately make the most of their situation" (p. 880). They reported their leisure interests and pursuits remained similar to activities prior to their injuries; especially related to activity engagement and personal meaning. In addition, self-worth was based on their ability to be independent and self-efficacious (11). Individuals having Muscular Dystrophy chose to "focus on today and dismiss thoughts about the future" (p. 1,394) and used their time to attend to elements of life that were valued including recreation, leisure, and social interaction (9). Individuals having Multiple Sclerosis (MS) identified self-management as integral to coping with their *individual* health situations. They identified coping strategies including having (a) positive attitude, (b) realistic perspectives about their abilities, (c) acknowledged their feelings about MS, (d) motivation to stay active to remain physically and emotionally healthy, (e) social interactions, and (f) empowered themselves with the most current information about MS (11).

Cultural

A specific culture is often represented by images it projects, language and discourse used, and stereotypes it reinforces or dispels (12). Terminology and language used within and outside of a culture can sustain or weaken it. For example, meanings and social values assigned to words change over time like words such as the past and present usage of the terms handicapped, retarded, crippled, and senile.

As previously discussed, the two models of disability (e.g., medical, social) assign definitions and labels about impairment. However, neither fully explicate cultural perceptions of disability and health, especially cultural discourse about the influence of disability on health and vice versa. Patston (13) stated:

> Whether it is from the medical or social model, we define
> people as impaired – and as a result disabled – in relation
> to their difference from a socially determined notion of
> what it is to be unimpaired or non-disabled. (p. 1626)

The concept of functional diversity is recent; however, its essence is appealing as a cultural context for framing a new and common position supporting the coexistence of disability and health (13). Within the notion of functional diversity, each individual is not labeled with terms such as "impaired" or "disabled" or "healthy" or "able-bodied"; rather a new language is employed that *constructively* changes cultural perceptions of each individual through use of positive or neutral terminology. For example, using this language, a person with a disability is a "person with unique function"; a person without a disability is a "person with common function." Thus, the model of Constructive Functional Diversity (CFD) suggests that each individual (not just individuals having disabilities) is "functionally diverse" (13). There is potential for CFD to have significant effects on cultural views as well as an essential paradigm shift about the coexistence of disability and health.

Although cultural perspectives of the relationship between disability and health may be simplified by using CFD as a lens for considering disability and health, it should be noted that perspectives can vary based on ethnicity, education, and social expectations (14, 15). This is important because culture and ethnicity can have an effect on the meaning of health (16). Numerous studies that compared ethnicity across perspectives of disability and health demonstrate significant differences across ethnicities related to perceptions of disability and health (14). Related to education, some findings suggest that lower levels of formal education was associated with increased perception of disability as abnormal and unhealthy (14). Social expectations are also different across cultures and ethnicities. For example, in some cultures, preferred socially acceptable behavior does not support independence by individuals with disability. Rather, it is socially expected that one demonstrates behavior that complies with the social expectations of others such as being "helpless," "attended to," or "waited on" (15).

Physical

Associating disability with health is complex when considering the physical domain. A great deal of health-related literature on individuals with disabilities focuses on function, how well a person can perform a physical task or skill. Function also includes performance of activities of daily living (ADLs), participation in active recreation and leisure, and engaging in sports.

Some research about the relationship between disability and health suggests that *perceptions* of health and *actual* health are related primarily to function; the higher level of functioning, the more the person is considered healthy. Other research suggests that perceptions and actual health are related to activity and participation. Specifically, health is equated with independent choice, rather than level of physical participation or degree of physical function. For example, an individual having a mobility impairment may not value being able to perform ADLs, but does value the physical capacity that promotes some or limited ability to participate in social activities or leisure pursuits.

One study related to valued life activities suggests that the physical domain of health for individuals with chronic conditions (i.e., rheumatoid arthritis) is complex; although the physical domain is associated with function, what is valued is what that function allows an individual to do. For example, the person's level of function allows him/her to engage in their favorite leisure activity with friends. Thus, functional skills in and of themselves were not as important. What was more important were the valued life activities, degree of independence, and the quality of the time spent with significant others permitted by the functioning (17).

In a study that examined individuals with intellectual disabilities, findings indicated that health meant that one could participate in various activities and spend time with friends and family. In addition, participants reported indicators of health that included social relationships, emotional states, energy level, ability to work, understanding healthy behaviors and culturally bound health beliefs (18). In a study that examined how young children perceive health using a multidimensional framework including the International Classification on Functioning, Disability, and Health (ICF Model) researchers found that preschool children indicated generally that being able to "do" and participate in preferred activities were hallmarks of health whether the activities were very active (e.g., running and playing with other children) or relatively sedentary (e.g., playing video games or playing with toys) (19).

Other research indicates that physical aspects of disability and health can be related to the purpose of the activity and its relationship to body image. In a study that compared active individuals with and without disabilities to their inactive peers, findings indicated that individuals who were physically active, whether with or without a disability, had a more positive body image than the inactive group and that the primary purpose for being physically active by individuals with acquired mobility disability (AMD) was that they were invested in their health to the degree that physical activity would decrease potential secondary conditions (e.g., pressure sores). In addition, they indicated interest in maintaining healthy physical appearance, health, fitness, and body satisfaction (20).

In summary, research findings support psychosocial, cultural, and physical aspects of the coexistence between disability and health. In addition, studies indicated complex and overlapping relationships between health aspects and human domains, presenting an opportunity to potentially strengthen the concept that coexistence of disability and health is not an illusion. Although this section addressed aspects of psychosocial, cultural, and physical domains separately, based on the research, it is likely that these aspects work together simultaneously to promote health in individuals with disabilities. Engagement in recreation and leisure provides evidence of how theses domains coincide to further promote health among those with disabilities.

Role of Recreation and Leisure for Individuals with Disabilities

Participation in everyday activities, including leisure, is a vital part of human development. National and global efforts over the past ten years have shaped how people around the world not only view health, but the role of active living in health promotion. They have also worked toward expanding the definition of health to include physical, mental, and social well-being (5). Additionally, in promoting their definition of health, the WHO asserts that an important and vital component of health and well-being is one's quality of life. Healthy People 2010, the U.S. Department of Health and Human Services (21) guide for identifying and addressing threats to health, has two main goals, (a) to increase quality of life and years of healthy life, and (b) eliminate health disparities among different segments of the U.S. population. With the notion of quality of life squarely at the center of health promotion, recreation and leisure plays a vital role in this effort as quality of life issues are inherent in leisure engagement (22).

Recreation and Well-being

Self-determination. Well-being is conceptualized as the integration of all parts of health (physical, mental, social, emotional, and spiritual) that results in a healthy active lifestyle and feeling good about oneself (23). Just as with individuals without disabilities, recreation and leisure can play an important role in the promotion of well-being with individuals who have disabilities. One tenet of well-being is concept of personal choice, or self-determination (24). Central to recreation and leisure involvement is personal choice or self-determination as it has shown to lead to enjoyment, satisfaction, and flow (25). Several studies examining the role of self-determination and the leisure behavior of individuals with disabilities have demonstrated that when individuals can make choices in leisure, they report a higher sense of well-being (26, 27, 28). Sable and Bocarro (29) reported that participants in a community-based therapeutic recreation program felt more engaged in activities that had meaning to them, and felt less socially isolated and more confident as a result of this recreation engagement. Schleien and Mactavish (30) found that when framing recreation involvement on self-determination, families who had a member with a disability reported having more balance and spontaneity in their leisure, and thus a better sense of well-being. Thus, recreation and leisure involvement can lead to greater feelings of well-being if individuals with disabilities are provided opportunities for self-determination.

Social Supports. Another connection between recreation engagement and well-being is social supports. Social supports include emotional support, friendships, family relationships, appropriate caregiving, social inclusion, and advocates to name a few (21). According to Coleman and Iso-Ahola (31), social supports can contribute to one's sense of well-being by reducing feelings of social isolation and increasing a sense of belonging. It is not uncommon for individuals with disabilities to experience social isolation, stigma, lack of friendships, or advocacy structures (2, 3, 4). One way to develop strong social supports is through engagement in recreation and leisure activities. Given the social nature of recreation and leisure environments, they are ideal for developing and sustaining social supports for individuals with disabilities. Social relationships that occur during recreation can offer connectedness, support, advice, encouragement, assistance, and a host of social resources important for one's well-being (24). *Healthy People 2010* urges people to develop social supports to reduce feelings of sadness, depression, or unhappiness that prevent them from being active. Recreation and leisure environments can promote social acceptance for individuals with disabilities, an important factor in developing social supports as well as a sense of belonging, which is an important precursor to friendship development (31, 32). According to Coyne and Fullerton (33), friendships can develop between people with and without disabilities through mutual leisure interests. Mutual recreation interests can build on natural supports that come from people sharing a common bond. Reducing stress, loneliness, frustration, and social isolation is an objective of Healthy People 2010 in health promotion, thus engagement in recreation and leisure is one way to improve these health indicators.

Recreation and Community Involvement

Adjustment and Transitioning. Leisure and recreation involvement are helpful to assist individuals with disabilities in adjustment to their disability and transitional planning. Adjustment to disability refers to individuals who are not born with a disability but have acquired one at some point throughout their life. Acquiring a disability is often a life altering experience impacting the person on multiple dimensions. The person's career/vocational path may change, his or her living situation may change, even his or her social support system, personal relationships, or friendships may change. In this period of significant adjustment, leisure can be a source of continuity. Dattilo and colleagues (34) reported participating in community recreation activities following discharge from a rehabilitation hospital was helpful in feeling like a person and not a disability. Recreation activities can also be a context that provides continuity to social support systems following the acquisition of a disability. By focusing on common leisure interests, individuals with newly acquired disabilities and their friends can maintain their social bonds.

Transition planning involves aiding someone in shifting from one life phase to another or finding services needed for a successful return to community life. For instance, with shorter hospital stays, people who acquire a disability are less prepared to transition back to their home and community life, resulting in fewer resources for promoting and maintaining health (29). Recreation engagement can assist in life transitions by providing a forum for using new and existing skills. For example, recreation can help someone with autism transitioning from school-based leisure activities to community leisure engagement by supporting the use of their existing social skills. Recreation can also be useful in assisting someone who has recently experienced a spinal cord injury learn new healthy behaviors by learning different ways to engage in his or her favorite activities. By using leisure activities to aid in transitioning back to community life following rehabilitation, individuals with disabilities can not only improve their health, but quality of life in general (29).

Inclusive recreation. Inclusive recreation is engagement in activities by individuals with and without disabilities. If organized and designed using certain guiding principles, inclusive recreation can promote community involvement, thus improving health and quality of life. Active engagement in community life has been identified as an important factor in predicting quality of life, a critical health indicator (35). Sherrill and Williams (36) asserted that inclusive sport programs foster feelings of normalcy, offer a social network, and provide a connection to one's community for participants with disabilities. The more connected people are to their communities, the less likely they will experience social isolation which can lead to a number of mental and emotional health issues (37). For example, Zabriskie, Lundgerg, and Groff (38) reported that individuals with disabilities who participated in physically active recreation perceived they gained new skills, which prepared them to pursue other independent leisure options in their community.

Involvement in inclusive recreation can also provide a training ground for individuals with disabilities to learn and utilize self-advocacy skills to seek and request leisure options that will promote their health. Recreation contexts have been in the forefront of inclusion since the inception of the Americans with Disabilities Act (ADA). In addition, most university curriculums are preparing their graduates to accommodate individuals with disabilities into leisure services. In turn, individuals with disabilities are being provided more opportunities to self-advocate for leisure preferences, compared to work or residential environments (39). While some studies have found that negative aspects associated with inclusion can impede self-advocacy for active recreation involvement (40, 41), others have found it provides more options and choices for leisure engagement.

Involvement in inclusive leisure can strengthen one's well-being by offering a variety of recreation options and one's that are sustained rather than brief. In addition, individuals with disabilities have reported that constraints such as a lack of social acceptance, negative societal attitudes, and perceptions of stigma negatively influenced them to seek or participate in community recreation activities (42, 32, 43). A recent study found that more park and recreation agencies are providing inclusive leisure options to patrons with disabilities as compared to 10 years earlier (44). Providing inclusive leisure options that will attract and meet the needs of those with disabilities requires health-promotion professionals to address environmental, social, and programmatic access issues (45, 46, 47). Inclusive leisure contexts should provide social support for individuals with disabilities to take risks and challenge stereotypes (40), particularly in physically active recreation and sport activities. By providing support to take risks, individuals with disabilities can be introduced to various leisure options as well as challenge stereotypes that prevent them from participating in regular physical activities.

Life-long Leisure Pursuits

Leisure and recreation can also develop health protection behaviors by creating leisure lifestyles, building active and regular leisure engagement into one's lifestyle, which can in turn promote life-long leisure engagement. The key to building one's leisure lifestyle is to center it on meaningful activities. Sable and Bocarro (29) reported that people with disabilities who participated in meaningful recreation activities had more motivation to sustain healthy behaviors that supported their participation in society. Meaningful inclusive leisure activities also play a critical role in developing skills, resources, and support systems to address activity limitations (38). Developing life-long leisure interests also requires options that offer longevity instead of shorter programs that can be less effective in honing skills or piquing interest. In the same study, Zabriskie and colleagues found that individuals with disabilities were willing to commit to and preferred longer and more consistent programs than briefer experiences. Lastly, lifelong leisure pursuits are critical to maintaining one's health throughout the lifespan and typically begin at a young age. Young people with disabilities who learn habits and behaviors that promote health are more likely to maintain those behaviors throughout their lifespan than those who don't (1).

Role of Leisure Engagement in Health and Wellness

Recreation and leisure research indicates that approximately twice as many adults with a disability (25.6%) are physically inactive compared to adults without a disability (12.8%) (1). A sedentary lifestyle is a serious public health concern for all Americans, but it is even more acute for people with disabilities who are at much greater risk for developing the types of health problems associated with inactivity. Several reports (2, 3) have suggested that the high levels of physical inactivity among people with disabilities predispose them to a significantly higher incidence and severity of secondary conditions (2, 4–7) and in particular, being overweight and obesity (8, 10).

The poorer health status of people with disabilities creates an additional burden on the individual, caregiver, and/or other family members (8, 11). Society is also impacted by the increased economic costs of supporting healthcare and community services that may be required, and poor health is known to predict higher rates of unemployment and reduced social participation (12). While most of the financial resources in public health have been directed at prevention of disease, injury, and *disability*, there is growing recognition among public policy experts that prevention of secondary conditions is an equally important issue among people with disabilities. Health promotion activities, especially increased participation in physical activity, can have an enormous positive impact on reducing secondary conditions and improving health in people with disabilities (13, 14). Promoting key health behaviors such as beneficial physical activity can be a universal solution to these multiple layers of issues and problems that effect the individual with a disability and society (12, 15, 16).

Barriers to Physical Activity among People with Disabilities

People with disabilities often experience barriers to regular physical activity beyond those experienced by the general population, including costs of membership and specialized transportation, lack of information on available, appropriate and accessible facilities and programs, lack of accessible exercise equipment, physical layouts challenging to people using mobility aids, lack of disability awareness and support in fitness staff, and the general perception that fitness facilities are unfriendly environments for those with a disability (17–20). Barriers such as these further reduce the likelihood of acquiring and practicing regular physical activity and result in a decline in physical function and health (see Figure 29.1). Recent research suggests people with disabilities are often confronted with so many barriers to participating in the types of physical and recreational activities they need to maintain their health and well-being that they decide such pursuits are not worth their time and effort (18, 20).

Benefits of Leisure Time Physical Activity

The benefits of leisure time physical activity are vast and not any different in people with or without disabilities. In anyone, exercise can help build healthy bones, muscles, and joints; may help one's immune system ward off illness and infection; can increase blood flow to all parts of the body; relieve chronic pain; and improve ability to perform activities of daily living (ADLs). Beyond improving physical health, psychological benefits of engaging in physical activity may be reduced feelings of depression and anxiety. Physical activity provides an outlet for socialization and stress release and may help one to maintain or extend independence and mobility into older age. Physical activity has also been found to be associated with reduced health care costs, better performance in school, lower worker absenteeism and turnover, and increased productivity.

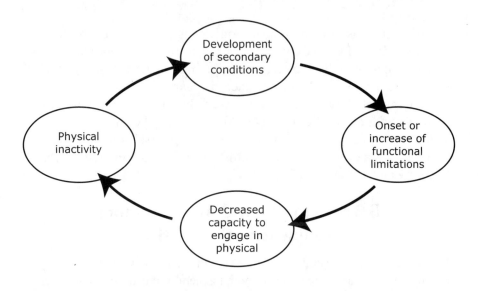

Figure 29.1 Cycle of Physical Inactivity and Deconditioning

Physical activity is defined as any bodily movement produced by skeletal muscles that result in increased energy expenditure (49). Often physical activity and exercise are used synonymously. However; exercise is a specific subcomponent of physical activity. Exercise is planned, structured, and includes repetitive movements for the purpose of improving or maintaining one or more components of physical fitness. Exercise has been shown to increase functional capacity (i.e., activities of daily living, household chores, and daily walking) more so than physical activity, however *any* activity is better than *in*activity (50). This is in agreement with previous studies that suggest participation in leisure activity unrelated to fitness improves other components of health such as a decrease in dementia and social isolation (51, 52, 53). Studies also suggest that by promoting leisure time physical activity in later life, older adults can maintain a greater level of independence which is associated with a decreased body mass index (BMI) (54, 55). Lastly, the greatest health improvements are seen when people who are the least fit become physically active (56). Some improvement include:

- Improved weight control and reduced abdominal adiposity

- Reduced levels of triglycerides (i.e., fats), increased high-density lipoprotein (HDL; i.e., good cholesterol), decreased low-density lipoprotein-HDL (LDL; i.e., bad cholesterol) ratio

- Improved glucose homeostasis and insulin sensitivity (57, 58)

- Reduced risk for cardiovascular disease

- Reduced risk for various chronic conditions (i.e., diabetes mellitus, cancer [colon and breast], obesity, hypertension, osteoporosis, and osteoarthritis) (48, 58)

- Reduced levels of stress, anxiety, and depression (56, 57, 59)

Disability Specific Research

Community-based physical activity programs provide a cost-effective and a convenient way for individuals with disabilities to reap the rewards of leisure time physical activity. A recent water-based exercise program that utilized moderate- to high-intensity exercise improved cardiovascular fitness and functional mobility in chronic stroke survivors (60). Pang and colleagues utilized a 19-week program for stroke survivors that incorporated fitness and mobility exercises three times weekly for an hour duration to maintain bone mineral density of the femoral neck. This is a notable outcome as stroke survivors are at greater risk of hip fracture in the paretic leg.

Research also demonstrates that progressive resistance training exercise can improve the unaffected and affected limb which results in improved functional abilities (i.e., stair climbing, prolonged walking) (61). Home-based exercise has been shown to be safe in subacute stroke and increase balance, endurance, and mobility greater than seen in spontaneous recovery and usual care (62). Another home-based program improved walking speed in individuals with multiple sclerosis after a 6-month exercise program that began during in-patient rehabilitation and transitioned into home-based activity (63). It is important for recreation professionals to support this transition from rehabilitation to community exercise for all individuals with disabilities. A slow walking speed can reduce the likelihood of participation in family, social, vocational, and leisure activity which results in a decrease in the quality of life that people with disabilities experience. Minimally supervised exercise has been demonstrated to be safe for individuals with multiple sclerosis without increase in symptoms or injury (63, 64).

For individuals with a spinal cord injury, a long-term, twice weekly exercise program improved physical fitness and psychological well-being (65). Ginis et al. found that individuals with spinal cord injury reported an improved satisfaction with physical function and physical appearance in addition to less stress, pain, and depression after a 3-month period of exercise participation (66). Individuals with intellectual disabilities also benefit from regular exercise participation. Adults with Down Syndrome report significant gains in cardiovascular fitness, muscular strength and endurance in addition to improvements in attitude toward exercise, life satisfaction, and a decrease in depression (67, 68).

Effects of Exercise on Health in Persons with Disabilities

Physical Activity Recommendations

Although the exact dose of beneficial physical activity for people with disabilities is unknown, recommendations have been developed as general public health guidelines. The United States Department of Health and Human Services *2008 Physical Activity Guidelines for American* (69) recommends 150 minutes of moderate-intensity activity per week, or 75 minutes of vigorous-intensity activity per week. According to basic recommendations from American College of Sports Medicine (ACSM) for adults over the age of 65, or adults with chronic conditions such as arthritis between the ages of 50–64:

1. To gain the health-related benefits of physical activity, moderately intense aerobic exercise should be performed 30 minutes a day, five days a week, or vigorously intense aerobic exercise 20 minutes a day, 3 days a week.
2. A comprehensive program should also include eight to 10 strength-training exercises, 10–15 repetitions of each exercise twice to three times per week.
3. Balance exercises should be included if the individual is at risk for falls.

Other general recommendations include My Pyramid, developed by the U.S. Department of Agriculture, which includes the following:

1. To prevent chronic disease, 30 minutes of moderate- to vigorous-intensity exercise.
2. To maintain weight, 60 minutes of moderate- to vigorous-intensity exercise while not exceeding caloric intake.
3. To maintain weight loss, 60 to 90 minutes of moderate- to vigorous-intensity exercise while not exceeding caloric intake.

To summarize these general guidelines, most individuals can meet the public health recommendations by participating in approximately 30 minutes of daily activity. The 30 minutes of recommended activity can be obtained by intermittent exercise throughout the day such as three 10-minute bouts and does not have to be done in one 30-minute session. This is especially important for people with disabilities who may be unable to sustain prolonged activity due to secondary conditions such as fatigue.

Until recently, specific guidelines for people with disabilities have been absent from general public health recommendations. In 2008, the U.S. Department of Health and Human Services designated a Physical Activity Guidelines Committee. This committee summarized the latest knowledge about activity and health, with efforts directed towards specific population subgroups, such as seniors, children, and people with disabilities. The guidelines were released in October 2008 and confirm that physical activity is beneficial for almost everyone. For instance, guidelines state that adults gain substantial health benefits from 2 and a half hours a week of moderate aerobic physical activity, and children benefit from 1 hour or more of physical activity per day. Specifically for adults with disabilities, recommendations are that "those who are able should get at least 2 and a half hours of moderate aerobic activity a week, or 1 hour and 15 minutes of vigorous aerobic activity a week." The recommendations further include muscle-strengthening activities which involve all major muscle groups performed 2 or more days a week. When people with disabilities are unable to meet the guidelines, the recommendations encourage regular physical activity according to their abilities and emphasize that people with disabilities should avoid inactivity. Individuals with disabilities or health conditions, who are not able to follow the guidelines, are encouraged to adapt their physical activity to meet their abilities. Moving is important for everyone. Overall, the evidence indicates that regular leisure time physical activity provides important health benefits for people with disabilities.

Summary

The message in this chapter is clearly that disability does not equal unhealthy, sedentary, inactive, or in continual need of medical attention. Individuals with disabilities can and do live active lifestyles engaging in a variety of recreation, leisure, and sports activities. These activities aid in maintaining their physical, mental, social, and emotional health. Engagement in recreation and leisure also promotes self-determination, which can generalize to other areas of their lives. Recreation can be a forum for developing and maintaining social support systems and be a way for individuals with disabilities to become more active it their communities.

In times of personal difficulty or life change, leisure and recreation engagement can be a source of continuity for individuals with disabilities as well. Engagement in active leisure can and should be a life-long pursuit. In doing so, individuals with disabilities can improve and maintain their physical, social, emotional, and cognitive health. Support for active leisure engagement is not only at the U.S. and Canadian federal levels but worldwide through the initiatives and support of the World Health Organization. Being cognizant and responsive to the health and wellness needs of individuals with disabilities will support these initiatives as well as serve to provide opportunities for greater community involvement for these individuals.

References

1. Sherrill, C. *Adapted Physical Activity, Recreation, and Sport: Crossdisciplinary and Lifespan 6th ed.*, McGraw Hill: New York, 2004.
2. Devine, MA., Sylvester, C. Disabling defenders?: The social construction of disability in therapeutic recreation. In C. Sylvester (ed) *Philosophies and issues in Therapeutic Recreation 3rd ed.* Ashburn, VA: National Recreation and Park Association, 2005, pp. 85–101.
3. Fine, M., Asch, A. Disability beyond stigma: Social interaction, discrimination, and activism. *J Soc Issues* 1988;**44/1**:3–21.
4. Oliver, M. *Understanding disability: From theory to practice*. MacMillan Press LTD: London, 1986.
5. World Health Organization. *International classification of functioning, disability, and health (ICF)*. Geneva, Switzerland: Author, 2001.
6. *Merriam-Webster collegiate dictionary* (11th ed.). Merriam-Webster: Springfield, MA, 2005.
7. World Health Organization. Constitution of the World Health Organization. *Chronicle of the World Health Organization* 1974;**1**:29–43.
8. Bergman S. Psychosocial aspects of chronic widespread pain and fibromyalgia. *Disabil Rehabil* 2005;**27/12**:675–683.
9. Boström K, Ahlström G. Living with a chronic deteriorating disease: The trajectory with muscular dystrophy over ten years. *Disabil Rehabil* 2004;**26/23**:1388–1398.
10. Malcomson KS, Lowe-Strong AS, Dunwoody L. What can we learn from the personal insights of individuals living and coping with multiple sclerosis? *Disabil Rehabil* 2008;**30/9**:662–674.
11. Saradjian A, Thompson AR, Datta D. The experience of men using an upper limb prosthesis following amputation: Positive coping and minimizing feeling different. *Disabil Rehabil* 2008;**30/11**:871–883.
12. Devlieger PJ. From handicap to disability: Language use and cultural meaning in the United States. *Disabil Rehabil* 1999;**21/7**:346–354.
13. Patston P. Constructive functional diversity: A new paradigm beyond disability and impairment. *Disabil Rehabil* 2007;**29/20–21**:1652–1633.
14. Brown S, McCauley SR, Levin HS, Contant C, Boake C. Perception of health and quality of life in minorities after mild-to-moderate traumatic brain injury. *Appl Neuropsychol* 2004;**11/1**:54–64.
15. Tamaru A, McColl MA, Yamasaki S. Understanding 'independence': Perspectives of occupational therapists. *Disabil Rehabil* 2007;**29/13**:1021–1033.
16. Freeman H. The meaning of race in science—considerations for cancer research: Concerns of special populations in the National Cancer Program. *Cancer* 1998;**82**:219–225.

17. Katz P, et al. Valued life activity disability played a significant role in self-rated health among adults with chronic health conditions. *J Clin Epidemiol* 2009;**62**:158–166.
18. Jurkowski JM, Rivera Y, Hammel, J. Health perceptions of Latinos with intellectual disabilities: The results of a qualitative pilot study. *Health Promot Pract* 2009;**10/1**:144–155.
19. Almqvist L, Hellnäs P, Stefansson M, Granlund M. 'I can play!' Young children's perception of health. *Pediatr Rehabil* 2006;**9/3**:275–284.
20. Yuen HK, Hanson CN. Body image and exercise in people with and without acquired mobility disability. *Disabil Rehabil* 2002;**24/6**:289–296.
21. U.S. Department of Health and Human Services. *Healthy People 2010*. (Conference edition in two volumes). U.S. Government Printing House: Washington, DC, 2000.
22. Sylvester C. Therapeutic recreation and the right to leisure. *Therapeutic Recreation Journal* 1992;**26/2**:9–20.
23. Sherril C, Rimmer JH, Pitetti KH. Fitness and healthy lifestyle. In C. Sherrill *Adapted Physical Activity, Recreation, and Sport: Crossdisciplinary and Lifespan 6th ed*. New York: McGraw Hill, 2004, pp. 356–389.
24. Bullock CC, Mahon MJ. *Introduction to recreation services for people with disabilities: A person-centered approach*. Sagamore: Champaign, IL, 1997.
25. Csikszentmihalyi M. *Flow: The psychology of optimal experience*. New York: HarperCollins, 1990.
26. Cory L, Dattilo J, Williams R. Effects of a leisure education program on social knowledge and skills of youth with cognitive disabilities. *Therapeutic Recreation Journal* 2006;**40**:144–164.
27. Dattilo, J., Hoge, G. Effects of a leisure education program on youth with mental retardation. *Educ Train Ment Retard Dev Disabil* 1999;**34**:20–34.
28. Williams, R., Dattilo, J. Effects of leisure education on self-determination, social interaction, and positive affect of young adults with mental retardation. *Therapeutic Recreation Journal* 1997;**31**:244–258.
29. Sable J, Bocarro J. Transitioning back to health: Participant's perspective of Project PATH. *Therapeutic Recreation Journal* 2004;**38**:206–224.
30. Schleien SJ, Mactavish J. Re-injecting spontaneity and balance in family life: parents' perspectives on recreation in families that include children with developmental disability. *J Intellect Disabil Res* 2004;**48**:123–141.

31. Coleman D, Iso-Ahola S. Leisure and health: The role of social support and self-determination. *J Leisure Res* 1993;**25**:111–128.

32. Devine MA. From connector to distancer: The role of inclusive leisure contexts in determining social acceptance for people with disabilities. *J Leisure Res* 2004;**36**:137–159.

33. Coyne P, Fullerton A. *Supporting individuals with Autism Spectrum Disorder in recreation*. Sagamore: Champaign, IL, 2004.

34. Dattilo J, Caldwell L, Lee Y, Kleiber DA. Returning to the community with a spinal cord injury: Implications for therapeutic recreation specialists. *Therapeutic Recreation Journal* 1998;**33**:13–27.

35. Djkers, MP. Correlates of life satisfaction among persons with spinal cord injuries. *Arch Phys Med Rehabil* 1999;**80**:867–876.

36. Sherrill C, Williams T. Disability and sport: Psychosocial perspectives on inclusion, integration, & participation. *Sport Sci Rev* 1996;**5**:42–64.

37. Gresham FM, Sugai G, Horner RH. Interpreting outcomes of social skills training for students with high incidence disabilities. *Exceptional Children* 2001;**67**:331–344.

38. Zabriskie RB, Lundgerg NR, Groff DG. Quality of life and identity: The benefits of a community-based therapeutic recreation and adaptive sports program. *Therapeutic Recreation Journal* 2005;**39**:176–191.

39. Devine MA, Koch L. The role of inclusive recreation participation by individuals with disabilities in the rehabilitation counseling process. *Work* 2003;**21/1**:83–88.

40. Bedini LA, Anderson DM. I'm nice, I'm smart, I like Karate: Girls with physical disabilities perceptions of physical recreation. *Therapeutic Recreation Journal* 2005;**39**:114–130.

41. Devine MA, Parr MG. Social capital and inclusive leisure contexts: A good fit or dichotomous? *Leisure Sci* 2008;**30/5**:391–408.

42. Henderson KA, Bedini LA, Hecht L. "Not just a wheelchair, Not just a woman": Self identity and leisure. *Therapeutic Recreation Journal* 1994;**27/2**:87–98.

43. Devine MA, Dattilo J. The relationship between social acceptance and leisure lifestyles of people with disabilities. *Therapeutic Recreation Journal* 2000;**34**:306–322.

44. Devine MA. (in review). A nationwide look at inclusion: Responses and best practices. Journal of Park and Recreation Administration.

45. Bedini LA. Just sit down so we can talk: perceived stigma and the pursuit of community recreation for people with disabilities. *Therapeutic Recreation Journal* 2000;**34**:55–68.

46. Devine MA, Lashua B. Constructing social acceptance in inclusive leisure contexts: The role of individuals with disabilities. *Therapeutic Recreation Journal* 2002;**36**:65–83.
47. Wilhite B, Devine MA, Goldenberg L. Self-perceptions of adolescents with and without disabilities: Implications for leisure programs and services. *Therapeutic Recreation Journal* 1999;**33:15**–28.
48. U.S. Department of Health and Human Services. *Healthy People 2010: Understanding and Improving Health, 2nd Ed.* U.S. Government Printing Office: Washington, DC, 2000.
49. Caspersen CJ, Powell KE, Christenson GM. Physical activity, exercise, and physical fitness: definitions and distinctions for health-related research. *Public Health Rep* 1985;**100/2**:126–131.
50. Brach JS, Simonsick EM, Kritchevsky S, Yaffe K, Newman AB. The association between physical function and lifestyle activity and exercise in the health, aging and body composition study. *J Am Geriatr Soc* 2004;**52/4**:502–509.
51. Fabrigoule C, Letenneur L, Dartigues JF, Zarrouk M, Commenges D, Barberger-Gateau P. Social and leisure activities and risk of dementia: a prospective longitudinal study. *J Am Geriatr Soc* 1995;**43/5**:485–490.
52. Musick MA, Herzog AR, House JS. Volunteering and mortality among older adults: findings from a national sample. *J Gerontol B Psychol Sci Soc Sci* 1999;**54/3**:S173–180.
53. Wilson RS, Mendes De Leon CF, Barnes LL, et al. Participation in cognitively stimulating activities and risk of incident Alzheimer disease. *JAMA* 2002;**287/6**:742–748.
54. Simoes EJ, Kobau R, Kapp J, Waterman B, Mokdad A, Anderson L. Associations of physical activity and body mass index with activities of daily living in older adults. *J Community Health* 2006;**31/6**:453–467.
55. Kaleta D, Makowiec-Dabrowska T, Jegier A. Occupational and leisure-time energy expenditure and body mass index. *Int J Occup Med Environ Health* 2007;**20/1**:9–16.
56. Warburton DE, Nicol CW, Bredin SS. Health benefits of physical activity: the evidence. *CMAJ* 2006;**174/6**:801–809.
57. Warburton DE, Glendhill N, Quinney A. The effects of changes in musculoskeletal fitness on health. *Can J Appl Physiol* 2001;**26/2**:161–216.
58. Blair SN, Brodney S. Effects of physical inactivity and obesity on morbidity and mortality: Current evidence and research issues. *Med Sci Sports Exerc* 1999;**31/11 Suppl**:S646–662.

59. Dunn AL, Trivedi MH, O'Neal HA. Physical activity dose-response effects on outcomes of depression and anxiety. *Med Sci Sports Exerc* 2001;**33/6 Suppl**:S587–597; discussion 609–510.

60. Chu KS, Eng JJ, Dawson AS, Harris JE, Ozkaplan A, Gylfadottir S. Water-based exercise for cardiovascular fitness in people with chronic stroke: a randomized controlled trial. *Arch Phys Med Rehabil* 2004;**85/6**:870–874.

61. Ouellette MM, LeBrasseur NK, Bean JF, et al. High-intensity resistance training improves muscle strength, self-reported function, and disability in long-term stroke survivors. *Stroke* 2004;**35/6**:1404–1409.

62. Ducan P, Richards L, Wallace D, et al. A randomized, controlled pilot study of a home-based exercise program for individuals with mild and moderate stroke. *Stroke* 1998;**29/10**:2055–2060.

63. Romberg A, Virtanen A, Ruutiainen J, et al. Effects of a 6-month exercise program on patients with multiple sclerosis: A randomized study. *Neurology.* Dec 14 2004;**63/11**:2034–2038.

64. DeBolt LS, McCubbin JA. The effects of home-based resistance exercise on balance, power, and mobility in adults with multiple sclerosis. *Arch Phys Med Rehabil* 2004;**85/2**:290–297.

65. Hicks A, Martin K, Ditor D, et al. Long-term exercise training in persons with spinal cord injury: Effects on strength, arm ergometry performance and psychological well-being. *Spinal Cord* 2003;**41/1**:34–43.

66. Ginis KAM, Latimer AE, McKechnie K, et al. Using exercise to enhance subjective well-being among people with spinal cord injury: The mediating influences of stress and pain. *Rehabilitation Psychology* 2003;**48/3**:157–164.

67. Rimmer JH, Heller T, Wang E, Valerio I. Improvements in physical fitness in adults with Down syndrome. *Am J Ment Retard* 2004;**109/2**:165–174.

68. Heller T, Hsieh K, Rimmer JH. Attitudinal and psychosocial outcomes of a fitness and health education program on adults with Down syndrome. *Am J Ment Retard* 2004;**109/2**:175–185.

69. Physical Activity Guidelines Advisory Committee. *Physical Activity Guidelines Advisory Committee Report, 2008.* U.S. Department of Health and Human Services: Washington, DC, 2008.

Chapter 30

Leisure and the Health of People Who are Lesbian, Gay, Bisexual, and Transgendered

Amy N. Thayer
M. Deborah Bialeschki

Introduction

Imagine a time when you've felt marginalized; perhaps you were singled out, misunderstood, or even discriminated against because something about you was different than the larger group of which you were a part. Maybe you felt uncomfortable, annoyed, or angry. Or possibly, this incident might have left you feeling distressed, ostracized, or sick. Consider now how you might have felt if these attitudes were much more widespread and their effects far more reaching, as is the reality for many lesbian, gay, bisexual, and transgender (LGBT) individuals. In our culture, the stigma frequently attached to and the prejudice often experienced by LGBT persons seriously impacts their quality of life; however, leisure serves as an integral component in improving the overall health and well-being of sexual minority members.

Generally characterized as freedom, enjoyment, and self-expression (1–5), leisure also has also been described as an activity specific term (6, 7) that provides individuals recreational experiences that are freely chosen and unrelated to work. When leisure is contextualized as physical activity offering freedom, pleasure, and self-expression, it is not difficult to understand the role leisure can play in sexual minority members' healthy living.

Before we are able to appreciate the importance of leisure in improving and maintaining the health and wellness of LGBT individuals, it would be wise to discuss a few of the social origins of the most prominent diseases and illnesses that afflict this community. More specifically, awareness of the sexuality norms in the United States is warranted. The constructs of homophobia and heterosexism provide heterosexuals with a privileged and advantageous social status that facilitates the notion of "heterosexist bias," described as "conceptualizing human experience in strictly heterosexual terms and consequently ignoring, invalidating, or derogating homosexual behaviors and sexual orientation, and lesbian, gay male and bisexual relationships and lifestyles" (8). Additionally, these group identities have been institutionalized within our American culture, and individuals are assigned status characteristics, or "attributes on which people differ and for which there are widely held beliefs in the culture associating greater social worthiness and competence with one category of the attribute than another" (9). For example, race, gender and sex, and sexual identity all have cultural beliefs attached to them, and as such, members of society apply somewhat standardized expectations and assumptions for individual behaviors based on those principles. As a result, it is not difficult to understand how social evaluations of these categorizations create and legitimize hierarchies that are stratified from the most privileged to the most disadvantaged (10). This hierarchy has not only organized our society in a way that minimizes and even excludes the lives and experiences of many minority groups, including lesbians, gays, bisexuals, and transgender persons, but it has also rendered them stigmatized merely because they do not meet the demographic requirements of the majority; the effects of this stigma can be extensive, and damaging to living a healthy life.

Disease and Illness—Considerations for the LGBT Community

Emotional Distress. "Sexual stigma" is the shared belief regarding homosexuals' devalued social status that deems their behaviors, desires, and relationships as negative, compared to those of heterosexuals (11, 12). This stigma results in sexual minority individuals having less power, less access to valuable resources, less influence over others, and less jurisdiction over their own fate (12, 13). Moreover, research (14, 15) has suggested stigmatized individuals who know their identity is devalued may harbor an excessive amount of distress trying to anticipate prejudice and discrimination. "Distress" is an unpleasant subjective state comprised of depression, anxiety, and anger as well as feelings that cause pain and misery. Distress has been described as dichotomous to wellbeing on the emotional states continuum and is caused by objective disadvantage and perceived powerlessness within society (16). Men and women who identify as LGBT are presented with distinctly different amounts of hardship, constraint, and perceived personal control, each of which contribute to a heightened level of distress not inherent in heterosexual women and men. Further, scholars conducting research in this area purport bisexual individuals may experience higher levels of distress than either gay men or lesbians, because they are marginalized by both homosexuals and heterosexuals (17). Similar reasoning has been suggested for transgender individuals (18). Another commonly known fact is that gay and bisexual males have a higher risk for suicidal thoughts, feelings, and behaviors that results from being members of a sexual minority (19). Another research finding is that LGBT youth attempt suicide two to six times more frequently than heterosexual youth (20). Consequently, coalescing stigma and distress gravely impacts LGBT individuals' health in significant ways as well as perhaps some less obvious ways.

Drug and Alcohol Use. Social oppression, shame, and anxiety, fostered through social stigma and manifested as distress, have commonly been believed to influence LGBT drinking and drug use and abuse (21). Research has indicated sexual minority women demonstrate higher levels of alcohol use and abuse than their heterosexual counterparts (22, 23, 24); gay men report drinking more often and in greater quantities than lesbians or heterosexual women, but have been found to have similar rates of alcohol-related problems as heterosexual men and fewer alcohol-related problems than bisexual women and lesbians (25). And, although not much is known about the substance use and abuse of bisexual or transgendered individuals, Hughes and Eliason (18) indicated bisexual men and bisexual women seem to follow the alcohol trends of gay men and lesbians respectively, while transgender men and women appear to engage in more drug use and abuse than that of alcohol.

Irrespective of which sexual minority category to which they belong, or their substance of choice, commonly identified reasons exist that explain the LGBT community's increased use of alcohol and drugs, which include: 1) reliance on bars for socialization and peer support, 2) emotional dissonance of "passing" as heterosexual and using substances to reduce anxiety related to these conflicts, and 3) interaction between discriminatory experiences (because of being a member of the sexual minority) and substance use (21). Although the use of substances may serve as a coping strategy for LGBT individuals, there is also concern that these behaviors could result in abuse and potential dependency on alcohol and drugs (26). This dependency not only potentially exacerbates incidences of depression (27) and some types of cancer (28), but can negatively impact the overall health and wellness of LGBT individuals by influencing other serious health conditions and illnesses such as overweight and obesity for sexual minority women, and HIV/AIDS for sexual minority men.

Overweight/Obesity and related illnesses. During the past 40 years, obesity rates in the United States have increased from 13% to 32% (29), and overweight adults now account for 66% of the American population (30). Obesity has been identified as a serious health concern, because of its contribution to other chronic diseases, such as diabetes, stroke, heart disease, osteoarthritis, as well as breast and colon cancer (31, 32). Moreover, it is estimated that obese persons have one-and-a-half to two times the risk of premature death than individuals who maintain their weight within the healthy range. Despite what is known about the health implications of obesity, it has still been associated with approximately 112,000 deaths in the U.S. In other words, obesity further complicated other significant health issues that often culminated in death (33). Although a myriad of data exist that indicates overweight and obesity issues are more prevalent in sexual minority women than in heterosexual women, there appears to be a lack of consensus as to why this increase in obesity occurs for this group of women.

While lesbians may comprise approximately four percent of the overall population (34), they have a much higher prevalence of overweight and obesity and are more likely to have a higher Body Mass Index (BMI) compared to heterosexual women (35). Some research has posited social gatherings located in bars (and therefore higher caloric intake from alcoholic beverages), diverse female roles (i.e., women asserting feminine, masculine, and/or androgynous qualities in the way they present themselves and behave), as well as greater acceptance of diverse body shapes and sizes that do not mirror our culturally-imposed belief that "thin is beautiful" or "thin is feminine" or "muscular is masculine" may contribute to increased instances of sexual minority women carrying unhealthy body weight (36). Although such philosophies are socially empowering, they may also be hazardous to their physical wellbeing. Whereas it is generally believed the etiology of this serious health condition is a result of the discrimination and distress derived from lesbians' and bisexual women's stigmatized identity (37), not much else is certain. Of no doubt, however, is the substantial role leisure can play in increasing self-confidence and reducing overweight conditions, obesity, and other serious illnesses in sexual minority women.

HIV/AIDS. While the Human Immunodificiency Virus (HIV) weakens individuals' immune systems and can cause Acquired Immune Deficiency Syndrome (AIDS), it is certainly possible for persons to live with this stage of HIV for many years (decades, even) without any serious health complications. In contrast, AIDS is a life-threatening illness that significantly compromises the immune system and allows for other serious conditions such as pneumonia and cancer. If uncontrolled, the outcome of AIDS is often death. AIDS is a disease that afflicts all factions of people throughout the world. In the United States, it is estimated that through 2006, there have been 1,014,797 AIDS cases, 565,927 AIDS deaths, and 509,681 people living with AIDS, with gay and bisexual men accounting for the highest proportion of new infections (38). Currently, estimates suggest that just over a half a million gay and bisexual men are living with AIDS (39). Obvious are the physical health ramifications of this illness, but there are also critical emotional consequences for sexual minority men who are HIV positive or who are living with AIDS. Both should be considered when investigating the health and wellness of gay and bisexual men.

Since the first incidence was reported in the early 1980s, AIDS has remained a highly stigmatized disease with many people associating it with homosexual and bisexual men and intravenous drug users. This stigmatization often breeds anger, disgust, and discrimination. As a result, those individuals stricken with the disease often experience heightened anxiety, ostracism, depression, and may exhibit negative coping strategies, such as substance use and abuse and in some cases, suicide. For sexual minority men with AIDS, the risk of substance abuse and suicide risk is intensified not only because they have AIDS (still a stigmatized disease), but also because of their nonconformist sexuality (they are not heterosexual). Unmistakably, leisure has a critical part in assisting with the physical health of AIDS patients (e.g., being physically active to keep the body stronger and decrease fatigue) and in coping with the mental and emotional strain (e.g. being physically active to enhance mood or spending time with people from whom they receive support) that accompanies AIDS (40).

Leisure—A Component to Health and Wellness in the LGBT Community

Leisure-time activities are an important element in all individuals' health and wellbeing. It allows for personal freedom, pleasure, and self-expression that are paramount to one's mental and emotional health, and it includes physical activity that improves and maintains both physical and mental health. Chronic illness and disease can be controlled and even eradicated by adopting a lifestyle that incorporates daily physical activity. Additionally, activities that promote freedom of self-expression often allow for confidence-building and empowerment. In the LGBT population, these aspects of leisure are essential components to the development and maintenance of community. While one can argue for the importance of community for all people, the creation of social networks and the sharing of social support may be even more critical to LGBT people for its role in providing positive health benefits to sexual minority people.

Leisure and Community. Community is a broad term characterized by collectives of people sharing common values and concerns regarding the welfare of their group. Interactions occurring within communities facilitate the development of social networks and the promotion of social support, both of which ultimately impact behaviors and preferences within the group. The notion of social support (41) includes *Emotional Support* (love, empathy, trust, and caring), *Instrumental Support* (aid and services offered to a person in need), *Informational Support* (advice, suggestion, and information provided to assist in addressing problems), and *Appraisal Support* (information used for self-evaluation purposes- e.g. constructive feedback, affirmation, and social comparison). Social networks include relationships and ties to other individuals observable as friendships, kinship, work ties, as well as means of communication, chains of command or a host of other social linkages (42). The LGBT community is built on common identity and collective strength in celebration of shared qualities, culture, and goals. These social relationships, which include the functions of social support and social networks, exert powerful influence on their health, health status, health behaviors, and health decision-making (43).

The interactions between and among members of these formal and informal social networks and social support systems serve as significant sources of influence on LGBT health behaviors. The offering of social support among the members of this community is imperative because it allows for the substantiating of positive leisure and health behaviors, such as exercise, physical activity, and sports. Likewise, social networks assist in providing access to useful resources that might provide leisure opportunities. Leisure also plays a monumental role in the cultivation of socially valued experiences within the LGBT community and is offered in many diverse forms. There are travel and tourism companies dedicated to the needs and experiences of LGBT people. Gay bars and coffee shops provide LGBT "space" where socialization among the community is fostered and encouraged and where identities can be expressed (44). LGBT recreational teams, sports leagues, and competitive events such as the Gay Games are also prominent forms of leisure. These sport opportunities are a good example of how leisure as physical activity is devoted to building and strengthening solidarity and acceptance within the LGBT community and the general public as well as promoting behaviors that positively influence their health and wellness.

Leisure as Physical Activity. The simple act of moving your body regularly can dramatically improve your physical health. For example, moderate and vigorous intensity physical activity for 30 minutes, five days a week, or a total of 150 minutes per week can prevent and/or manage chronic health conditions such as diabetes, stroke, heart disease, osteoarthritis, as well as the contributing factor of obesity. Doubling this amount of physical activity can produce significant gains in health and fitness. (45). While being physically active is important to everyone, it may be particularly important to the physical health of LGBT individuals. Physical activity not only protects against overweight and obesity, which is of particular concern within the lesbian community, but it also has been identified as an integral factor in the self-care and health promotion of those individuals living with HIV/AIDS (40). Additionally, coping with physical illness or attenuating mental and emotional distress can also be a benefit of participation in physical activity, because it provides physiological changes known to improve mood and reduce depression (i.e., the release of endorphins and serotonin).

Interestingly, relationships with significant others and/or close friends outside the family and the social support provided from these relationships dramatically improves the incidence of physical activity behavior in GLBT communities. For example, the Task Force on Community Preventive Services (TFCPS) reported 44% increase in time spent being physically active, a 20% increase in frequency of physical activity, and improved fitness levels and decreased body fat when social support was present within an individual's social networks (46). Even observing others within your social network being physically active has been shown to assist in increasing physical activity participation, as Henderson and Ainsworth (47) discovered when studying women's physical activity habits. Clearly, the value of leisure, particularly as opportunities to be physically active on a variety of levels and in an array of settings, is well-recognized among LGBT individuals.

Gay Recreation Teams and Leagues. Recreational and competitive sports opportunities are excellent examples of how the LGBT community values leisure as a manifestation of freedom in self-expression, as well as physical activity. LGBT recreation teams and sports leagues are plentiful in every state throughout the United States and cater to both the competitive and recreational sports/activity enthusiast by offering a myriad of physical activities. Examples of teams and leagues include sports such as running, skiing, hiking, cycling, camping, rodeo clubs, rugby, soccer, football, tennis, soccer, golf, volleyball, and softball. While these teams/clubs/leagues are generally comprised of LGBT people, many also include supportive heterosexual friends and family. So, why is there a need for recreational clubs or sports leagues designed to serve LGBT individuals, specifically? These beneficial leisure activities are the context for caring for the physical health of one's body, building and strengthening community, while enjoying time spent within an atmosphere where being a person in the sexual minority is celebrated, rather than denounced. In this way, individuals can share in a sense of pride regarding their sexual identity in a supportive and healthy environment while also reaping the benefits of friendships and camaraderie with other LGBT people.

Federation of Gay Games. The Gay Games, as they are commonly referred, is the largest international LGBT athletic and cultural event. Conceived by a past Olympian and first hosted in San Francisco almost 30 years ago, the Gay Games purpose is "to foster and augment the self-respect of lesbians and gay men throughout the world and to engender respect and understanding from the non-gay world, primarily through an organized international participatory athletic and cultural event held every four years" (48). During each competition, there are core sports in which athletes can participate as well as a variety of performance and visual art opportunities, all of which draw approximately 12,000 athletes from around the world. Through sport and culture, the Gay Games tout the importance of inclusivity, self-expression, and achieving one's personal best, within an atmosphere that is safe, accepting, and empowering not only for sexual minority people, but for all people, without regard to sexual orientation, gender, race, religion, nationality, ethnic origin, political belief, physical ability, athletic/artistic ability, or HIV status. The Gay Games, another positive context of leisure for LGBT people, encourages authenticity and community by cultivating an environment that is liberating and supportive, which are essential components to individuals' physical, mental, and emotional health and well-being.

A Brief Word about Non-Active Leisure. While we have focused primarily on physically active leisure pursuits, the value of non-physically active leisure to the emotional and mental health and well-being of GLBT individuals is a good reminder of the importance of all types of leisure pursuits. Just as community and social capital are built through physical activities in leisure, the same parallels can be found in leisure focused on cultural arts and performance. For example, women's music has been a mainstay of the lesbian community for decades through live performances and recorded music by lesbian musicians for the women's community. There are also opportunities to participate in GLBT choral groups, community bands, and other performance groups that come together for cultural events as well as community celebrations such as Gay Pride parades and events. Some of these cultural opportunities have national organizations. A good example is the Lesbian and Gay Band Association (LGBA) that is comprised of gay marching and concert bands from US and international cities. The LGBA meets annually in different cities to plan events and share the gift of music with gay and non-gay audiences. As stated on their website (49):

> By uniting men and women who share this love, bands
> help create and enhance the "community" their members
> call home. Through musical performance, LGBA bands

make a powerful political statement in a non-political way. Whether marching or playing a concert, we proudly proclaim "We Are Who We Are." LGBA bands are sources of pride within their cities, as well as positive symbols of the same communities. Making music creates a family where affection means more than affectional preference. By "banding together," LGBA shows that people of different sexes, ages, creeds, races, and challenges can build a strong community.

All of these non-active leisure pursuits offer opportunities to build communities of support and personal enjoyment that add to the mental and emotional health and well-being of many LGBT people.

Summary

As indicated in previous chapters, leisure has a place in every culture and is experienced in a myriad of ways. Not surprisingly, its presence within the LGBT subculture is no exception. Leisure is a powerful element in both directly affecting LGBT individuals' health, as observable through effects of physical activity, and indirectly as witnessed in its function of building and strengthening community by providing opportunities for growth and positive ways to cope with and reduce stigma and depression. In either case, the profound influence leisure asserts in the lives of LGBT people reveals it as an integral ingredient in their healthy living.

References

1. Bammel G, Bammel L. *Leisure and Human Behavior*. Wm. C. Brown Publishers: Dubuque, IA, 1992.
2. Henderson KA. The contribution of feminism to an understanding of leisure constraints. *J Leisure Res* 1991;**23**:363–377.
3. Henderson KA, Rannells JS. Farm women and the meaning of work and leisure: An oral history perspective. *Leisure Sci* 1988;**10**:41–50.
4. Kelly JR. *Freedom To Be: A New Sociology of Leisure*. Macmillan Publishing Company: New York, 1987.
5. Samdahl DM. A symbolic interactionist model of leisure: Theory and empirical support. *Leisure Sci* 1988;**10**:27–39.
6. Edginton CR, Jordan DJ, DeGraaf DG, Edginton SR. *Leisure and Life Satisfaction: Foundational Perspectives*. Brown & Benchmark Publishers: Dubuque, IA, 1995.
7. Kraus R. *Recreation and Leisure in Modern Society*. Addison-Wesley: Reading, MA, 1997.
8. Herek GM, Kimmel DC, Amaro H, Melton GB. Avoiding heterosexual bias in psychological research. *Am Psychol* 1991;**46**:957–963.
9. Correll SJ, Ridgeway CL. Expectation states theory. In Delamater J (ed). *Handbook of Social Psychology*. New York: Kluwer Academic/Plenum, 2003.
10. Della Fave LR. The meek shall not inherit the earth: Self-evaluation and the legitimacy of evaluation. *Am Socio Rev* 1980;**45/6**:955–971.
11. Herek GM. The psychology of sexual prejudice. *Curr Dir Psychol Sci* 2000;**9/1**:19–22.
12. Herek GM. Confronting sexual stigma and prejudice: Theory and practice. *J Soc Issues* 2007;**63/4**:905–925.
13. Link BG, Phelan JC. Conceptualizing stigma. *Annu Rev Sociol* 2001;**27**:363–385.
14. Barefoot JC, Brummett BH, Clapp-Channing NE, Siegler IC, Vitaliano PP, Williams RB, et al. Moderators of the effect of social support on depressive symptoms in cardiac patients. *Am J Cardiol* 2000;**86/4**:438–442.
15. Sartore ML, Cunningham GB. The lesbian stigma in the sport context: Implications for women of every sexual orientation. *Quest (00336297)* 2009;**61/3**:289–305.
16. Ross CE, Mirowsky J. Social structure and psychological functioning: Distress, perceived control, and trust. In J. Delamater (ed). *Handbook of Social Psychology*. New York: Kluwer Academic/Plenum, 2003, pp. 411–447.

17. Weber GN. Using to numb the pain: Substance use and abuse among lesbian, gay, and bisexual individuals. *J Ment Health Counsel* 2008;**30/1**:31–48.

18. Hughes TL, Eliason M. Substance use and abuse in lesbian, gay, bisexual and transgender populations. *J Prim Prev* 2002;**22/3**:263–298.

19. Abelson J, Lambevski S, Crawford J, Bartos M, Kippax S. Factors associated with 'feeling suicidal': The role of sexual identity. *J Homosex* 2006;**51/1**:59–80.

20. Gould MS, Greenberg T, Velting DM, Shaffer D. Youth suicide: A review. *Prevention Researcher* 2006;**13/3**:3–7.

21. Center for Substance Abuse Treatment. *A Provider's Introduction to Substance Abuse Treatment for Lesbian, Gay, Bisexual, and Transgender Individuals*. 2001.

22. Burgard SA, Cochran SD, Mays VM. Alcohol and tobacco use patterns among heterosexually and homosexually experienced California women. *Drug Alcohol Depend* 2005;**77/1**:61–70.

23. Cochran SD, Keenan C, Schober C, Mays VM. Estimates of alcohol use and clinical treatment needs among homosexually active men and women in the U.S. population. *J Consult Clin Psychol* 2000;**68/6**:1062–1071.

24. Wilsnack SC, Hughes TL, Johnson TP, Bostick WB, Szalacha LA, Benson P, et al. Drinking and drinking-related problems among heterosexual and sexual minority women. *J Stud Alcohol Drugs* 2008;**69**:129–139.

25. Amadio DM, Adam T, Buletza K. Gender Differences in Alcohol Use and Alcohol-Related Problems: Do They Hold for Lesbians and Gay Men? *J Gay Lesb Soc Serv* 2008;**20/4**:315–327.

26. Cabaj RP. Substance abuse, internalized homophobia, and gay men and lesbians: Psychodynamic issues and clinical implications. In Guss JR, Drescher J (eds). *Addictions in the Gay and Lesbian Community*. New York: Haworth Press, 2000, pp. 5–24.

27. Sandfort TG, de Graaf R, Bijl RV, Schnabel P. Same-sex sexual behavior and psychiatric disorders: Findings from the Netherlands Mental Health Survey and Incidence Study (NEMESIS). *Arch Gen Psychiatr* 2001;**58/1**:85–91.

28. MacMahon B. Epidemiology and the causes of breast cancer. *Int J Canc* 2006;**118/10**:2373–2378.

29. Weight-control Information Network. Statistics Related to Overweight and Obesity. Washington, DC: National Institute of Diabetes and Digestive and Kidney Diseases and National Institutes of Health. http://win.niddk.nih.gov/statistics/#preval. Accessed September 19, 2009.

30. Christakis NA, Fowler JH. The spread of obesity in a large social network over 32 years. *N Engl J Med* 2007;**357/18**:370–379.
31. United States Department of Health and Human Services. Healthy People 2010: Understanding and Improving Health, 2001. http://www. health.gov/healthypeople/default.htm. Accessed November 17, 2009.
32. United States Department of Health and Human Services. *The Surgeon General's Call to Action to Prevent and Decrease Overweight and Obesity Prevent and Decrease Overweight and Obesity*. US Department of Health and Human Services, Public Health Service. Office of the Surgeon General: Washington, DC, 2001.
33. Flegal KM, Graubard BI, Williamson, DF, Gail MH. Excess deaths associated with underweight, overweight, and obesity. *J Am Med Assoc* 2005;**293/15**:1861–1867.
34. Mravcak S. Primary care for lesbians and bisexual women. *Am Fam Physician* 2006;**74/2**:279–291.
35. Boehmer U, Bowen DJ, Bauer GR. Overweight and obesity in sexual minority women: Evidence from population-based data. *Am J Public Health* 2007;**97/6**:1134–1140.
36. Aaron DJ, Markovic N, Danielson ME, Honnold JA, Janosky JE, Schmidt NJ. Behavioral risk factors for disease and preventive health practices among lesbians. *Am J Public Health* 2001;**91/6**:972–975.
37. Boehmer U, Bowen DJ. Examining factors linked to overweight and obesity in women of different sexual orientations. *Prev Med* 2009;**48/4**:357–361.
38. Centers for Disease Control and Prevention. 2006 HIV/AIDS Surveillance Report. http://www.cdc.gov/hiv/topics/surveillance/resources/ reports/2006report/pdf/2006SurveillanceReport.pdf. Accessed November 17, 2009.
39. Joint United Nations Programme on HIV/AIDS (UNAIDS) and World Health Organization (WHO). AIDS Epidemic. http://www.unaids.org/ en/KnowledgeCentre/HIVData/EpiUpdate/EpiUpdArchive/2007/ default.asp. Accessed November 17, 2009.
40. Clingerman EM. Participation in physical activity by persons living with HIV disease. *J Assoc Nurses AIDS Care* 2003;**14/5**:59–70.
41. House JS. *Work Stress and Social Support*. Addison-Wesley: Reading, MA, 1981.
42. Felmlee DH. Interaction in social networks. In Delamater J (ed). *Handbook of Social Psychology*. New York: Kluwer Academic/Plenum, 2003, pp. 389–409.
43. Heaney CA, Israel BA. Social networks and social support. In Glanz K, Rimer BK, Lewis FM (ed). *Health Behavior and Health Education*. San Francisco: Jossey-Bass, 2002, pp. 185–209.

44. Johnson C. 'The first step is the two-step': Hegemonic masculinity and dancing in a country-western gay bar. *Int J Qual Stud Educ* 2005;**18/4**:445–464.
45. Physical Activity Guidelines Advisory Committee. *Physical Activity Guidelines Advisory Committee Report 2008*. United States Department of Health and Human Services. Washington, DC, 2008.
46. Kahn EB, Ramsey LT, Brownson RC, Heath GW, Howze EH, Powell KE, et al. The effectiveness of interventions to increase physical activity. *Am J Prev Med* 2002;**22/4S**:73–107.
47. Henderson KA, Ainsworth BA. A synthesis of perceptions about physical activity among older African Americans and American Indian women. *Am J Public Health* 2003;**93/2**:313–317.
48. Federation of Gay Games. Concept and Purpose. http://www.gaygames.com/. Accessed November 17, 2009.
49. Lesbian and Gay Band Association. About LGBA. http://www.gaybands.org. Accessed November 17, 2009.

Chapter 31
Health Disparities and Physical Activity, Parks, and Recreation

Melicia Whitt-Glover
Myron Floyd

On most days after school, 12-year-old La'Teisha comes home and finds whatever snacks are in the kitchen and shares them with her siblings as they watch music videos until their mother arrives home from work. When she arrives home, La'Teisha is only allowed outside to play on the front steps because the streets and the playground down the street are considered dangerous because of random violence from gang fights. Because of limited daily outdoor leisure time and access to healthy snacks, it is not surprising that La'Teisha is overweight[1] and at risk for type 2 diabetes.

La'Teisha spends several hours in the afternoons talking on the phone or chatting on the internet with her 14-year-old cousin, Sharon, who lives in a neighboring suburb in an upper middle class neighborhood. Sharon has several parks within a mile of her house but she has to travel down a busy road with no sidewalks to get to the parks. Sharon's parents work full time and her parents do not allow her to go to the parks alone because of the dangerous route to get there. Because Sharon cannot drive and because both of her parents work full time, Sharon is not able to participate in after-school activities. Sharon helps her parents by getting dinner started when she gets home from school; however, because Sharon's cooking skills are limited, she mainly prepares meals using boxed or frozen dinners.

La'Teisha and Sharon's mothers are sisters and both have metabolic syndrome (2). The sisters constantly encourage each other to practice healthier behaviors and made a pact to start walking for exercise together. However, because of the long hours each woman works, it is difficult for them to get together to walk more than a few times per month. It is safer to walk in Sharon's neighborhood. Unfortunately, La'Teisha's mother does not drive and has to rely on public transportation or rides from family members and friends to gain access to safe park and recreation areas. Both women are trying to lose weight and improve their health but are frustrated by the lack of time and opportunities for leisure time physical activity. In addition, both women are determined to involve their daughters in activities to prevent them from developing metabolic syndrome, but with long working hours and no way to get their daughters to after school activities, it appears to be a no-win situation.

Overview/Introduction

The vignette above is likely similar to the reality of low income and racial and ethnic minority groups who live in the United States. In this chapter, we consider how racial and ethnic disparities in physical activity and health can be combated through parks and recreation services. First, we review statistical data on physical activity prevalence for racial and ethnic minority groups in the U.S. and describe what we mean by *disparity*. Following this, we consider the role of parks and recreation facilities play in addressing racial and ethnic health disparities. We conclude with recommendations for the public health and recreation and park professions.

Background

Estimates from the 2005–2007 American Community Survey indicated that the total U.S. population was just under 300 million and was comprised of a large proportion of racial and ethnic minorities (~26%), including ~37 million Blacks/African Americans (12.1%), ~13 million Asians (4.3%), ~2.4 million American Indian and Alaska Natives (0.8%), just over 400,000 Native Hawaiians and other Pacific Islanders (0.1%), and ~44 million Hispanics/Latinos (14.5%)(24). Although racial and ethnic minorities make up only 26% of the U.S. population, they share a disproportionate burden of chronic disease. In 2005, four of the ten leading causes of death among racial and ethnic minorities, as well as among the general population, were chronic diseases directly related to modifiable risk factors associated with lifestyle behaviors (21). These chronic diseases were heart disease, cancer (specifically colon and breast cancer), diabetes, and stroke. For each of these health outcomes and their related risk factors, morbidity and mortality rates are higher among racial and ethnic minorities compared to non-Hispanic whites. The prolonged course of illness and disability from these diseases, as well as their related risk factors, such as obesity and hypertension, results in a decreased quality of life with much pain and suffering as well as enormous health care costs (21).

When one observes differences in a certain factor between one group compared to another group or groups, the difference could indicate a *disparity*. The information presented above highlighting differences in morbidity and mortality rates among racial and ethnic minority groups compared to non-Hispanic whites indicates the existence of *health disparities*. No consensus definition exists for the term "health disparity," or the related terms "health inequality" and "health inequity." Generally, each of these terms refers to health associated differences among groups. The National Institutes of Health (NIH) defines health disparities as "...differences in the incidence, prevalence, mortality, and burden of diseases and other adverse health conditions that exist among specific population groups in the United States" (26). Health disparities are measured by comparing the health of one group (usually defined as the reference group) to that of different groups. Health disparities reveal important information about the health of a population that is not as evident using population-wide health measures. Health disparities indicate that certain groups of individuals are experiencing worse health or are at greater risk of poor health compared to other groups in a population.

Despite major advances in public health, medicine, economic prosperity, and wealth, health disparities have persisted during the 20th century and have even increased for certain health indicators, such as diabetes. Because physical activity is a primary risk factor for many of the diseases that are observed in higher proportions among racial and ethnic minority groups and because physical activity is a risk factor that is modifiable, focusing on physical activity may be an important step toward reducing or eliminating health disparities for certain health outcomes. Addressing and reducing morbidity and mortality rates among racial and ethnic minorities, particularly from diseases with modifiable risk factors (e.g., physical activity) that could be ameliorated with preventive health measures and behavior modification, is a major public health priority. Assessing the underlying causes of health disparities can help provide policy makers, health care providers and educators, public health officials, and the lay public with important information related to how the distribution of efforts and resources are used to reduce or eliminate disparities.

How Much Physical Activity are People Getting (or not Getting)?

Physical activity is one of the most important modifiable risk factors for several of the leading causes of morbidity and mortality among U.S. adults, including heart disease, stroke, hypertension, noninsulin-dependent (type 2) diabetes mellitus, overweight and obesity, and breast and colon cancer (25). Although the association between physical activity and health-related factors has been researched and clear relationships between increased levels of daily physical activity and better health have been observed, the knowledge has not translated to increased physical activity for all populations.

Three national surveys—the Behavioral Risk Factor Surveillance System (BRFSS), the National Health Interview Survey (NHIS), and the National Health and Nutrition Examination Survey (NHANES)—provide population-level estimates of self-reported physical activity participation among U.S. adults. Typically, data are collected using self-reported surveys that ask individuals to provide an estimate of their "usual" physical activity or of their physical activity during the week prior to survey administration. Although there are known limitations with using self-reported data, these surveys provide the only source of national-level information about physical activity type, frequency, intensity, duration, and achievement of national physical objectives. The surveys assess leisure-time physical activity. The BRFSS also includes household and transportation activity. The BRFSS collects data only on adults ($\geq$ 18 years of age) while the NHANES and NHIS include data on children as well as adults.

Self-reported data from the 2003 BRFSS, the 2004 NHIS, and the 1999–2004 NHANES showed that anywhere from 24% to 36% of African American adults reported meeting national physical activity recommendations (28). For the BRFSS and NHIS, respondents were labeled as meeting recommendations if they reported participation in moderate- or light/moderate-intensity physical activity for $\geq$ 30 minutes on $\geq$ 5 days/week or vigorous intensity physical activity for $\geq$ 20 minutes on $\geq$ 3 days/week. NHANES respondents were labeled as meeting recommendations if they reported participation in moderate-intensity physical activity for $\geq$ 600 total minutes over $\geq$ 20 of the past 30 days or vigorous-intensity physical activity for $\geq$ 240 minutes on $\geq$ 12 of the past 30 days. Self-reported data from the 2001–2004 NHANES showed that a higher percentage of Mexican-American and non-Hispanic black children engaged in low levels of active play (defined as reported to play or exercise hard enough to sweat or breathe hard less than 7 times per week) compared to non-Hispanic white children (3).

In 2003, the NHANES data collection protocol was expanded to include objectively-monitored data collected on physical activity levels using accelerometers. Because monitors were designed to be worn all day and to capture all types of physical activity (not limited to leisure-time, household, or transportation), the data collected provided a more complete picture of physical activity levels. Figure 31.1 shows that, when all types of physical activity were captured using an objective monitor, non-Hispanic blacks and Mexican Americans appeared to engage in more moderate-to-vigorous physical activity than non-Hispanic whites at all ages except among those 60 years of age or older. These data are in contrast to data collected using self-report measures, and the findings may be related to the fact that self-report measures may not accurately capture the types of physical activity in which minority adults participate, thus underestimating physical activity participation (1). It is also possible that efforts focused on eliminating health disparities for health-outcomes associated with physical activity may have led to interventions that have truly been effective at increasing physical activity in racial and ethnic minority groups. Additional research

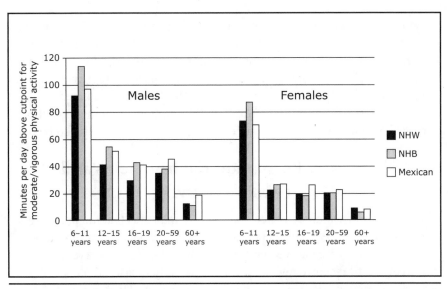

Figure 31.1 Physical Activity Participation Using Data from NHANES 2003–2004 (NHW=non-Hispanic White, NHB=non-Hispanic Black)

may be needed to determine whether physical activity participation levels are truly higher in racial and ethnic minority communities and, if so, why higher levels of physical activity are not accompanied by lower rates of poor health outcomes in which physical activity is a primary risk factor.

National surveys are also used to collect information on sedentary behaviors, most commonly referred to as screen time (use of computers, watching television/videos, playing computer/video games). Self-reported data from NHANES 2001–2004 showed that a higher percentage of non-Hispanic black boys and girls, compared to non-Hispanic white and Mexican American boys and girls, reported high screen time (defined as > 2 hours per day) (3). Objectively monitored data from NHANES 2003–2004 showed that, in general, there was no difference in the amount of time spent in sedentary behavior between non-Hispanic whites and non-Hispanic blacks; however, the data showed that Mexican Americans tended to be less sedentary than non-Hispanic whites and non-Hispanic blacks.

Decisions and opportunities to engage in physical activity are influenced by a variety of factors including descriptive characteristics (boys/men are generally more physically active than girls/women; those with more education and higher income levels are generally more physically active than those with lower education and lower income levels; individuals who are normal weight are generally more physically active than individuals who are overweight or obese; younger people are generally more physically active than older people). In reference to the vignette included at the beginning of this chapter, environmental characteristics also influence a person's decision to be physically active. If facilities are not available and/ or are not easy to access, opportunities to engage in physical activity are limited. Finally, there are also cultural differences associated with the importance placed on physical activity versus other pursuits (e.g., rest, spending time with family) that can influence whether an individual decides to engage in physical activity (2). Additional discussion about the impact of personal and environmental factors on physical activity in included below.

Parks and Recreation Environments and Physical Activity

Accumulating research evidence consistently indicates that the presence of parks and other recreation facilities in neighborhoods helps individuals become physically active and thus healthier. While this makes sense intuitively, until recently few studies have actually measured physical activity associated with park and recreation behavior. Historically, the primary emphasis for parks and recreation researchers and managers was to monitor amount of use, activity preferences, and park users demographics and satisfaction with facilities and services (12). Increased interest in and recognition of the health value of parks has stimulated more scientific research on physical activity.

One reason parks and recreation facilities are increasingly considered vital to health promotion is because they are widely available. Parks are generally accessible to people in urban areas and most people report using them. Approximately 70 percent of U.S. residents live within walking distance of an urban park and 3 of 4 adults report visiting local parks (13). Not much is known, however, about whether park use varies by race and ethnicity because there are few definitive studies on this issue. For example, a Cleveland-based study found that African Americans are less likely to be park users than *non-Hispanic whites* (23). Studies conducted in Atlanta and Philadelphia found that Caucasians and Hispanics were more likely to use parks than African Americans and Asian Americans (17). Other studies suggest that African Americans used urban parks at *greater* frequency than non-Hispanic whites (22, 27). An important research priority then is to examine race and ethnic differences in park use and to identify barriers and constraints that might prevent use of parks by members of racial and ethnic minority groups. This is of particular importance for low income minority individuals and families who are less able to pay for private or commercial recreation services.

As mentioned, awareness of the health value of parks, particularly for physical activity, is increasing. Studies to date suggest that people living in closer proximity to parks and recreation facilities are more likely to be physically active than people who live further away (20). Kaczynski and

Henderson (20) reviewed all scientific studies that examined the relationship between proximity of parks and recreation facilities and participation in physical activity. The majority of the studies they reviewed (8 of 13, or 61%) found that parks were associated with increased levels of physical activity. In fact, a national study representative of the adult U.S. population showed that people with access to parks were more likely to meet recommended levels of physical activity (5).

For children and adolescents, neighborhood parks are a potential double source of physical activity because they provide destinations for walking, cycling, or skating and because specific types of park facilities support on-site physical activity. For example, a study set in Atlanta demonstrated that youth with one or more parks near their residences were 2 to 3 times more likely to engage in walking than youth without parks close by (9). Another study involving children's use of parks conducted in 10 parks in Tampa and 18 parks in Chicago found that parks with trails or walking paths, sports facilities, and playgrounds (8) were associated with higher levels of moderate intensity physical activity. Attractiveness of neighborhoods and parks also plays an important role in supporting physical activity. Not surprisingly, people are more likely to use parks that are attractive (11) and youth are more likely to be physically active if they perceive their neighborhood as aesthetically pleasing (7).

Disparities in Parks and Recreation

Even though parks and recreation facilities provide opportunities to engage in physically active leisure, there is growing concern about whether parks and recreation facilities are equally available for all racial and ethnic groups. Moreover, there is concern that unequal availability of parks contributes to lower prevalence of physical activity among racial and ethnic minority groups. An emerging hypothesis among researchers suggests that racial and ethnic disparity in physical activity prevalence results from disparities in access to parks and other types of "activity-friendly" environments. Stated differently, individuals from racial and ethnic minority populations get less physical activity because the neighborhoods in which they live are not conducive to outdoor physical activity. Even though this is a new area of research, a number of studies lend support to this hypothesis. National studies have shown that public parks, recreation facilities, and private facilities are three times more likely to be found in majority communities than in minority communities (16). The research also demonstrates that greater availability of physical activity facilities is related to more activity and less overweight among youth. This particular finding provides some of the best empirical evidence of the association between parks and health. Not only did the study link recreation facilities to physical activity, it showed that youth with access to parks and recreation facilities were less likely to be overweight. Consequently, there is "strong" evidence that increasing access to parks, trails, and other recreation services can support broader efforts to improve community health and well-being. Establishing relationships between recreation facilities and physical activity and weight status also suggests how provision of parks and recreation services (or lack of provision) can influence health disparities.

Neighborhood Environments and Physical Activity

In addition to parks, community design, safety perceptions, and aesthetics have been found to be important for physical activity. A number of studies show that presence of sidewalks is associated with increased physical activity (10, 18, 19). As mentioned earlier, parks are important destinations for community residents, including adults and youth. Sidewalks are also important for connecting neighborhood residents to schools, shops, and businesses making neighborhoods activity friendly. Quality of streets and sidewalk is also paramount however. A walkable street may not always be a safe street. For example, an Austin (TX) study observed that low-income Hispanic neighborhoods were highly walkable in terms of presence of sidewalks (compared to white-non Hispanic neighborhoods) (29). However, in the low income Hispanic areas crime, traffic, and poor maintenance presented barriers to walking and outdoor leisure.

Greater perceptions of safety and low crime make neighborhoods and parks more conducive to outdoor physical activity. Concern for safety and exposure to crime deter outdoor activity generally, but research findings indicate racial and ethnic minorities may be affected most. Results from a national study of adolescents found that African-American and Hispanic youth were more likely to live in high crime areas, and that youth from high crime areas had lower levels of physical activity (15). In a San Antonio study involving Mexican-American youth, the number of violent crimes in neighborhoods was associated with less physical activity among girls, but not among boys (14).

Regarding aesthetics, past research suggests that racial and ethnic minorities rate their neighborhoods as less pleasant for physical activity (4, 6). Moreover, for youth, a neighborhood that is perceived as attractive or pleasant is more conducive to physical activity (7).

Parks and other neighborhood factors can influence opportunities for obtaining recommended levels of physical activity. Public parks may also be important for promoting healthy lifestyles among racial and ethnic minorities, thereby reducing disparities in physical activity, obesity, and related conditions. As mentioned, one reason public parks and recreation facilities are regarded as important to public health is their wide availability. Another reason is because parks and recreation facilities (planning, developments, funding, etc.) are under the influence of policy makers, professional managers, and citizen-residents. Individuals in these various roles make a range of decisions that affect access to parks and recreation opportunities.

Decisions about building new parks, renovating facilities, expanding or cutting services, etc. have consequences for availability of recreation opportunities within communities. Because of increasing research evidence about connections between parks and health and potential sources of health disparities, there is increased potential for policy makers and recreation managers to be better informed about the impact of their decisions.

Conclusion and Practical Implications

Within this chapter, we have highlighted disparities in physical activity participation using data from national surveys. We also provided information about and highlighted disparities in the availability of parks and recreation resources and the association between presence of parks and recreation facilities in neighborhoods and physical activity participation. As presented, the information indicates that racial and ethnic minority groups participate in lower levels of leisure-time physical activity compared to non-Hispanic whites (though racial and ethnic minorities may participate in slightly more overall physical activity than non-Hispanic whites) and that leisure-time physical activity participation may be influenced by limited availability of well-maintained and easily accessible park and recreation facilities.

Eliminating health-related disparities is a public health priority and is a matter that can be addressed by individuals in all walks of life including individuals (e.g., everyday citizens), decision makers (e.g., council members, elected officials, principals, advisory board members), and researchers (e.g., academic faculty members, research firms). Individuals, decision makers, and researchers can work together to address issues/concerns that impact physical activity-related disparities. For example, lack of resources/ facilities, safety concerns, and aesthetics were mentioned previously as factors that might impact use of park and recreation facilities in neighborhoods with high concentrations of racial and ethnic minority groups. These factors, in turn, impact individual physical activity levels. Individuals could help to address these factors and work toward eliminating health disparities by advocating for maintenance and improvement of sidewalks in disadvantaged neighborhoods, coordinating cleanup events in public recreational

Table 31.1 Additional Resources

Website	Description
www.activelivingresearch.org	Active Living Research supports research to identify environmental factors and policies that influence physical activity.
www.walkableamerica.org	The Partnership for a Walkable America (PWA) is a national coalition working to improve the conditions for walking in America and to increase the number of Americans who walk regularly.
www.americaonthemove.org	Our mission is to improve health and quality of life by promoting healthful eating and active living among individuals, families, communities and society.
www.activelivingresources.org	The role of the Active Living Resource Center (ALRC) web site is to provide you the resources and tools to help you make walking and bicycling part of your community's healthy lifestyle.
www.policylink.org	PolicyLink connects the work of people on the ground to the creation of sustainable communities of opportunity that allow everyone to participate and prosper. Such communities offer access to quality jobs, affordable housing, good schools, transportation, and the benefits of healthy food and physical activity.
www.activelivingbydesign.org	Active Living By Design creates community-led change by working with local and national partners to build a culture of active living and healthy eating.
www.saferoutesinfo.org	Safe Routes to School programs enable community leaders, schools and parents across the United States to improve safety and encourage more children to safely walk and bicycle to school.
www.walktoschool.org	Whether your concern is safer and improved streets, healthier habits, or cleaner air, Walk to School Day events are aimed at bringing forth permanent change to encourage a more walkable America—one community at a time.

facilities, taking personal responsibility to report areas with known traffic or safety risks, and cooperating with public safety and law enforcement departments to reduce fear of crime. Decision makers could help to address factors that may impact physical activity participation by developing and/or supporting programs and policies that increase opportunities for physical activity (e.g., more parks, policies for physical activity breaks in schools or at worksites), developing and/or supporting policies to slow traffic near parks and playgrounds, and providing incentives to local residents and organizations to get involved with park cleanup. Researchers can help by conducting additional research on physical activity prevalence and the impact of park and recreational facilities on physical activity participation, as well as research on factors associated with use or non-use of park and recreational facilities by different racial and ethnic minority groups.

Several national organizations have been formed to focus on promoting healthful living, including physically active lifestyle, in communities across the country. Table 31.1 provides some examples of organizations, including web address and a brief description of the organization. These organizations were chosen because in addition to their focus on promoting physically active lifestyle in communities, each organization includes a toolkit or action plan that can help individuals get involved with supporting the cause. Working together, we can all play an important role in eliminating health disparities that are associated with low levels of physical activity.

Footnotes

1. For children and adolescents (aged 2–19 years), the BMI value is plotted on the CDC growth charts to determine the corresponding BMI-for-age percentile. Overweight is defined as a BMI at or above the 85th percentile and lower than the 95th percentile. Obesity is defined as a BMI at or above the 95th percentile for children of the same age and sex. These definitions are based on the 2000 CDC Growth Charts for the United States and expert committee. A child's weight status is determined based on an age- and sex-specific percentile for BMI rather than by the BMI categories used for adults. Classifications of overweight and obesity for children and adolescents are age- and sex-specific because children's body composition varies as they age and varies between boys and girls. (Available at: http://www.cdc.gov/obesity/childhood/defining.html; accessed August 19, 2009)

2. Metabolic syndrome is characterized by a group of metabolic risk factors in one person. They include abdominal obesity (excessive fat tissue in and around the abdomen); atherogenic dyslipidemia (blood fat disorders—high triglycerides, low HDL cholesterol and high LDL cholesterol—that foster plaque buildups in artery walls); elevated blood pressure; insulin resistance or glucose intolerance (the body can't properly use insulin or blood sugar); prothrombotic state (e.g., high fibrinogen or plasminogen activator inhibitor–1 in the blood); and proinflammatory state (e.g., elevated C-reactive protein in the blood). People with the metabolic syndrome are at increased risk of coronary heart disease and other diseases related to plaque buildups in artery walls (e.g., stroke and peripheral vascular disease) and type 2 diabetes. The metabolic syndrome has become increasingly common in the United States. It's estimated that over 50 million Americans have it. (Available at: http://www.americanheart.org/presenter.jhtml?identifier=4756; accessed August 19, 2009).

References

1. Ainsworth BE, Irwin ML, Addy CL, Whitt MC, Stolarczyk LM. Moderate physical activity patterns of minority women: the Cross-Cultural Activity Participation Study. *J Womens Health Gend Based Med* 1999;**8/6**:805–813.

2. Airhihenbuwa CO, Kumanyika S, Agurs TD, Lowe A. Perceptions and beliefs about exercise, rest, and health among African Americans. *Am J Health Promot* 1995;**9/6**:426–429.

3. Anderson SE, Economos CD, Must A. Active play and screen time in US children aged 4 to 11 years in relation to sociodemographic and weight status characteristics: A nationally representative cross-sectional analysis. *BMC Publ Health* 2008;**8**:366.

4. Boslaugh SE, Luke DA, Brownson RC, Naleid KS, Kreuter MW. Perceptions of neighborhood environment for physical activity: Is it "who you are" or "where you live"? *J Urban Health* 2004;**81/4**:671–681.

5. Brownson RC, Baker EA, Houseman RA, Brennan LK, Bacak SJ. Environmental and policy determinants of physical activity in the United States. *Am J Public Health* 2001;**91**:1995–2003.

6. CDC. Neighborhood safety and the prevalence of physical inactivity -- selected states, 1996. *MMWR* 1999;**48/7**:143–146.

7. de Bruijn G-J, Kremers SPJ, Lensvelt-Mulders G, de Vries H, van Mechelen W, Brug J. Modeling individual and physical environmental factors with adolescent physical activity. *Am J Prev Med* 2006;**30/6**:507–512.

8. Floyd MF, Spengler JO, Maddock JE, Gobster PH, and Suau L. Park-based physical activity in diverse communities of two U.S. cities: An observational study. *Am J Prev Med* 2008;**34**:299–305.

9. Frank L, Kerr J, Chapman J, Sallis J. Urban form relationships with walk trip frequency and distance among youth. *Am J Health Promot* 2007;**21/4**:S1–S7.

10. Fulton JE, Shisler JL, Yore MM, Caspersen CJ. Active transportation to school: Findings from a national survey. *Res Q Exerc Sport* 2005;**76/3**:352–357.

11. Giles-Corti B, Broomhall MH, Knuiman M, Collins C, Douglas K, Ng K, Lange A, Donovan RJ. Increasing walking: How important is distance to, attractiveness, and size of public open space? *Am J Prev Med* 2005;**28** (2 Suppl 2):169–176.

12. Godbey GC, Caldwell LL, Floyd M, Payne LL. Contributions of leisure studies and recreation and park management research to the active living agenda. *Am J Prev Med* 2005;**28** (2 Supp 2):150–158.

13. Godbey GC, Graefe A, James SW. *The Benefits of Local Recreation and Park Services: A Nationwide Study of the Perceptions of the American Public*. National Recreation and Park Association: Ashburn, VA, 1992.

14. Gomez JE, Johnson BA, Selva M, Sallis JF. Violent crime and outdoor physical activity among inner-city youth. *Preventive medicine* 2004; 39/5:876–881.

15. Gordon-Larsen P, McMurray RG, Popkin BM. Determinants of adolescent physical activity and inactivity patterns. *Pediatrics* 2000;**105/6**:E83.

16. Gordon-Larsen P, Nelson MC, Page P, Popkin BM. Inequality in the built environment underlies key health disparities in physical activity and obesity. *Pediatrics* 2006;**117/2**:417–424.

17. Ho C-H, Sasidharan V, Elmendorf W, Willits FK, Graefe A, Godbey G. Gender and ethnic variations in urban park preferences, visitation, and perceived benefits. *J Leisure Res* 2005;**37/3**:281–306.

18. Jago R, Baranowski T, Baranowski JC. Observed, GIS, and self-reported environmental features and adolescent physical activity. *Am J Health Promot* 2006;**20**:422–428.
19. Jago R, Baranowski T, Zakeri I, Harris M. Observed environmental features and the physical activity of adolescent males. *Am J Prev Med*. 2005;**29/2**:98–104.
20. Kaczynski AT, Henderson KA. Environmental correlates of physical activity: A review of evidence about parks and recreation. *Leisure Sci* 2007;29/4:315–354.
21. National Center for Health Statistics. *Health, United States, 2008 with Chartbook*. Hyattsville, MD, 2009.
22. Paxton RJ, Sharpe PA, Granner ML, Hutto B. Associations of sociodemographic and community environmental variables to use of public parks and trails for physical activity. *Int J Health Promot Educ* 2005;**43/4**:108–116.
23. Scott D, Munson W. Perceived constraints to park usage among individuals with low incomes. *J Park Recreation Admin* 1994;**12/4**:79–96.
24. U.S. Census Bureau. *2005–2007 American Community Survey*. http://factfinder.census.gov/servlet/ACSSAFFFacts?_submenuId=factsheet_0&_sse=on. Accessed August 19, 2009.
25. U.S. Department of Health and Human Services. *Physical Activity and Health: A Report of the Surgeon General*. U.S. Department of Health and Human Services, Centers for Disease Control and Prevention, National Center for Chronic Disease Prevention and Health Promotion: Hyattsville, MD, 1996.
26. U.S. Department of Health and Human Services. *Strategic Research Plan and Budget to Reduce and Ultimately Eliminate Health Disparities: Volume 1, Fiscal Years 2002–2006*. NIH: Bethesda, MD, 2000
27. West PC. Urban region parks and black minorities: Subculture, marginality, and interracial relations in park use in the Detroit metropolitan area. *Leisure Sci* 1989;**11**:11–28.
28. Whitt-Glover MC, Taylor WC, Heath GW, Macera CA. Self-reported physical activity among blacks estimates from national surveys. *Am J Prev Med* 2007;33/5:412–417.
29. Zhu X, Lee C. Walkability and safety around elementary schools: Economic and ethnic disparities. *Am J Prev Med* 2008;**34/4**:282–290.

Chapter 32
Leisure, Health, and Adjustment of Immigrants

Adriana Perez
Colleen Keller
Martha Nuñez

Leisure-time physical activity (LTPA) is defined as physical activity associated with exercise and recreation; this includes activity that is any other time than that associated with regular housework, occupation, or transportation (1). In the U.S., 52.5% of older adults report no LTPA, falling far short of Healthy People 2010 target objectives (2). Those reporting the least amount of LTPA include ethnic minorities, women, and those with reported lower education and income levels. The benefits of LTPA include decreased risk for all-cause mortality for many chronic conditions, including cardiovascular disease (3).

Between 1900–2000, the foreign-born population of the U.S. increased by 57% (4). Over half, representing 16 million persons, were from Latin America, and more than a third of foreign-born persons live in the Western U.S. Data regarding engagement in physical activity are sparse among recent and even generational immigrants. Those data that are available focus primarily on Latinos and Asian populations (5). Understanding the health behavior of immigrants, such as that of LTPA, is important because of their rapid growth rate and their impact on the health status of the U.S. Studies that have focused on determinants of LTPA among immigrants acknowledge the role of intrapersonal and contextual factors, as well as environmental factors that influence LTPA (6). This chapter focuses on three aspects of foreign-born subgroups and issues surrounding their engagement in LTPA: acculturation, socioeconomic status and the built environment. The patterns of LTPA and culture-centric barriers to LTPA are coupled to present clear strategies for the development of resources for encouraging LTPA in foreign-born immigrants.

LTPA Among the Foreign-Born

Californians participating in the California Health Interview Survey (California has the U.S. largest population of foreign born immigrants) showed that across all ages and gender, Asian Americans, especially immigrants, had high levels of physical inactivity and low levels of LTPA compared to U.S. born non-Asians (1). However, the data from this survey does suggest that Asian Americans were more likely to participate in physical activity related to work and work transportation. Similarly, Im and Choe found that while Korean immigrant women reported high levels of physical activity related to everyday tasks, including walking to complete errands and household work, they were less likely to engage in LTPA (7). Comparing Latino and Asian immigrant adolescents, Allen and colleagues determined that Asian adolescents' health-promoting behaviors, including LTPA improved with each generation and remained better than whites, while Latino adolescents showed generally worsening behaviors, including declining LTPA (8).

There are over 2.4 million Chinese in the U.S. and over 69% are foreign born (9). The results of a Seattle community-based health survey among Chinese immigrants showed that less than one third engaged in recommended levels of physical activity. The results also showed that younger Chinese immigrants were significantly less likely to engage in recommended levels of physical activity, and individuals who had lived in the U.S. for longer than 10 years were less likely to exercise than more recent immigrants (10). Among older Chinese, length in U.S. residence was associated with declining levels of physical activity (11).

Using data from the National Health and Nutrition Examination survey and the Behavioral Risk Factor Surveillance System showed that among Latinos, the prevalence of engaging in PA was 32% and LTPA was 42.8%, respectively (12). These cumulated data further showed that acculturation was associated with an increase in LTPA. Transportation and work PA, however, was not associated with acculturation. Qualitative data from the Mothers' Child Feeding Practices study showed dramatic differences in physical activity practices between native countries and the U.S. and showed in the latter decreased physical labor, colder climates to preclude outdoor activity and increased television viewing affecting decreased participation of their children in LTPA (13).

The Hmong ethnic subgroup, migrating primarily from Thailand, has settled primarily in Wisconsin, Minnesota and California. Using qualitative research methods, focus group data indicates that barriers to LTPA among the Hmong include safety, lack of information, language, and financial resources (14).

Acculturation

Acculturation is defined as the process of psychosocial change that occurs when groups or individuals acquire values, language, and norms of the dominant society, which may play an important part in the health behavior of immigrant people. Acculturation is a long-term process during which individuals simultaneously learn about and/or modify certain aspects of a new culture and their culture of origin (15). Among Hispanics, the effect of acculturation on health-related behaviors is complex, and not clearly tied to the level of LTPA or physical activity. For example, as Hispanics become more acculturated, they may be at greater risk for selected adverse health outcomes and engage in less physical activity (16). Conversely, there is some evidence that resistance to acculturation may confer protective benefits.

The relationship is further clouded by the notion that travel between residence of origin and the U.S. is frequent and consistent. "Selective acculturation," the individual choice whether to adopt or not adopt Western lifestyles related to physical activity behavior, becomes an opportunity for intervention among foreign born ethnic groups during the transition to the U.S. culture (17, 18). For immigrant populations in general, acculturation to U.S. norms can lead to the adoption of a more sedentary lifestyle (19, 20).

Studies that have focused on the measurement of acculturation and the adoption of health behavior have mostly included measures that have been developed primarily for Hispanics, in particular, Mexican Americans (21). There is currently no universal measure for acculturation, and those that have been used have shown varying results. However, when examining the relationship between acculturation and LTPA, studies have found that higher acculturation is often linked to higher LTPA (6).

Socioeconomic Status

Socioeconomic status is an important consideration in racial and ethnic differences regarding attitudes about physical activity, exercise and LTPA. Economic defined socioeconomic status, employment, marital status, and educational status, have been shown to have a significant impact on the initiation and maintenance of regular physical activity (22). Research has shown direct relationships between risk reducing behaviors, such as physical activity and LTPA and level of income, education, and occupational status (23, 24). Material deprivation was associated with higher BMI and low levels of physical activity; for Blacks, residential racial segregation was associated with greater odds of being sedentary and overweight (25).

Adults of all ages, regardless of ethnicity, with limited education are less likely to engage in LTPA. Some research shows that individuals with eight or fewer years of education were less physically active than those with nine or more, even controlling for differences in income, past health, functional status, body mass, and chronic disease. A direct relationship has been identified between educational level and the performance of regular physical activity (26, 27).

The Built Environment

While it is acknowledged that individual-level motivational factors might influence healthy eating and physical activity, there is no question that neighborhood environments contribute to a structure and context that influence health behavior (28). Built environment neighborhood factors that contribute to healthy behaviors—such as healthy eating and physical activity—include safety, lighted streets, curbs, neighborhood food purchase accessibility, and crime.

Place of residence has been shown to be related to decreased physical activity. Several possible explanations are evident for this association with various populations. Some authors suggest that Hispanic immigrants have on average lower educational attainment and are less likely to speak English, in turn reducing upward social mobility and constraining life opportunities, including making it less likely that they would move to better neighborhoods (29). Other authors have shown that the built environment is associated with neighborhood-level socioeconomic status, lower levels of LTPA, and related behaviors (30). Hispanics have been shown to be more socioeconomically limited in their ability to live in or move to better neighborhoods than other groups, and living in more disadvantaged neighborhoods decreases opportunities for LTPA (29, 20).

Neighborhoods, an essential framework for the built environment, are an important element in immigrant participation in physical activity and LTPA. Among Hispanics, living in a housing tract with a higher proportion of immigrants was associated with lower level of physical activity. The investigators propose that immigrant enclaves insulate individuals from neighborhood-based resources, social cohesion, safety, and civic participation (31).

Conclusions and Recommendations

Participation in LTPA has been shown to be low among immigrant groups. The growing immigrant population to the U.S. has perpetuated an interest in exploring the relationship of specific factors related to the adoption of LTPA, including intrapersonal and contextual factors. Early intervention focused on promoting LTPA among U.S. immigrants is an important public health challenge, yet presents an opportunity to prevent chronic disease among ethnic minorities. The following recommendations build upon existing research emphasizing the role of acculturation, socioeconomic status, and the built environment.

Acculturation

Evenson et al. suggest that the process of acculturation can provide for opportunities to plan for physical activity interventions since it is during this process that individuals can form new and lasting health habits, including those related to LTPA (26). Focus group data on acculturation indicates that strategies that consider the level of acculturation of immigrants can help promote LTPA by fostering social support from family and friends, especially among immigrant women that describe experiencing loneliness and isolation from family and friends in their native country (26).

Physical activity interventions that consider the level of acculturation among immigrant women can include and encourage LTPA as part of daily life activities and family roles. For example, Latinas have often described the importance of doing things with family or around the home as acceptable ways to remain physically active. And because most immigrants are employed in physically demanding jobs, it would be beneficial to include ways other than occupational physical activity in which individuals can maximize LTPA for health benefits.

Recommendations to promote LTPA among U.S. immigrants include developing ways to offer resources and LTPA activities that are culture-centric. For example, dancing activities for older Latinas and family-centered courses in multiple languages. Walking has also been described as a safe and acceptable form of LTPA across different cultures. Messages that promote LTPA should emphasize the benefit of physical activity to the family and not only the individual. An English as a Second Language curriculum was developed for Chinese immigrants in Seattle to increase physical activity among that subgroup of foreign-born Asians and was predicated on qualitative research that indicated several culture-centric barriers to physical activity: lack of time, financial concerns, weather conditions, safety issues, and lack of culturally specific organized physical activities. Recommendations from this study included the development of educational materials that reflect traditional Chinese beliefs about appropriate exercises for different age groups (32). Latina immigrant women have not only recommended bilingual information; they have also recommended clear and concise instructions for physical activity, as well as education geared towards their husbands provided by another male, perhaps who serves as a lay health advisor (26).

Socioeconomic Status

Among Korean female immigrants, older women without children used environmental resources for physical activity more than younger Korean

women with children (33). Developing ways to share childcare responsibilities as well as developing improved neighborhood LTPA resources can
contribute to improved engagement among immigrant people. Similarly,
Latina immigrant women have recommended interventions that include
activities with children instead of those that offer childcare, since leaving
children with others is often difficult and physical activity can be beneficial
to children as well (26).

Increasing LTPA might be considered a commodity requiring discretionary income and free time. As a result, recommendations to promote
LTPA should include free, affordable, and sustainable interventions that
are community-based, which would involve participation and support from
community leaders, as well as lay health advisors.

The Built Environment

Since foreign-born individuals might not be acquainted with safe places
and resources to engage in LTPA, strategies such as mapping out walking
trails, education on community resources, and actual community introduction tours can be effective. A built environment can also be enhanced
through policy initiatives that include the development of sidewalks, parks,
and supporting partnerships with local schools, community centers, and
churches that would facilitate indoor activities. Other policy initiatives
recommended by immigrant women can be carried out through worksite
interventions that provide enough time during breaks for leisure walks or
financial support that includes LTPA incentives or help to offset health club
membership (26). Lastly, public access and multimedia advertising in multiple languages about LTPA resources have been shown to be effective in
contributing to an environment that promotes LTPA among all individuals.

These are only brief recommendations with examples of how strategies
can be employed among several immigrant groups. Testing interventions
that consider important factors, specific to these populations, can potentially help to improve the overall public health.

References

1. Kandula NR, Lauderdale DS. Leisure time, non-leisure time, and occupational physical activity in Asian Americans. *Ann Epidemiol* 2005;**15/4**:257–265.
2. Hughes JP, McDowell MA, Brody DJ. Leisure-time physical activity among US adults 60 or more years of age: Results from NHANES 1999–2004. *J Phys Act Health* 2008;**5/3**:347–358.
3. Peterson JJ, Lowe JB, Peterson NA, Nothwehr FK, Janz KF, Lobas JG. Paths to leisure physical activity among adults with intellectual disabilities: Self-efficacy and social support. *Am J Health Promot* 2008;23/1:35–42.
4. Malone N, Baluja KF, Costanzo JM, Davis CJ. The foreign-born population: 2000, census 2000 brief. Washington, DC: U.S. Department of Commerce, Economics and Statistics Administration, 2003, C2KBR-34. http://www.census.gov/prod/2003pubs/c2kbr-34.pdf. Accessed July 12, 2010.
5. Bolen JC, Rhodes L, Powell-Griner EE, Bland SD, Holtzman D. State-specific prevalence of selected health behaviors, by race and ethnicity--behavioral risk factor surveillance system, 1997. *MMWR CDC Surveill Summ* 2000;**49/2**:1–60.
6. Evenson KR, Sarmiento OL, Ayala GX. Acculturation and physical activity among North Carolina Latina immigrants. *Soc Sci Med* 2004;**59/12**:2509–2522.
7. Im EO, Choe MA. Physical activity of Korean immigrant women in the U.S.: Needs and attitudes. *Int J Nurs Stud* 2001;**38/5**:567–577.
8. Allen ML, Elliott MN, Morales LS, Diamant AL, Hambarsoomian K, Schuster MA. Adolescent participation in preventive health behaviors, physical activity, and nutrition: Differences across immigrant generations for Asians and Latinos compared with whites. *Am J Public Health* 2007;**97/2**:337–343.
9. U.S. Census Bureau. Census 2000 gateway. http://www.census.gov/main/www/cen2000.html. Accessed September 19, 2009.
10. Taylor VM, Yasui Y, Tu SP, Neuhouser ML, Li L, Woodall E, et al. Heart disease prevention among Chinese immigrants. *J Community Health* 2007;**32/5**:299–310.
11. Parikh NS, Fahs MC, Shelley D, Yerneni R. Health behaviors of older Chinese adults living in New York City. *J Community Health* 2009;**34/1**:6–15.
12. Ham SA, Yore MM, Kruger J, Heath GW, Moeti R. Physical activity patterns among Latinos in the United States: Putting the pieces together. *Prev Chronic Dis* 2007;**4/4**:A92.

13. Sussner KM, Lindsay AC, Greaney ML, Peterson KE. The influence of immigrant status and acculturation on the development of overweight in Latino families: A qualitative study. *J Immigr Minor Health* 2008;**10/6**:497–505.

14. Pham KL, Harrison GG, Kagawa-Singer M. Perceptions of diet and physical activity among California Hmong adults and youths. *Prev Chronic Dis* 2007;**4/4**:A93.

15. Marin G, Gamba RJ. Changes in reported awareness of product warning labels and messages in cohorts of California Hispanics and non-Hispanic whites. *Health Educ Behav* 1997;**24/2**:230–244.

16. Amaro H, de la Torre A. Public health needs and scientific opportunities in research on Latinas. *Am J Public Health* 2002;**92/4**:525–529.

17. Yeh MC, Viladrich A, Bruning N, Roye C. Determinants of Latina obesity in the united states: The role of selective acculturation. *J Transcult Nurs* 2009;**20/1**:105–115.

18. Viladrich A, Yeh MC, Bruning N, Weiss R. "Do real women have curves?" paradoxical body images among Latinas in New York City. *J Immigr Minor Health* 2009;**11/1**:20–28.

19. Bowie JV, Juon HS, Cho J, Rodriguez EM. Factors associated with overweight and obesity among Mexican Americans and Central Americans: Results from the 2001 California health interview survey. *Prev Chronic Dis* 2007;**4/1**:A10.

20. Do DP, Dubowitz T, Bird CE, Lurie N, Escarce JJ, Finch BK. Neighborhood context and ethnicity differences in body mass index: A multilevel analysis using the NHANES III survey (1988–1994). *Econ Hum Biol* 2007;**5/2**:179–203.

21. de la Cruz FA, Padilla GV, Agustin EO. Adapting a measure of acculturation for cross-cultural research. *J Transcult Nurs* 2000;**11/3**:191–198.

22. Crespo CJ, Smit E, Andersen RE, Carter-Pokras O, Ainsworth BE. Race/ethnicity, social class and their relation to physical inactivity during leisure time: Results from the third national health and nutrition examination survey, 1988–1994. *Am J Prev Med* 2000;**18/1**:46–53.

23. Kumanyika S, Grier S. Targeting interventions for ethnic minority and low-income populations. *Future Child* 2006;**16/1**:187–207.

24. Barnett E, Armstrong DL, Casper ML. Evidence of increasing coronary heart disease mortality among black men of lower social class. *Ann Epidemiol* 1999;**9/8**:464–471.

25. Chang VW. Racial residential segregation and weight status among US adults. *Soc Sci Med* 2006;**63/5**:1289–1303.

26. Evenson KR, Sarmiento OL, Tawney KW, Macon ML, Ammerman AS. Personal, social, and environmental correlates of physical activity in North Carolina Latina immigrants. *Am J Prev Med* 2003;**25** (3 Suppl 1):77–85.

27. Eyler AA, Matson-Koffman D, Rohm Young D, et al. Quantitative study of correlates of physical activity in women from diverse racial/ethnic groups: Women's cardiovascular health network project--introduction and methodology. *Am J Prev Med* 2003;**25** (3 Suppl 1):5–14.

28. French SA, Story M, Jeffery RW. Environmental influences on eating and physical activity. *Annu Rev Public Health* 2001;**22**:309–335.

29. Sanchez-Vaznaugh EV, Kawachi I, Subramanian SV, Sanchez BN, Acevedo-Garcia D. Differential effect of birthplace and length of residence on body mass index (BMI) by education, gender and race/ethnicity. *Soc Sci Med* 2008;**67/8**:1300–1310.

30. Taylor WC, Poston WSC, Jones L, Kraft MK. Environmental justice: Obesity, physical activity, and healthy eating. *J Phys Activ Health* 2006;**3**:S30–S54.

31. Osypuk TL, Roux AV, Hadley C, Kandula NR. Are immigrant enclaves healthy places to live? The multi-ethnic study of atherosclerosis. *Soc Sci Med* 2009;**69/1**:110–120.

32. Taylor VM, Cripe SM, Acorda E, et al. Development of an ESL curriculum to educate Chinese immigrants about physical activity. *J Immigr Minor Health* 2008;**10/4**:379–387.

33. Choi J, Wilbur J, Miller A, Szalacha L, McAuley E. Correlates of leisure-time physical activity in Korean immigrant women. *West J Nurs Res* 2008;**30/5**:620–638.

Chapter 33
Healthy Sexual Expression

Tina M. Penhollow
Melissa A. Jackson
Rose Hartzell

"Few are those who see with their own eyes and feel with
their own hearts" - Albert Einstein

The range of sexual expression is limited only by the magnitude of human creativity. A traditional theme in Western culture has been that sexual activity is serious or for greater ends such as reproduction or bonding in marriage. There are, however, many approaches to sexual expression and one may define it primarily as a leisure-pleasure medium. Our current media culture promotes a sex-saturated society and nonmarital sex continues to be condemned by abstinence education advocates, conservative religious groups, as well as some medical professionals and government officials. Between the extremes of irresponsible sex and mandated virginal standards, our society must embrace the reality of the variety of sexual expressions. This chapter is divided into the following sections: Sexuality and Sexual Health; Emotional, Physical, Sociocultural, and Spiritual Health; Healthy Sexual Relationships; Protective and Contraceptive Strategies; and Summary.

Sexuality and Sexual Health

Sexuality is an integral part of human existence and plays an important role in sustaining and improving quality of life and wellness for a large proportion of the population. A satisfying sex life is a critical element of overall health and happiness for many individuals, as sexuality plays a considerable role in intimate relationships and is an important aspect of all dimensions of health. Sexuality refers to a "core dimension of being human which includes sex (female or male), gender (condition or character of being female or male), sexual and gender identity, sexual orientation, eroticism, emotional attachment/love, and reproduction. It is experienced or expressed in thoughts, fantasies, desires, beliefs, attitudes, values, activities, practices, roles, and relationships. Sexuality is the result of the interplay of biological, psychological, socio-economic, cultural, ethical, and religious/spiritual factors. Sexuality is experienced and expressed in all that we are, what we feel, think, and do" (1, p. 6). This definition encompasses individual behaviors within the bounds one may choose, which can include abstinence, casual encounters (hookups), mutual relationships, committed long-term partnerships, and marriage.

Sexual health is recognized both at the individual and societal level. At the intrapersonal level, there are specific behaviors which characterize a sexually healthy individual (Table 33.1). At the societal level, societies protect and prioritize sexual rights, policies, legislation, education, infrastructure, research, and culture conducive to sexual health. Sexual health is evidenced in the free and responsible expressions of sexual capabilities that foster harmonious personal and social wellness, which enriches individual and social life. It is not merely the absence of dysfunction, disease, or infirmity.

Emotional, Physical, Sociocultural, and Spiritual Health

There is a paucity of research on the health benefits of sexual expression, as most published reports focus on the potential negative outcomes of

Table 33.1 Essential Elements of a Sexually Healthy Adult

☑ Demonstrate honest and effective communication

☑ Exhibit respect for oneself and others

☑ Obtain partner(s) consent for each act of sexual activity

☑ Take responsibility for one's own actions

☑ Seek protection against physical and emotional harm

☑ Practice effective contraceptive strategies to prevent against unwanted pregnancy

☑ Avoid contacting or transmitting a sexually transmitted infection (STI)

☑ Care about partner(s) pleasure

☑ Practice effective decision-making

☑ Demonstrate appreciation for one's own body

☑ Exhibit skills that enhance personal relationships

☑ Identify and live according to personal values

☑ Express one's sexuality while respecting the rights of others

☑ Practice health behaviors such as regular check-ups, breast and testicular self-exams

☑ Make informed choices about family options and reproduction as needed

☑ Discriminate between life-enhancing and harmful sexual behaviors

☑ Demonstrate tolerance for individuals with different sexual values and lifestyles

☑ Enjoy and express one's sexuality throughout the lifespan

sexuality. Sexual expression has been measured as sexual thoughts (sexual arousal, sexual desire, lust); wanted sexual behaviors; and occurrence of sexual behaviors (hugging/cuddling, kissing, sexual touching, sexual penetration including sexual intercourse, oral sex, or anal sex) (2). In 2007, the Planned Parenthood Federation of America (PPFA), in cooperation with the Society for the Scientific Study of Sexuality, published an updated manuscript on the Health Benefits of Sexual Expression (3). Research on published data demonstrates a positive benefit of sexual expression on emotional, physical, sociocultural, and spiritual health. The potential negative impact of sexual expression on physical health, including sexually transmitted infections (STIs) and unintended pregnancy have been widely reported. According to the PPFA (2007), less publicized research suggests both masturbation and partnered sexual activity may enhance well-being in many ways by fostering happiness, immunity, decreased mortality, pain management, as well as sexual and reproductive health. Recent studies even suggest sexual activity may be associated with reducing the risk of the two leading causes of death in the United States, heart disease and cancer (3).

Sexuality has an impact on all aspects of health, including emotional health. In all types of close relationships there is an ebb and flow in the way partners relate sexually and in the intensity of emotions experienced. Positive feelings toward one's partner on a daily basis have been associated with sexual arousal, sexual desire, and sexual behavior for males and females in both heterosexual and same-sex relationships (2). Thus, in all types of close relationships, sexual expression is robust when positive feelings toward one's partner are experienced. There is a growing body of research demonstrating sexual expression may have emotional health benefits which include reducing stress, depression, and suicide, as well as improving self-esteem and overall quality of life (3).

A number of studies have been conducted to examine the relationship between sexual expression and physical health (3, 4). It has been well established that a physically active lifestyle decreases the risk of chronic diseases; however, exercise may also have implications for enhancing sexual health. Sexual activity does burn calories and fat, and it has been demonstrated that people who have active sex lives tend to exercise more frequently and have better dietary patterns compared to those who are less sexually active. Research reports that college students who exercised frequently and reported themselves as physically fit were significantly more likely to rate themselves higher with regard to sexual performance and sexual desirability, as compared to those who exercised less and reported themselves as less fit. Other findings demonstrate that physical fitness and body image variables account for a statistically significant amount of variation in sexual satisfaction (4). For females, the three most important variables were concerns about being nude, fitness level, and exercise frequency. For males, the three main variables predicting sexual satisfaction included strength and build, exercise frequency, and concerns about being nude. Thus, exercise and fitness (physical health) has been shown to impact a number of sexual health variables, including sexual desire and sexual satisfaction.

The sociocultural health benefits of sexual expression have been acknowledged in the literature. Research has shown the expression of sexual desire is a key ingredient in pair-bonding, which is an essential social unit of all kinship structures, cultures, and societies. It has also been demonstrated that being in a relationship is associated with reduced morbidity and mortality rates (3). Sexuality is circumscribed by a particular historic and cultural context, organized into mores, traditions, and values. Social conditioning, or the process by which people learn norms and expectations over time, as well as motivations and emotions, have a crucial impact on sexual behavior, values, and attitudes. Sexuality in historical periods in our society and other societies reveals a broad range of acceptable behavior. Societies shape and constrain the diversity of sexual expression among its members. Sociocultural components or shared meanings of sexuality are essential for the conceptualization of human sexuality. There is a clear trend in theoretical approaches that sexuality refers both to reproductive capabilities and to pleasure.

Early pioneers of sexual reproductive rights believed sexuality was a way in which women and men could gain spiritual insight. In fact, most religious traditions include positive messages regarding sexuality and eroticism in their writings (3, 5). Many cultures and religions view sexual expression as a powerful form of spiritual enlightenment. The integration of sexual expression and spirituality has been reported to have a beneficial effect on quality of life and strength of relationships. A one-year study was conducted surveying 3,810 Americans, including women and men who identified themselves as heterosexual, homosexual, and bisexual (6). Participants reported a variety of relationship experiences, including long-term monogamy, serial monogamy (a succession of short monogamous relationships), nonmonogamous relationships, and some reported no sexual relationships. Individuals who indicated they associated their sexual experiences with their spirituality were more likely to report stronger relationships and an overall better quality of life.

Healthy Sexual Relationships

Expressing sexuality may serve as a healthy leisure activity for many individuals. It is healthy to express oneself sexually as a heterosexual, homosexual, or bisexual person. Healthy forms of sexual expression are wide-ranging and can include touching, kissing, solo or mutual masturbation, sexual intercourse, oral sex, and anal intercourse. Fantasy, role playing, and the use of toys are common forms of sexual expression as well. Many of these sexual practices have been considered taboo but are now more broadly accepted as common human sexual behaviors.

A healthy and safe form of sexual expression is masturbation. Masturbation is a leisure activity in which individuals can release built up sexual tension without putting themselves at risk of STIs or pregnancy. Women can stimulate themselves by rubbing their clitoris or inserting a finger or object within their vagina. Men can stimulate themselves through massaging their penile shaft and the head of their penis. It is possible to find many masturbation enhancers including vibrators, lubricants, erotica, dildos, and anal beads at sex shops or online.

Some couples may choose to mutually masturbate. Mutual masturbation occurs when individuals masturbate themselves in the company of their sexual partner, while their partner is stimulating themselves as well. Mutual masturbation can be a safer sex activity as long as there is no genital-to-genital rubbing or ejaculate that is deposited near a mucus membrane. Other couples find they can best express their sexuality through role-playing. Couples may choose to dress up, take on the personas of people other than themselves, and engage in a variety of sexual activities. Role-playing may allow couples to act out their sexual fantasies while still in the context of a safe and consensual relationship.

Healthy relationships are built on honest communication and mutual respect. This is true of all relationships, not just romantic or sexual ones. While expression of sexuality can include eroticism, emotional attachment, love, sex, gender, and reproduction—not all of these need to be expressed. Although various expressions and influences affecting sexuality may change across time, sexuality is present throughout the lifespan. Sexual relationships are personal and intimate, even if the relationship is casual or short-lived. There are several characteristics which comprise a sexually healthy adult. Responsible people respect their partner's feelings and desires. Healthy sexual expression always includes obtaining consent. A healthy sexual adult makes informed choices about reproduction options, practices monthly self-exams, and uses personal protective devices. Individuals exhibiting responsible sexual behavior do not intend to cause harm, and refrain from any form of discrimination, exploitation, harassment, and manipulation. Table 33.1 illustrates the essential elements of a healthy sexual adult.

Protective and Contraceptive Strategies

It is important to understand that individual sexual behaviors can carry with them a level of risk, and consequently, warrant a discussion of appropriate protective and contraceptive strategies. It is necessary to be aware of the available protective and contraceptive options in order to be healthy when expressing oneself sexually. Safer sex is anything during sex play to reduce the risk of getting a STI while enhancing one's sexuality. Not having sex, abstinence, including abstinence from intercourse, oral sex, anal sex, and genital-to-genital contact is the only sure way to eliminate the risk for STIs. Massaging, caressing, hugging, dry kissing, and masturbation are no-risk or extremely low-risk practices. Even though many people say "safe sex" instead of "safer sex," there is no kind of skin-to-skin sex play with a partner that is totally risk-free. But being "safer" is something that can be done by everyone. Risk-taking behavior occurs when an individual decides to become sexually active, in which semen, blood, or vaginal fluids could be exchanged. Safer sex is for anyone who is sexually active, with males and/or females. Safer sexual health practices to reduce the risk of contracting a STI are encouraged. It is recommended to utilize as many types of protection as possible.

There are many forms of protective and contraceptive strategies available. Barrier options include condoms (male and female) and dental dams. Condoms are used for oral sex, penile-vaginal intercourse, and anal intercourse. Condoms are the only temporary birth control method available for men. A male condom is a latex or polyurethane sheath that fits over the erect penis. Condoms prevent the escape of ejaculated semen during vaginal, oral, or anal intercourse or manual play. Male condoms are one of the most popular contraceptive methods in the United States and, next to the birth control pill, the most commonly used by college age adults (7). Condoms are highly effective at protecting against both pregnancy and STIs. There are a variety of different kinds and brands of condoms available on the market. It is up to the consumer as to which brand or type of condom they feel most comfortable. When using a condom it is imperative to use it correctly, since most condom error is due to errors on the part of the user. The first step to correct condom use is to purchase condoms that are the correct size, fit, and feel for the user. Using a condom that is the incorrect size can increase the user's chance of having breakage or slippage problems during intercourse. Various sizes can usually be found without at most places where condoms are sold. Once purchased, condoms should not be stored in an environment in which they are in direct sunlight or heat. Sunlight or heat may weaken the condom, causing an increase in the chance of the condom breaking while in use. The expiration date on the condom should also be checked before application occurs. In order for the condom to be most effective, it must be placed on the penis before any penetration occurs. During application, the tip of the condom must be pinched so that once it is placed on the penis there is an open space for ejaculatory fluid to accumulate. Once ejaculation has occurred, the condom should be removed immediately, and another one applied each time sexual intercourse occurs. The use of lubrication can also increase the efficacy of condoms. Water-based lubricants, such as Astroglide and KY, may be applied to the outside of the condom before intercourse in order to decrease the chance of condom breakage (8).

Lubricants are products which increase sexual pleasure by making contact surfaces wet and slippery and by decreasing friction and possible irritation. Lubricants offer no contraceptive or STI protection. The majority of lubricants available are water-based, which are recommended by doctors and health care professionals. Water-based lubricants are considered safer compared to the old style oil-based lubricants, since water-based lubricants do not damage condoms and they flush in and out of the body with more ease than oils. Oil-based lubricants such as hand creams, massage oils, and Vaseline should not be used, as they weaken condoms making them much more likely to leak or to break.

Female condoms are used less frequently than male condoms in the United States. Female condoms resemble male condoms and are made of polyurethane or latex as well, but are worn internally by the woman. A female condom is a loose-fitting, pre-lubricated, 7-inch polyurethane pouch. One flexible plastic ring at the closed end of the sheath fits loosely against the cervix and the other ring encircles the labial area (7). A female condom can be inserted up to eight hours before intercourse, and is one method in which women can protect themselves from both pregnancy and STIs without having to rely on their partner. The female condom should not be used at the same time as a male condom, since this may increase the chance of one of the condoms breaking.

Dental dams are another barrier option used for oral-vaginal (cunnilingus) or oral-anal sex. Dental dams are small, thin, rectangular sheets of latex used to reduce the transmission of STIs during oral sex by acting as a barrier to vaginal and anal secretions which contain bacteria and viruses. Condoms, rather than dental dams, should be used for fellatio, the act of performing oral sex on a man. Due to the risk of STIs, all individuals are recommended to wear a condom and/or use dental dams when coming into contact with another person's bodily fluids. Only individuals who have tested negative for STIs and are in mutually exclusive relationships have the clear option of not using barrier protection (9).

Spermicides are a contraceptive method available in many forms including foam, cream, gel, vaginal contraceptive film (VCF), and suppositories. Spermicides contain the chemicals nonoxynol-9 (N-9) or octoxynol that prevent pregnancy by immobilizing and killing sperm; however, spermicides offer no protection against STIs. Spermicides have been found to irritate the vaginal wall, making women more susceptible to STIs and HIV. Therefore, it is not recommended that couples use any type of spermicide, including spermicidal condoms, unless both partners are in a monogamous relationship and have tested negative for STIs and HIV (10).

Many of the most common birth control methods used by women work by artificially altering hormone levels. Hormone-based contraceptives potentially have several effects, including inhibiting ovulation, altering the mucous lining of the cervix for the blockage of passing sperm, and preventing a fertilized egg from implanting successfully in the uterus. Oral contraceptives are a reversible method of birth control most commonly used by women in the United States today, including women of college age (7). Four basic types of oral contraceptives are available on the market: constant-dose combination, triphasic, Seasonale, and the progestin-only birth control pill.

The NuvaRing and Ortho Evra are two hormone-based contraceptives that do not require taking a pill each day. Both synthetic estrogen and pro- gestin are embedded in either a 2-inch diameter soft and transparent vaginal ring (NuvaRing) to release hormones through the vaginal lining, or a beige match-booked sized transdermal patch (Ortho Evra) to release hormones through the skin into the bloodstream (7). The NuvaRing and Ortho Evra both work in the same way as the birth control pill to prevent pregnancy.

Depo-Provera is a long-acting progestin (hormone) form of birth control. It is injected into the muscle every 11 weeks. It is effective 24 hours after the first injection if given within five days of the beginning of menstruation. The Depo-Provera shot inhibits the secretion of hormones that stimulate the ovaries, which prevents ovulation. It also thickens the cervical mucus to prevent the entrance of sperm into the uterus.

Implanon is a new form of hormonal contraceptive approved by the United States Food and Drug Administration in 2006. Implanon is a small, thin, implantable flexible rod the size of a matchstick surgically placed under the skin of the arm. It contains a hormone called etonogestrel, a progestin-only method of birth control, which does not contain estrogen. Implanon prevents pregnancy by stopping the release of eggs from the ovary, as well as changing the mucus in the cervix and the lining of the uterus. Women can use a single Implanon rod for up to three years.

Intrauterine devices, commonly referred to as IUDs, are small, T-shaped contraceptive devices made of flexible plastic and are surgically implanted into a women's uterus. Both the copper and progesterone in IUDs are ef- fective in preventing fertilization. There are three IUDs available on the market: Copper-T (ParaGard), Progestasert T, and Mirena (7). Depending on the type of IUD a woman chooses, she may be protected from pregnancy for up to 5–10 years.

Another method of contraception that has become more common in recent years is sterilization, which is the most effective form of birth control excluding abstinence. Sterilization is the leading method of birth control in the United States and around the world (7). Sterilization is an option for individuals who do not want more children or prefer to remain childless. Female sterilization, referred to as tubal ligation, is the surgical procedure performed on a woman. Sterilization using the tubal ligation technique is accomplished by severing or tying the fallopian tubes. Male sterilization, referred to as a vasectomy, is the permanent birth control method performed on a man. A vasectomy is accomplished by removing a section from each vas deferens, the sperm-carrying duct located in the testicles. In general, male sterilization is safer, has fewer complications following surgery, is considerably less expensive, and is as equally effective as female sterilization.

It should be noted that hormone-based contraceptives, IUDs, and permanent surgical procedures help prevent against pregnancy, but do not prevent against STIs. Each method of birth control described has advantages and disadvantages relative to effectiveness, safety, cost, and convenience. It is essential to be familiar with the various methods of birth control, as many individuals will likely use several forms of contraception and new practices and procedures will become increasingly available. Whether an individual is having sex or not, both men and women need to have regular checkups to make sure they are sexually healthy. STI testing should be conducted every six months for individuals who have multiple sex partners. Women should have annual gynecological exams. Protective and contraceptive strategies provide the tools for healthy sexual expression. A list of safer sexual health practices is provided in Table 33.2.

Summary

Research in human sexuality should continue to explore the full scope of sexual health by identifying the potential health benefits of sexual expression as well as the risks. The emotional, physical, sociocultural, and spiritual health benefits of sexual expression cannot be ignored. Couples may choose to engage in a variety of leisure sexual behaviors, all of which can be healthy if they occur in a consensual and safe way. Healthy relationships are built on honest communication and mutual respect. There are many forms of protective and contraceptive strategies available, and it is possible for individuals to engage in sexual activities in a manner that decreases their risk for pregnancy and acquisition of STIs. Sexuality plays an important role in sustaining and improving quality of life and wellness for a large proportion of the population and can serve as a healthy leisure activity.

Table 33.2 Safer Sexual Health Practices

☑ If you have multiple sex partners, ask your health care provider to check for STIs every 6 months, even if you do not have any symptoms

☑ Have a STI test before sexual encounter(s) with a new partner

☑ Women should have annual gynecological exams

☑ For oral-vaginal sex (cunnilingus) and oral-anal sex, use latex dental dams

☑ Use latex or polyurethane barriers, such as condoms (male or female) for oral-penile sex (fellatio) and sexual intercourse

☑ Avoid the use of oil-based or petroleum products, such as Vaseline

☑ Use water-based lubricants, such as Astroglide or KY

☑ Never have sex (even with a condom) if you or your partner has a visible sore, ulcer, or lump on the genital or anal area

☑ Change latex/polyurethane barriers prior to each act of genital contact and/or oral sex

☑ Avoid sexual contact with anonymous partner(s) whose health practices are unknown

☑ Utilize birth control method(s) of choice

☑ Avoid having sex while under the influence of alcohol or drugs

☑ For additional protection, use spermicidal foams, jellies, or creams with nonoxynol-9

☑ After manual sexual contact with another person's genital area, wash your hands and genitals with hot water and an antibacterial soap

☑ Do not share vibrators or any type of sex toy

☑ Utilize condoms on sex toys and clean with hot water and an antibacterial soap between each use

☑ Seek immediate medical treatment if you think you or your partner has a STI

References

1. Pan American Health Organization. *Promotion of Sexual Health: Recommendations for Action* 2000. http://www.paho.org/English/HCP/HCA/PromotionSexualHealth.pdf. Accessed July 12, 2010.

2. Ridley C, Ogolsky B, Payne P, Totenhagen C, Cate R. Sexual expression: Its emotional context in heterosexual, gay, and lesbian couples. *J Sex Res* 2008;**45/3**:305–315.

3. Whipple B, Knowles J, Davis J, Gianotten W, Golub D. The health benefits of sexual expression. *Planned Parenthood Federation of America, Inc.* 2007.

4. Penhollow TM, Young M. Predictors of sexual satisfaction: the role of body image and fitness. *Electron J Hum Sex* 2008;**11**. http://www.ejhs.org/volume11/Penhollow.htm. Accessed July 12, 2010.

5. Keesling B. *Rx Sex: Making Love is the Best Medicine*. Alameda, CA: Hunter House, Inc, 2000.

6. Ogden G. Spiritual passion and compassion in late life sexual relationships. *Electron J Hum Sex* 2002;**4**. http://www.ejhs.org/volume4/Ogden.htm. Accessed July 12, 2010.

7. Crooks R, Baur K. *Our Sexuality (9ᵗʰ ed)*. Wadsworth Publishers: Belmont, CA, 2005.

8. Crosby RA, Sanders SA, Yarber WL, Graham CA, Dodge B. Condom use errors and problems among college men. *Sex Trans Diseases* 2002;**29/9**:552–557.

9. Strong B, Yarber W, Sayad B, DeVault C. *Human Sexuality: Diversity in Contemporary America (6ᵗʰ ed)*. McGraw Hill: New York, 2008.

10. Centers for Disease Control and Prevention. Nonoxynol-9 spermicide contraception use: United States 1999. *MMWR* 2002;**51/18**:389–392.

Chapter 34

Healthy Dining: Eating for Pleasure, Leisure, and Wellness

Christopher Wharton
Linda Vaughan

The seemingly simple act of eating serves many purposes, many of which have evolved over the history of mankind. Early in the evolution of our species, eating was simply a survival mechanism. Humans ate what was available and what didn't kill them. With the invention of fire, it is presumed that pleasurable eating softened what had previously been a strictly utilitarian process and, according to many, proved a crucial distinction between humans and animals. Over time, food choices expanded; food storage, preservation, and preparation techniques became more advanced; and the social role of dining magnified. Throughout the centuries, food became a symbol of wealth as gluttony amongst the royal and upper classes contrasted strongly with the starvation faced by the poor. Specific foods and dining patterns came to represent one's identity through political, religious, and/or cultural affiliations. Food represented power during wars, political conflicts, and even within family units. How has such a simple act of survival turned into what is currently viewed as a minefield of conflicting medical, economic, ethical, sociocultural, and political viewpoints? As we explore the process of healthy dining, some of these questions will be addressed but certainly not resolved. For the purpose of this chapter, we have elected to frame our discussion around the times we eat at home and the times we eat away from the home. While not a perfect line of distinction, it offers a strong point of contrast for examining how one might eat for pleasure, leisure, and wellness.

Eating at Home

The family unit, however it may be defined, is anchored by a Home. Homes come in many shapes and structures but are readily recognizable by all within a community. Home represents safety and security; for most, home is where our earliest memories of eating are born. Up until the past several decades, home was also where the majority of eating took place. In today's world, how does home-based eating influence our ability to enjoy and benefit from the foods we consume?

Establishing a Healthful Base for Eating at Home

The stimulus to eat can be triggered internally, through signals received by the area of the brain known as the hypothalamus, or externally, in response to environmental sights, sounds, and aromas. *Hunger* is viewed as a physiologic response, typically unpleasant in nature, that triggers a search for food, any acceptable food. In contrast, *appetite* is more of an emotional response, often occurring in the absence of hunger and frequently directed towards a specific food, such as a brownie, or a type of food, such as a salty, crunchy snack. Whether the urge to eat is grounded in hunger or appetite, the outcome is largely defined by the *"food environment"* of the home.

Nutrition educators often refer to the importance of the home's *gatekeeper*: the person who (largely or totally) controls the decisions related to food purchasing. This individual, often the female head of household, exerts tremendous influence on the availability of food within the home. In the same way that new parents "baby-proof" their home, the gatekeeper can establish a healthful stock of foods from which the family can choose. Simply put, if the majority of foods brought into the home is healthy, family members are more likely to eat health-promoting meals and snacks.

What, then, is the definition of "healthy foods" or "health promoting diet"? Although modified somewhat by certain medical conditions, exercise/performance goals, and other individualized factors, the basics of good nutrition are easily summarized. The U.S. Departments of Health and Human Services and of Agriculture have published *Dietary Guidelines for Americans* (http://www.cnpp.usda.gov/DGAs2010-DGACReport.htm), with a new edition due in 2010, that provide easy-to-understand, easy-to-implement recommendations. "Feel better today. Stay healthy for tomorrow." is a major theme that reinforces the concept that healthful habits of today lowers future risk of many chronic diseases, including heart disease, diabetes, osteoporosis, and certain cancers. Specific themes and recommendations related to healthy food choices are summarized in Table 34.1.

One of the more common recommendations for healthy eating is increased consumption of fruits and vegetables. Although most produce purchased for the home comes from grocery stores, corner markets, and other food outlets, a renewed interest in local foods has spurred the development of alternative sources of healthful whole foods. *Farmers' markets* and *community supported agriculture programs* (CSAs), in particular, have gained in popularity in the last decade as a source of food for home use. Farmers' markets provide a venue in which the consumer not only has the opportunity to buy "farm fresh" whole foods, such as fruits, vegetables, and grain products, but also the opportunity to meet the producers of those foods. The chance to interact with food producers offers a unique social experience in food purchasing: rather than pulling produce from a grocery shelf to bring home, a consumer receives produce from the producer, who can explain where and how that produce was grown. Such experiences can be educational, allowing for a deeper appreciation of the source of one's food and the effort involved in growing it.

CSAs operate in a slightly different fashion than farmers' markets. Although many different CSA models exist, the average CSA is usually run

Table 34.1 Basic Guidelines for a Healthy Diet

Website	Description
Focus on Fruits	Select fresh, dried, canned, and frozen fruits from across the color spectrum. Red, orange, yellow, purple, green, and blue fruits are packed with phytochemicals, vitamins, and minerals.
Vary your Veggies	Dark green, orange, deep yellow, and red vegetables pack the most power in a healthy diet. Legumes such as black beans, pinto beans, split peas and lentils are low fat, high protein foods that are also rich in minerals and vitamins. Fresh, frozen, and canned vegetables are all healthful choices; avoid vegetables packaged with added salt or sauces and all fried vegetables.
Go Low with Calcium Rich Foods	After the age of 2 years, select low fat or fat-free milk, yogurt, and cheese to meet your calcium needs. Every day, aim for 3 cups of milk/yogurt or the equivalent in cheese. If regular cow's milk is not part of your typical diet, choose lactose-free milk, calcium fortified orange juice and/or soy milk, and other calcium-fortified foods.
Make Half your Grains Whole	Read food labels carefully to choose breads, cereals, crackers, rice, and pasta products where the first ingredient is specifically identified as a "whole" grain. Brown rice, whole wheat pasta, stone ground corn tortillas, bulgur, barley, and oatmeal are popular examples of whole grain foods that provide fiber, B-vitamins, and minerals.
Go Lean with Protein	Select leaner cuts of meat; prepare all meats, fish, and poultry by broiling, grilling, baking, or roasting it. Rotate your protein-rich foods by including legumes as a main dish a few times each week. Although high in fat, nuts and nut butters are protein rich and provide so-called healthy fats.
Know Your Limits	Use the Nutrition Facts label to select foods low in saturated and trans fats. Select and serve foods low in added sugars and salt. If you choose to drink alcohol, do so in moderation [up to 1 drink a day for women and up to 2 drinks a day for men].

[1] Adapted from Dietary Guidelines for Americans, 2005, 6th Edition. U.S. Departments of Health and Human Services and Agriculture. U.S. Government Printing Office.

out of a single farm. In the context of a CSA, the consumer signs a contract at the beginning of a growing season, paying up front for a "share" of produce being grown at the farm. In return, the farmer provides weekly allotments of produce to CSA members for the duration of the growing season. By paying for all weekly shares up front, the consumer provides the farmer with needed capital—and financial security—to run farm operations. By purchasing from a local farmer, the consumer is guaranteed fresh, seasonal whole foods on a consistent basis. Studies on such programs note that CSA members take satisfaction not only in receiving seasonal goods, but also in participating in a community event that supports the efforts of local small businessmen and women—the farmers growing the food (1).

In addition to foods purchased and brought into the home by the gatekeeper, foods can be made available to the household in other ways. Some families, rural or urban, are embracing home or community gardening as a means of introducing fresh produce into their diets. Home gardening is the establishment of in-ground, raised box, or potted plant gardens in and around the property on which a family is living. Community gardens are usually small areas of land within a neighborhood that have been partitioned into multiple 'plots' that an individual or family may rent. The individual or family may then grow plants of their choice but are also responsible for the upkeep of that particular plot.

Hands-on experiences with gardening have proven an effective means of increasing fruit and vegetable intake in children, including experimentation with new fruits and vegetables (2). For many households, gardening becomes a leisure-time activity that is very satisfying, provides a flexible opportunity for outside activity, and offers a time for informal nutrition education.

Establishing a Nurturing Environment for Eating at Home

The provision of healthy foods within the home is a multi-step process that begins with the purchase or acquisition of food, continues through the food preparation stage, and ends with the actual serving and consumption of the food. The home environment is key to bringing pleasure back into dining.

Without question, family meals benefit all members of the household. Whenever possible, given the demands of today's children and adults, family members are encouraged to make it a priority to sit down for an uninterrupted meal. No television or electronic devices; no books or toys; no coming and going. The atmosphere should be pleasant, as you would find when dining with friends. No nagging, fighting, or yelling. Family members should look forward to shared mealtimes, not dread them. A pleasant meal offers the opportunity to connect and communicate. Regular family meals have been associated with enhanced academic, emotional, and social outcomes, including a long term reduction in adolescent addictive behaviors (3), a lower rate of overweight in school aged children (4), a more healthful pattern of food intake (5), and an increased consumption of breakfast, itself a predictor of many academic and health benefits (6). There is even a national campaign "Eat Better, Eat together" that promotes family mealtimes in order to improve dietary intake and strengthen the family.

"Feeding" is very different from "eating." Feeding is a process in which the actions and decisions of one or several persons are imposed upon others. Eating is a self-initiated, largely self-regulated process. Within many households, the process of feeding comes into conflict with process of eating. When these conflicts occur between parents/caretakers and children, there is an increased potential for future eating disorders and body dysmorphia (abnormal perception of one's body image). While there are numerous recommendations on "how to feed" a family, child, or household, one popular approach is based on a clearly defined division of responsibility (7). In this family-oriented model, the parent/caretaker is responsible for the "*what, when, and where of feeding*" while the (younger) child is responsible for the "*how much and whether of eating.*" Older children and adolescents gradually assume the responsibilities of feeding and eating as they mature and gain independence. Feeding decisions include what foods to serve, when to provide meals and snacks, and where to dine. The process of feeding sets the stage. Eating decisions are individualized: the individual himself or herself decides which foods to eat and how much (if any) to eat. While some parents/caretakers find it difficult to give up control over the eating process, the research literature confirms that controlling, restrictive parental feeding styles increase risk for subsequent overweight, eating disorders, and body dissatisfaction (8). In contrast, positive parental role modeling at meals and involving children in the food selection and preparation processes are predictors of more healthful food choices and avoidance of excess weight.

The provision of a supportive, nurturing environment enhances the health-promoting qualities of nutritious foods and meals. Even the healthiest of meals cannot overcome the negative impact of a conflict-ridden household.

Bringing Pleasure and Leisure into the Home Dining Experience

Opening one's home to others to share in the dining experience defines many cultures across the globe. As host or hostess, there is the opportunity to provide a leisurely and pleasurable experience. While some prefer to do all the planning and preparation on their own, many hosts are embracing the model of communal dining, inviting all participants to take an active role. The event may play out as a pot-luck meal, where everyone brings a specific food item/dish, or a progressive meal, where participants travel from one location to the next as the meal transitions from one course to the next. Increasingly, a "hands-on" meal is gaining in popularity. Invited guests are literally put to work: they may be asked to prepare their own pizza, help in making the salad or pasta, or prepare the vegetables for roasting. Whatever the arrangement, a participatory meal eases the burden on the host or hostess and increases conversation and enjoyment among all.

Sharing the dining experience with others provides a great opportunity to experience unfamiliar cuisines, foods and beverages, and cultural practices. Spending time with a family who retains traditional Hispanic meal patterns will introduce others to the communal activities of making holiday tamales. Other families may invite guests into their home for an afternoon of holiday cookie baking or to take part in a pre-Thanksgiving tradition of deep-frying turkeys. These events broaden one's definition of a "healthful diet" and break down communication and other barriers between persons of differing backgrounds.

Eating Outside the Home

The many benefits of eating at home have received attention from the media and researchers alike because, ironically, eating at home is becoming increasingly less common. The amount of time and money spent on home food preparation declined steadily from the 1970s through today, while money and time spent eating meals and snacks away from the home increased rapidly. Fewer than half of all U.S. households report cooking at home even once a day. And, by 2004, money spent in the U.S. on food away from the home exceeded that spent on food for the home for the first time (9).

Understanding the Food Environment Outside the Home

The reasons for such a change in where individuals, friends, and families share snacks and meals are many. Primary among them, however, is the ever-evolving complexion of the food environment outside the home. Recall that the food environment within the home—including what foods are available, when, and where—often is regulated by a gatekeeper. Outside the home, the food environment is influenced by multiple factors. For instance, the many and varied food advertisements found in the food environment drive consumer purchasing behaviors, emphasizing packaged, processed, and pre-cooked foods. Similarly, the availability of food both within food outlets and non-food outlets (gas stations, book stores, and other consumer goods venues) gives the consumer the opportunity to purchase food more easily and more readily than ever before. This unrelenting availability of food also leads to increased competition among those selling food, driving down prices and making it more affordable for consumers to eat away from the home. Finally, the more urbanized and mobile culture cultivated in the U.S. has led to a demand for readily available convenience foods made for the on-the-go lifestyle.

As a result, the food environment outside the home now is saturated not only with a variety of restaurants offering sit-down or take-home meals, but also with non-traditional food and non-food venues offering an extensive array of ready-to-eat foods.

Taking Advantage of a Rich Food Environment

The overcrowded food environment described above offers many benefits for consumers. From the perspective of health and leisure, a rich food environment offers a wide variety of novel cuisines and atmospheres in which to enjoy new foods. Trying foods from other cultures can be an ideal opportunity to be introduced to new flavors, customs, and ideas, and to develop an appreciation for those cultures. Because "eating out" is often a fun, social venture, trying new foods can also feel more adventurous, without the pressure that might come with attempting an unfamiliar food or meal at home.

As noted earlier, food has been linked to social events in every culture studied. Whether the food or meal is presented within a family, religious, or other cultural event, the activity becomes more enjoyable, more interactive, and more meaningful. Some events held outside the home are defined by the foods served: ask any child what he/she remembers about the circus or the state fair and specific foods will no doubt be part of the response. While many are (rightfully) concerned about what has been termed "the toxic food environment" of the U.S., it is equally important to remember that a healthful diet is flexible enough to accommodate occasional splurges! Dietary phobias, such as fear of fat or refined sugars, should never be allowed to interfere with the normal enjoyment of social events that include or are based upon eating outside the home.

Although eating out means being served food rather than preparing one's own food, it does not preclude the chance to enjoy food grown or produced locally. In fact, a new trend has developed, especially within the last decade, for restaurants to secure and purchase local ingredients. For instance, some restaurants work with individual farms to purchase ingredients for their dishes and note on their menus the farms providing these ingredients. Other restaurants literally grow ingredients on site, harvesting fruit from fruit trees, herbs and spices from the surrounding landscaping, and other products for daily meal preparations. As with purchasing local produce through farmers' markets and CSAs, "going local" when eating out also means supporting local, non-chain restaurants, an important aspect in maintaining a vibrant local economy.

Navigating the Pitfalls of Eating Outside the Home

The outside food environment, while offering numerous opportunities for enjoyable dining experiences, can also be treacherous in terms of its impact on health and wellness. As a result, consumers must take care when enjoying meals away from the home. Numerous strategies are available to maximize the healthfulness of the leisurely experience of eating away from the home.

Of greatest concern when eating out is the nutritional make-up of the foods consumed. Individual meals and snacks purchased and eaten outside the home generally are higher in calories, fat, saturated fat, and salt compared to those prepared inside the home (10). A lifestyle characterized by frequent "away from home" eating has broad implications as well: overall diet quality is negatively associated with the number of meals eaten away from the home (11). One important reason for this negative dietary nutritional profile is probably the venue in which consumers eat away-from-home foods. Americans are eating at sit-down restaurants less often than in the past and, at the same time, are increasing the number of occasions they purchase fast foods, in particular from drive-through windows. Fast foods are often *calorie-dense*, meaning they contain a high number of calories by weight of food. Fast foods also can be high in fat and sodium, and low in fiber, vitamins A and C, and other critically important nutrients.

Being mindful of one's food choices, however, can help improve the nutritional quality of snacks and meals purchased outside the home. For instance, many fast food chains post nutrition information of their offerings. Most often, this information can be found online or in pamphlets in the store. In some locations in the U.S., fast food chains are required to post this information on store menu boards. Federal legislation has been introduced that would require this practice in many U.S. restaurant chains. Consumers can then take nutrition information into account when purchasing foods to ensure they buy items that are not only enjoyable but healthful as well. Consumers can also seek out restaurants that promote the use of healthy ingredients or healthy food offerings, especially those using whole, local foods. These restaurants often provide a more healthful set of options from which to choose.

Portion size is another very important consideration when eating away from home. Many restaurants (fast food or otherwise) maximize portion sizes in an attempt to convince consumers they are receiving maximal value for the money spent. Faced with larger portions, consumers will generally eat more than necessary as visual cues, like the amount of food on one's plate, can override internal body signals of satiety or fullness. By eating more slowly and mindfully, especially while socializing with friends and family, one can give the body time to feel full on less food. Consumers can also split meals with friends or family, which also can contribute to the social enjoyment of the eating occasion, or bring extra food home to enjoy at a later time.

Conclusion

Eating food, whether in the home or outside of it, is a surprisingly complex process. Eating is not only about immediate sustenance, but also about social relationships, local customs and culture, long-term health, and overall wellness. Within the home, families often define themselves through the ways they prepare and provide food. Children learn the value of food and develop relationships with food—healthy or unhealthy—that are often life-long. Eating outside the home can be a great pleasure, connecting individuals more closely with friends, family, and the place they live. It can also expose individuals to international cuisines, new food customs, and local businesses. But, without mindful consideration of the places and types of foods one eats, eating away from home can also have a detrimental impact on one's long-term health and wellness.

Thoughtful purchasing, preparation, provision, and consumption of food can optimize both the pleasurable and healthful aspects of eating. Using current guidelines for healthful eating and employing strategies to navigate the challenges of the external food environment are important ways to attain and maintain optimal health while enjoying eating in the home or outside the home.

References

1. Brehm JM, Eisenhauer BW. Motivations for participating in community supported agriculture and their relationship with community attachment and social capital. *South Rural Sociol* 2008;**23**:94–115.
2. Heim S, Stang J, Ireland M. A garden pilot project enhances fruit and vegetable consumption among children. *J Amer Diet Assoc* 2009;**109**:1220–1226.
3. Eisenberg ME, Neumark-Sztainer D, Fulkerson JA, Story M. Family meals and substance use: Is there a long-term protective association? *J Adolesc Health* 2008;**43**:151–156.
4. Gable S, Change Y, Krull JL. Television watching and frequency of family meals are predictive of overweight onset and persistence in a national sample of school-aged children. *J Amer Diet Assoc* 2007;**107**:53–61.
5. Rockett HRH. Family dinner: More than just a meal. *J Amer Diet Assoc* 2007;**107**:1498–1501.
6. Pearson N, Biddle SJH, Gorely T. Family correlates of breakfast consumption among children and adolescents. A systematic review. *Appetite* 2009;**52**:1–7.
7. Satter E. Your Child's Weight: *Helping Without Harming (Birth through Adolescence)*. Kelcy Press: Madison, WI, 2005.
8. Clark HR, Goyder E, Bissell P, Blank L, Peters J. How do parents' child-feeding behaviours influence child weight? Implications for childhood obesity policy. *J Public Health* 2007;**29**:132–141.
9. Ebbin R. Midwest tops in restaurant spending. Restaurants USA Online, July, 2002. http://www.restaurant.org/rusa/magArticle. cfm?ArticleID=797. Accessed July 12, 2010.
10. Guthrie JF, Lin BH, Frazao E. Role of food prepared at home in the American diet, 1977–78 versus 1994–96: Changes and consequences. *J Nutr Ed Behav* 2002;**34**:140–150.
11. Woodruff SJ, Hanning RM. Effect of meal environment on diet quality rating. *Can J Diet Pract Res* 2009;**70**:118–124.

Chapter 35
Health and Television Viewing
Kelley K. Pettee Gabriel

Introduction

The examples used to portray types of leisure activities can be either active or passive in nature. Active leisure activities involve expending physical energy and can range in intensity from light to very hard (e.g., causal strolling to running). Alternatively, passive leisure activities involve little or no energy expenditure and are usually characterized by sedentary activities (i.e., watching television (TV), internet use, reading, or sleeping). *Physical inactivity* is defined as a state in which body movement is minimal and is quantified as the amount of time spent in *passive leisure* or *sedentary* activities (1, 2).

Television Viewing in U.S. Adults and Children

The U.S. Surgeon General's Report supports the link between physical inactivity and risk for health-related outcomes (3). As such, leading federal initiatives, such as *Healthy People 2010* (4), have begun to establish objectives for reducing physical inactivity as well as for increasing physical activity levels. In both children and adults, specific inactivity-related objectives have been identified in order to achieve the larger goal, which is to improve health, fitness, and quality of life through physical activity. In adults, that objective is more general with the goal to reduce the proportion of adults who do not participate in any active leisure physical activities. In children, goals that specifically target passive leisure activities have been established (i.e., increase the proportion of children who watch two or fewer hours of TV per day). State and national initiatives for reducing physical through a reduction in time spent watching TV are currently being monitored in surveillance systems in order to track the *Healthy People 2010* goals. In adults, TV viewing, in addition to nonoccupational computer use, is tracked through the National Health and Nutrition Examination Survey (NHANES), and in children, TV viewing and nonschool related computer use is monitored by the Youth Risk Behavior Survey (YRBS).

In a 2007 report by Yore et al., which utilized NHANES survey data from 1999–2002, approximately 43% of adults aged 20 or more years reported watching three or more hours of TV per day (5). In children, 2007 YRBS data indicated that 35.4% of children in grades 9–12 reported watching TV for three or more hours per day on an average school day, a rate which has declined from 1999 (42.8%). However, the proportion of children watching TV for three or more hours has remained largely unchanged from 2005 (37.2% in 2005).

TV Viewing in Public Health Research

The growing national interest in reducing physical inactivity levels among U.S. children and adults has trickled down into the research community. Currently, there is growing interest in developing methods that accurately quantify time spent being sedentary in order to determine the impact of physical inactivity on health-related outcomes or for use in intervention efforts designed to reduce the amount of time spent in passive leisure activities in order to improve the health and well-being of study participants. When focusing on strategies that target a reduction in physical inactivity levels, researchers often focus on passive leisure activities that provide no real health benefit and are easily modifiable (1).

One strategy to combat rising physical inactivity rates that is particularly appealing to researchers is to reduce time spent watching TV, which is an analogous approach to existing state and national initiatives. TV watching is an extremely popular leisure time activity in the U.S. Based on 2008 data from Neilson Media Research, more than 65% of U.S. homes receive digital cable or satellite broadcasting—services that provide one hundred or more channel options. Further, 25–35% of U.S. homes have Digital Video Recorder (DVR) or video on demand capabilities or time-shifted TV. Together, these factors contribute to an exorbitant amount of available programming, and on an individual-basis, can lead to an increased amount of time spent watching TV. According to Neilsen Media Research (2008) (6), the TV was on in the typical household for more than one hundred hours per month, which is equivalent to approximately 4–5 hours of TV watching per day. From 2007, the total amount of time spent watching TV has increased by 4%. In addition to TV, individuals also have the capability to watch TV and videos using the internet and mobile phones, which adds to the already overabundant opportunity to view TV programming.

Measuring TV Viewing in Public Health Research

Overall, the quantification of physical activity has received less attention than physical activity (1). As such, there is limited information regarding the psychometric properties (i.e., reliability and validity) of measures used to assess TV watching. However, due to the recent research interest in this topic, methods are becoming more refined.

In adults, researchers have primarily relied on self-report measures to ascertain the amount of time spent watching TV. TV programming is more structured when compared with other sedentary behaviors as it is typically scheduled in 30 to 60 minute increments. Structured programming may provide a more accurate assessment when individuals are asked to recall this particular sedentary activity. Unfortunately, there is no clear consensus regarding question wording, recall time frame, or activity or activities included. Some questions ask participants to recall the total number of TV hours watched in a usual or typical week, while others use a more definitive time frame (e.g., past week). For some individuals, responding to a question that is framed in terms of a usual or typical week may require longer-term recall than responding to a question about the past week, especially if the pattern of the particular behavior is irregular. For example, if the amount of time spent watching TV varies from week to week, the individual would need to first identify a week that he/she considers typical. The longer the interval between the time of recollection and the week identified as most reflective of the usual number of hours spent watching TV, the higher the possibility of an inaccurate estimate. Similarly, with some questions individuals are asked to recall the number of hours spent watching television per day, while others use other periods of reference (e.g., past week). It may be easier for individuals to recall an activity done over the past day, rather than per week basis, which may cause discrepancies in TV watching estimates that are reported by different surveillance systems or research studies. Further, some questions are one-item, while others inquire about TV watching and additional activities (i.e., videos or Internet use). The recall of additional activities beyond TV watching may also lead to greater variability in responses given.

In children, ascertaining TV watching via self-report measures may not be appropriate. In general, children may have more difficulty recalling activities, as such; the strategies that have been identified to measure TV viewing in this population are largely age dependant. Subjective approaches include the use of a parent proxy for younger children or daily habits diary for older children and adolescents, while event loggers provide an objective measure of time spent watching TV. Briefly, appliances that promote study targeted sedentary behaviors (e.g., television or computer) are attached to an event logger, which are commercially available devices that record minute-by-minute electrical activity data of the appliance of interest. Thus, the data from event loggers provide an objective measure of the amount of time that the appliance was in use. Finally, although physical inactivity should not be thought as the inverse of physical activity, there is considerable interest within the research community to measure physical inactivity levels using accelerometery. Data are outputted as counts at user-defined intervals, or epochs. It has been proposed that a zero count may indicate time spent in sedentary, passive leisure activity, especially if zero counts are accumulated over long periods of time. For example, zero counts accumulated over 30 minutes may indicate that the individual was inactive during those 30 minutes. However, zero counts may also be associated with monitor removal; therefore, the use of a supplemental monitor diary where individuals record the time the monitor was put on in the morning and taken off in the evening is recommended.

The practice of *media multitasking* is an important limitation for researchers to consider when quantifying time spent watching TV, regardless of whether TV viewing was measured via subjective or objective methods. Media multitasking is defined as participating in more than one medium at a time (e.g., using the internet while watching TV) (7). With regards to subjective ascertainment, individuals may have more difficulty accurately recalling TV watching if another form of media was used at the same time. Likewise, an event logger only provides information on appliances that it is attached to. Further, the event logger is only capable of quantifying the amount of time that the appliance was powered on and; therefore, not able to determine whether or not the TV was watched for the entire time by the same individual.

Television Viewing and Health Outcomes

The recent national and research-based interest in reducing sedentary behaviors is primarily due to observed associations between TV watching and health-risk factors, including obesity. The mechanism to support the relationship between TV watching and obesity can simply be attributed to an imbalance between energy intake and energy expenditure. Given that there are limited hours in the day that are not already designated for work or school and other compulsory activities, how one spends his/her leisure or free time is particularly important. The discretionary amount of time that was once allotted during the day for more active pursuits, such as walking and sports participation, is now competing with more passive leisure activities. Therefore, time spent watching TV may reduce time spent participating in other activities that may have higher associated metabolic costs than watching TV, which reduces overall energy expenditure. On the other side of energy balance, research suggests that TV viewing is associated with greater energy intake through prompting and distraction. It is thought that commercials that advertise products during TV programming may prompt viewers to eat when they are not hungry and to make unhealthy food choices. Also, watching TV may also affect energy intake by distracting the viewer so that he/she becomes unaware of what and how much food they are consuming.

Television Viewing and Obesity

Robust findings from research in adults clearly support the direct association between TV watching and risk for obesity (8). In these studies, TV watching was typically assessed using self-report while obesity was measured using a variety of anthropometric markers including body weight, body mass index, percent body fat, waist-to-hip ratio, and waist circumference obtained using either subjective or objective means. Regardless of measurement strategy, findings clearly indicate that the more time that is spent watching TV, the greater the probability of being overweight or obese. Further, significant relationships generally remained after additional adjustment for potential confounding variables, including demographic factors, dietary intake, and physical activity level.

In children and adolescents, TV viewing has been shown to reinforce negative healthy lifestyle behaviors. In children, the time spent watching TV is consistently high from one year to the next. Similar to adults, an increased amount of time spent watching TV leaves little or no time for youth to be physically active during the day, thereby reducing total daily energy expenditure. TV viewing is also related to excessive snacking, overconsumption of unhealthy foods that are advertised during commercial programming, and persuading parents to purchase unhealthy food options at grocery stores. Not surprisingly, studies have also shown a positive relationship between increased TV viewing and risk for childhood obesity (9). Unfortunately, obesity developed during childhood or adolescents typically carries over into adulthood (10).

In order to prevent the risk of obesity in adulthood, intervention studies have been designed in children that target an overall reduction in TV viewing levels. Typically, these studies are family-based in which parents are encouraged to make the same behavioral changes as their children. Strategies for reducing time spent watching TV include self-monitoring, positive reinforcement, and stimulus control, including unplugging the TV or using a TV allowance device. Typically, a TV allowance device is connected between the TV and electrical supply and allows parents or guardians to preprogram the child's weekly TV viewing time. Children access the TV using a code and the time is automatically deducted from their account. Once the child's allotted TV time is used up, the TV will automatically shut off and will not turn back on for that child until the beginning of the next week. These devices can also be used to monitor nonschool-related computer or Internet use. A TV allowance device can be useful when attempting to reduce viewing time since allotted time can be systematically decreased from one week to the next. Finally, studies that are interested in increasing physical activity levels as well as reducing TV viewing, have made TV viewing contingent on physical activity. In research studies, television sets are connected to a cycling ergometer by a power controller. The power controller measures the revolutions per minute outputted by the cyclist and, if the pedaling is above a prescribed threshold, electrical power is transmitted to the TV. Studies have shown that when children are required to be physically active in order to participate in sedentary activities, physical activity levels increase, time spent watching TV decreases, and body weight improves (11). TV viewing that is conditional on physical activity can also be done in an informal way. Through positive reinforcement, parents could reward children for being physically active by allowing them to participate in more sedentary pursuits.

The undeniable association between TV viewing and overweight and obesity is thought to increase one's risk for the development of related comorbidities. However, the research examining the associations of TV viewing with obesity-related chronic conditions is not clear.

Television Viewing and Cardiovascular Disease Risk Factors

Several studies have examined the association of TV viewing with CVD risk factors (8). It has been hypothesized that an increased amount of time spent watching TV would be positively related to total cholesterol, low density lipoprotein (LDL), and triglyceride levels and inversely related to high density lipoprotein (HDL) levels. However, results from studies examining these associations have been mixed, with the relationship between TV viewing and triglycerides demonstrating the most consistent pattern. There is also thought that TV viewing may negatively influence blood pressure levels; leading to an increased risk for developing hypertension. Again, findings from studies examining this association are inconclusive, which may be due to the known confounding effect of obesity on TV viewing and risk factors for cardiovascular disease and support the need for additional studies in this area.

Television Viewing and Metabolic Disorders

Previous investigations have examined whether TV viewing is inversely associated with metabolic disorders, including type 2 diabetes mellitus and metabolic syndrome (8). In these studies, type 2 diabetes mellitus was defined in a number of different ways, which may complicate the interpretation of the findings. For example, some studies used self-reported diagnosis of type 2 diabetes, while other investigations used clinical indicators including impaired fasting glucose or insulin resistance to define presence of type 2 diabetes mellitus. For that reason, the research findings of previous studies examining the relationship of type 2 diabetes mellitus with TV viewing are largely mixed and may be due to the confounding effect of obesity. Similarly, several studies have also examined the relationship between watching TV and metabolic syndrome (8). Since an increased amount of time spent watching TV is negatively associated with health risk factors that characterize metabolic syndrome (e.g., increased waist circumference and elevated triglyceride levels), the hypothesized inverse relationship between TV viewing and metabolic syndrome seems logical. However, similar to the relationship of TV viewing with other health outcomes, findings are inconclusive. The mixed results may be due to differences in how metabolic syndrome is defined (i.e., WHO vs. National Cholesterol Education Program Adult Treatment Panel III criteria) or because obesity, which is included in both definitions, is driving the relationship between TV viewing and metabolic syndrome.

Conclusions

With the competing demands of work or school, household chores, eating and sleep, the activities that individuals choose to do during their free or leisure time are particularly important. Since many compulsory activities (i.e., work, school, sleep) involve little to no physical exertion, it becomes imperative for individuals to participate in more active activities during their leisure time to improve overall health and well-being. Unfortunately, many adults and children choose to spend a large proportion of their discretionary time in passive leisure activities that are mostly sedentary and provide no real physical benefit, which is confirmed by the alarming rates of TV viewing that have been documented in both industry and research settings. A reduction in daily energy expenditure, coupled with an increase in associated food consumption, results in a positive energy balance that may lead to obesity and an increased risk for the development of obesity-related health outcomes, including cardiovascular and metabolic diseases. Research suggests that strategies aimed at reducing TV viewing may be a useful when attempting to increase physical activity levels for general health and well-being. However, additional research is needed to more closely examine the independent contribution of TV viewing on health outcomes beyond obesity and to determine which strategies work most effectively in a given population.

References

1. Dietz WH. *The role of lifestyle in health: the epidemiology and consequences of inactivity.* Proc Nutr Soc 1996;**55/3**:829–840.
2. Epstein LH, Roemmich JN. Reducing sedentary behavior: role in modifying physical activity. *Exerc Sport Sci Rev* 2001;**29/3**:103–108.
3. U.S. Dept of Health and Human Services. *Physical Activity and Health: A Report of the Surgeon General.* US Dept of Health and Human Services, Centers for Disease Control and Prevention: Atlanta, GA, 1996..
4. *Healthy People 2010.* http://www.healthypeople.gov/. Accessed September 23, 2008.
5. Yore MM, Fulton JE, Nelson DE, Kohl HW 3rd. Cigarette smoking status and the association between media use and overweight and obesity. *Am J Epidemiol* 2007;**166/7**:795–802.
6. The Nielsen Company. *Television, Internet and Mobile Usage in the U.S.: Nielsen's Three Screen Report.* 2008.
7. Foehr UG. *Media Multitasking Among American Youth: Prevalence, Predictors and Pairings.* http://www.kff.org/entmedia/entmedia121206pkg.cfm. Accessed August 23, 2007.
8. Williams DM, HA Raynor, Ciccolo JT. A review of TV viewing and its association with health outcomes in adults. *American Journal of Lifestyle Medicine* 2008;**2/3**:250–259.
9. Epstein LH, Roemmich JN, Paluch RA, Raynor HA. Physical activity as a substitute for sedentary behavior in youth. *Ann Behav Med* 2005;**29/3**:200–209.
10. Nieto FJ, Szklo M, Comstock GW. Childhood weight and growth rate as predictors of adult mortality. *Am J Epidemiol* 1992;**136/2**:201–213.
11. Faith MS, Berman N, Heo M, Pietrobelli A, Gallagher D, Epstein LH, et al. Effects of contingent television on physical activity and television viewing in obese children. *Pediatrics* 2001;**107/5**:1043–1048.

Chapter 36
Healthy Drinking
Abraham G. Kocheril

Wine has been enjoyed by human beings as a libation for thousands of years. For much of that time, it has also been used for various medicinal purposes. It has played an integral role in culture and religion. Since the reporting of the French paradox in 1991, wine consumption in the United States has been increasing. Historically, beer is older than wine, and the earliest beers may have been made accidentally. Although there is less literature concerning their health implications, beer and spirits are also enjoyed by many. Since alcohol abuse continues to be a societal problem, I will stress that moderation is essential. Recent studies demonstrate that the health benefits seen at moderate levels can be lost at excessive levels of alcohol consumption.

The French Paradox

The French paradox is that the French consume a diet high in fat, and yet have a low incidence of heart disease. When analyzed, moderate alcohol consumption (defined as 1–3 glasses of wine or beer per day, less for women based on body weight and physiology) is associated with a 25–45% reduction in coronary artery disease (CAD) risk. This was reported in the U.S. on Nov. 17, 1991, on the CBS program "60 Minutes." I will discuss possible explanations, such as the flavonoids (natural antioxidants) in wine. Alcohol is known to raise high density lipoprotein (HDL), or the "good" cholesterol. Some of the benefit in France may arise from the French lifestyle (e.g., having wine with a relaxed dinner, with family and friends). The metabolism of alcohol may be different in these settings than when one is drinking alone and without food.

A Review of the Medical Literature

The medical literature is replete with studies showing benefit to regular moderate alcohol consumption. In a review of 25 studies on alcohol and CAD, involving 350,000 men and women, with 1.8 million person-years of follow-up, all types of alcohol were associated with a lower risk of CAD. The authors concluded that the benefit was related to alcohol rather than other components (1).

In a large study of U.S. male physicians, moderate regular alcohol consumption reduced angina pectoris and myocardial infarction (MI) events

(2). An earlier report from this study group established the cardiovascular benefit of aspirin in this relatively high-risk group.

The largest population study was a prospective study of 128,934 northern California residents, in a prepaid health plan, looking at CAD hospitalizations. Enrollment started in 1978–85 and the participants were followed until December 31, 1991. During this time, 3,931 were hospitalized for CAD. The analysis found that total alcohol consumption was inversely related to risk of CAD hospitalizations in both sexes. The association was weakest for liquor and strongest for beer in men and wine in women. Controlled for total alcohol consumed, the benefit of beer in men, and of both red and white wine in all persons, was still significant (3).

Coronary calcification, measured by chest computed tomography, correlates with the burden of atherosclerosis and CAD. Regular consumption of less than or equal to 2 drinks per day was inversely associated with extensive coronary calcification in a general population. In fact, the risk was 50% less with 1–2 drinks per day than in nondrinkers (4).

Heart rate variability (HRV) is a measure of heart health, which has significant prognostic value in predicting mortality risk. One study examined the impact of alcohol use on HRV in women with CAD, using ambulatory 24-hour electrocardiography. Wine, but not spirits or beer, was positively and independently associated with increased HRV in women with CAD (5). This would predict a better survival for these women who consume wine.

Several studies have established the benefit of moderate wine consumption in the reduction of CAD events. Recent investigations extend those findings, into such areas as congestive heart failure (HF), especially for older adults. Among older persons in one study, increasing levels of moderate alcohol consumption were associated with a decreasing risk of HF; this was not entirely mediated by a reduction in the risk of myocardial infarction (6). This is important since one of the risks of alcohol abuse is the potential to cause a weakened heart with limited pumping capacity (cardiomyopathy) and HF. A report from the Framingham Heart Study had also shown that moderate alcohol consumption confers protection against HF (7).

In another study of 2,594 subjects hospitalized for HF, heavy alcohol consumption (more than 3 drinks per day) was associated with a higher risk of non-CAD HF. In general, alcohol use was inversely related to CAD HF. Moderate alcohol consumption was inversely related to non-CAD HF in diabetics (8). Yet another study correlated a 28% drop in HF risk with one drink per day (9). This was in an analysis of the Cardiovascular Health Study, which further documented a U-shaped curve, meaning that the benefit seen with some alcohol, was lost at higher levels of alcohol consumption.

One of the risks of binge drinking is the development of a common heart rhythm disorder known as atrial fibrillation (AF). The Copenhagen City Heart Study followed 16,415 women and men, in whom there were 1071 cases of AF. Moderate alcohol was not associated with AF; the cardiac benefits found in other studies are therefore not contradicted. Heavy drinking, however, was associated with the development of AF. Statistically, the hazard ratio (HR) was 1.45 (i.e., a 45% risk increase) when consuming 35 or more drinks per week among men. In this study, 5% of the AF was associated with heavy alcohol, and this was unrelated to CAD or hypertension (10).

Some of the health benefits appear to arise from the raising of HDL cholesterol levels and lowering of the blood concentration of lipoprotein (a). The anti-inflammatory effects of the flavonoids in (especially red) wine may be involved. In the search for mechanisms of benefit, alcohol's effects on inflammation are becoming more prominent. Moderate alcohol consumption raises plasma adiponectin (i.e., a protein hormone secreted from adipose [fatty] tissue, that modulates a number of metabolic processes) levels, which may curb inflammation and reduce CAD. Interestingly, moderate alcohol in combination with higher dietary fat increased adiponectin levels, while a carbohydrate-rich diet with a high glycemic load produced lower adiponectin levels. In fact, obesity and diabetes mellitus are associated with low levels of adiponectin. Dose dependency has also been shown, with increasing adiponectin levels from 5.0–29.9 grams of alcohol daily (roughly 0.5 to 3 drinks per day), as opposed to decreasing levels at over 30 grams of daily alcohol (11).

A potentially important discovery is the compound resveratrol. This is found in red grape skins and seeds, particularly those made in cooler climates like that of Burgundy and upstate New York. Resveratrol may prolong life by activating an ancient survival reflex; this mimics the effect of a low-calorie diet. Dr. David Sinclair of the Harvard Medical School has demonstrated that it prolongs life in yeast by 70%. Animal and human studies are in progress.

Resveratrol may even provide some stroke protection. A study done by researchers at Johns Hopkins University fed mice resveratrol prior to inducing stroke. The effect was that it reduced the area of stroke damage by 40%. The explanation may be in building cell resistance against free radical damage. An increased level of heme oxygenase (i.e., an enzyme that is induced in response to oxidative stress and may provide tissue protection) was noted, in association with resveratrol (12).

Procyanidins have been noted in red wine. This is a type of flavonoid polyphenol, with potent protective effect on blood vessels. Procyanidins are condensed tannins, and may be part of the reason that wines improve with age. Red wine from traditional wine making areas such as Southwest France and Sardinia seem to have higher levels (5–10 times more than wines from elsewhere) (13). People from these locations tend to live long lives.

A study measuring markers of inflammation found lower levels of Interleukin-6 (i.e., IL-6, a cytokine secreted by white blood cells, part of the inflammatory process) and C-reactive protein (i.e., CRP, a protein in the blood whose levels rise in response to inflammation) in individuals consuming 1 to 7 drinks per week, compared to those who were not drinking. These benefits were lost when the consumption was more than 7 drinks per week. This provides a possible explanation of benefits in reduction of heart attacks and strokes. The study was conducted on 2,574 healthy seniors, aged 70–79. Adjusted for age, race, gender, education, smoking, diabetes, and physical activity, the IL-6 and CRP benefits persisted. One drink was defined as a can of beer, glass of wine, or shot of liquor (14).

In a study of college students (25 men and women), the average CRP was 0.9 mg/L. Excess alcohol consumption was associated with above normal CRP (1.25). Moderate alcohol was associated with a level of 0.7, a healthier CRP than little or no alcohol (0.85). For reference, a low risk CRP is <1 mg/L, moderate risk 1–3, and high risk >3 mg/L (15).

Ocke et al. presented the initial results of the Zutphen Study (Netherlands) at the American Heart Association's Cardiovascular Disease Epidemiology and Prevention conference on March 1, 2007. They studied 1,373 men, born between 1900 and 1920. Alcohol consumption, adjusted for other risk factors, was analyzed. They found that 1–2 glasses(≤20 g) per day led to a 36% lower all cause mortality and a 34% lower risk of cardiovascular disease death. Greater reduction was seen with wine than with other types of alcohol. In the analysis, 1.5 ounces of wine led to a 40% lower risk of death and a 48% lower risk of cardiovascular disease death. Wine drinkers lived 2 years longer than those drinking beer or liquor. Those drinking moderate alcohol lived 1.6 years longer than teetotalers. Of note, 70% of all wine consumed was red (16).

Some of the cardiovascular benefits may derive from nitric oxide (NO), which promotes endothelium-dependent vasodilation (i.e., the inner lining of blood vessels use NO to cause the surrounding smooth muscle to relax, thereby increasing blood flow through these vessels). An increase in the enzyme that produces NO has been shown in association with red wine (17). Red wine has an abundance of phenolic acids, polyphenols, and flavonoids (i.e., natural antioxidants).

Diabetes is considered a coronary heart disease risk equivalent, based on the high risk of cardiovascular events in this population. Investigation shows that alcohol and polyphenols from wine have favorable effects on glucose metabolism and insulin sensitivity. A recent review of the literature summarized that 1–3 drinks per day reduces risk of developing diabetes by

33–56% (18). Among diabetics, the risk of developing CHD was reduced 34–55%. In addition, the alcohol consumption did not interfere with standard medications for diabetes mellitus.

Healthy Ageing: a Longitudinal study in Europe (The HALE Project) studied lifestyle factors in subjects aged 70–90 years (19). A lower risk of all-cause mortality was associated with the Mediterranean diet, HR 0.77; moderate alcohol use, HR 0.78; physical activity, HR 0.63; non-smoking, HR 0.65. Incorporating all four healthy behaviors had the most powerful impact, with a HR 0.35, or a 65% reduction in the risk of premature death.

In the health professionals follow-up study, 8,867 healthy men were evaluated over a significant period of time. In general, these were non-drinking men following a healthy lifestyle. Those consuming 2 drinks per day were 60% less likely to have an MI over 16 years. This finding came out of a multivariate model adjusting for age, family history of MI, aspirin use, hypertension, and hypercholesterolemia (20).

Benefits other than cardiac are also being reported. Consumption of 1–6 drinks weekly is associated with a lower risk of incident dementia among older adults (21). Rather than being exclusively due to alcohol, it is possible that the older people who were drinking were also socializing and engaging their brains, thus delaying the onset of dementia. Small studies have shown benefits in peripheral arterial disease, age-related macular degeneration, kidney stones, food poisoning, and psychological distress.

Too Good to be True?

The Centers for Disease Control & Prevention (CDC) expressed skepticism about all the good news on alcohol consumption (22). They interviewed 250,000 patients in 2003 telephone survey. Moderate drinkers tended to be in better health, better educated, wealthier, and more active than nondrinkers. Nondrinkers had more risk factors for CAD. It is therefore possible, at least in earlier studies, that the benefits of alcohol were overestimated.

In a University of California San Francisco review of 30 studies on moderate alcohol consumption, abstainers run a 25% higher risk of CAD. They found it a common error to lump "abstainers" into drinkers who had quit. Advancing age or poor health may have led to quitting. In an analysis by Fillmore et al. of 54 studies, only 7 did not mingle former drinkers and abstainers; these found no significant differences in health. Dr. A. Klatsky responded that his first study in 1981 contained the flaw but that subsequent studies took this confounder into consideration. He further pointed out that alcohol raises HDL and has anti-clotting effects (23).

Despite skepticism, studies have continued to show benefit to moderate alcohol consumption. A large study (2487 men and women, aged 70–79, followed for 5 years) examined the rate of mortality and cardiovascular events in people consuming 1–7 drinks per week. They found a relative risk reduction (RRR) of 26% in death compared to drinking less than 1 ounce per week. The authors also found a RRR of 30% in cardiovascular events. The risk reductions were fully adjusted for confounding variables. The event rates higher at consumption of over 7 drinks per week. The effect of alcohol in this study was independent of anti-inflammatory and HDL effects (24).

It appears that the health benefit can be realized regardless of when one starts drinking. Initiating moderate alcohol consumption in middle age in one study was found to produce a 38% reduction in cardiovascular events over 4 years compared with nondrinkers (25). This was a substudy of the Atherosclerosis Risk in Communities study (ARIC), which looked at 15,792 middle-aged black and white men and women, who had no cardiovascular disease or diabetes mellitus at baseline.

Could it be good for bone health? Well, one drink a day has been associated with a 20% reduced risk of hip fracture compared to nondrinkers. In this study, more than 2 drinks daily led to a 40% higher risk of fracture. Further analysis showed that bone mineral density increased from abstinence up to 2 drinks per day. Some of the mechanism could be alcohol's effect on circulating estrogen levels (26).

Excessive Consumption

The definition of "one drink" is sometimes debated. By convention, one drink is 1.5 ounces of 80-proof spirits (bourbon, Scotch, vodka, gin), 1 ounce of 100-proof spirits, 4 ounces of wine, or 12 ounces of beer. For wine, "moderate" consumption, as defined in various studies, is typically 1–3 glasses of wine per day.

There is data on higher levels of alcohol consumption. In Switzerland, a study of 5,769 adults, aged 35–75, defined high consumption as 14–34 drinks per week, and very high as over 35 drinks per week. Their analysis utilized the Framingham 10-year CAD risk. The protective effect of moderate alcohol was lost in the very high drinkers, where the HDL benefit was offset by increases in blood pressure (27).

The Fear of Cancer

One of the great fears with alcohol consumption is the potential cancer risk suggested by some studies. Unfortunately, the Million Women Study added significantly to these concerns. A total of 1,280,296 women, median age 55, were recruited in breast cancer screening clinics in the United Kingdom, from 1996–2001. In this group of women, 75% drank alcohol, and most drank wine. After 7.2 years of follow-up, 68,775 women were diagnosed with cancer. Nondrinkers (compared to 2 drinks per week or less) had a 40% increase in liver and esophageal cancer. The authors questioned whether they were drinking until health problems arose. Trend analysis suggested that each additional drink per day would cause 11 additional breast cancers per 1000 women up to age 75, and a total of 15 cancers per 1000 women (28). Unfortunately, the investigators were not able to comment on any impact on cardiovascular health. Additional analyses are under way.

The announcement of these results created a stir, to say the least. Additional findings were reported in the New York Times of March 12, 2009. For instance, moderate drinking decreased risk of thyroid cancer, renal cell cancer, and non-Hodgkin's lymphoma. The author commented on the finding that women who were not drinking at all had a higher rate of cancer than those drinking up to 6 drinks per week. Included was a comment that Donald Berry, chairman of biostatistics at the University of Texas M.D. Anderson Cancer Center in Houston, considered the study meaningless.

Other studies also cast doubt on these results. Esophagitis and Barrett's esophagus are thought to be precursors of esophageal cancer. In a Kaiser Permanente study of 953 men and women in northern California, those consuming ≥1 glass of red or white wine per day were 56% less likely to develop Barrett's esophagus (29). Interestingly, beer or liquor did not lower the risk. Possible explanations proposed were antioxidants and the consumption of food with wine. Separately, an Australian study found that wine drinkers were less likely to develop adenocarcinoma, a specific type of esophageal cancer. An Irish study showed that wine reduced the risk of esophagitis by 50%.

A U.S. study of 6,237 women from 3 states with breast cancer was undertaken with 7,558 women also aged 20–69 as controls. This study found that 14 or more drinks per week were associated with a 24% increase in breast cancer compared with nondrinkers. No difference was evident between red and white wine. The lead author's advice was moderation, specifically no more than one drink per day (30).

Given the information so far on cancer, there is no clear reason to avoid alcohol completely. Further research is needed to clarify the breast cancer issue. Some cancers may be prevented by wine consumption. Based on the available information, moderation can provide drinking enjoyment and prevent an increase in cancer risk.

Longevity

It stands to reason that the cardiovascular benefits of alcohol, especially wine, should translate into better longevity. In fact, a recent paper suggested that men·who consumed half a glass of wine daily may their boost life expectancy by five years (31).

In this Dutch study with 40 years of follow-up, light, long-term alcohol consumption of all types of beverages, whether wine, spirits, or beer, increased life by 2.5 years among men compared with abstention. Light meant up to 20 grams, or about 0.7 ounces a day. Further, they noted that drinking wine was strongly linked with a lower risk of dying from heart disease, stroke, or other causes. Although there wasn't specific information on the applicability to women, the investigators felt that specific compounds found in wine, especially red wine, produced the cardiac benefits.

Conclusion

A vast literature supports the notion of health benefits of moderate alcohol consumption. As I have discussed, some of the studies show a clear advantage to wine over other types of alcohol, for cardiovascular and other benefits. The recent research clearly shows that while moderate alcohol consumption is beneficial, the benefit is lost at higher levels of consumption. The literature also suggests plausible mechanisms for health benefit, including the raising of HDL cholesterol, reduction of platelet clotting, and lowering of inflammation.

Although one does not need support from the medical literature to appreciate and enjoy wine, it is nice to know that it can be part of a healthy lifestyle. As a cardiologist, I encourage the reader to incorporate a balanced diet and regular exercise as well. The enjoyment of wine, as well as the artful pairing of food with wine, is an increasing trend in the U.S. Furthermore, the quality of wine available and the variety of wines available continually improve over the years. For the beer fans, beer is also available in much more variety than in the past, and the appreciation of beer has advanced along lines similar to wine appreciation. Cheers!

References

1. Rimm EB, Klatsky A, Grobbee D, Stampfer MJ. Review of moderate alcohol consumption and reduced risk of coronary heart disease: Is the effect due to beer, wine, or spirits. *BMJ* 1996;**312**:731–736.
2. Camargo CA Jr, Stampfer MJ, Glynn RJ, Grodstein F, Gaziano JM, Manson JE, Buring JE, Hennekens CH. Moderate alcohol consumption and risk for angina pectoris or myocardial infarction in U.S. male physicians. *Ann Intern Med* 1997;**126**:372–375.
3. Klatsky AL, Armstrong MA, Friedman GD. Red wine, white wine, liquor, beer, and risk for coronary artery disease hospitalization. *Am J Cardiol* 1997;**80**:416–420.
4. Vliegenthart R, Oei HH, van den Elzen AP, van Rooij FJ, Hofman A, Oudkerk M, Witteman JC. Alcohol consumption and coronary calcification in a general population. *Arch Intern Med* 2004;**164**:2355–60.
5. Janszky I, Ericson M, Blom M, Georgiades A, Magnusson JO, Alinagizadeh H, Ahnve S. Wine drinking is associated with increased heart rate variability in women with coronary heart disease. *Heart* 2005;**91**:314–318.
6. Abramson JL, Williams SA, Krumholz HM, Vaccarino V. Moderate alcohol consumption and risk of heart failure among older persons. *JAMA* 2001;**285**:1971–1977.
7. Walsh CR, Larson MG, Evans JC, Djousse L, Ellison RC, Vasan RS, et al. Alcohol consumption and risk for congestive heart failure in the Framingham Heart Study. *Ann Intern Med* 2002;**136**:181–191.
8. Klatsky AL, Chartier D, Udaltsova N, Gronningen S, Brar S, Friedman GD, Lundstrom RJ. Alcohol drinking and risk of hospitalization for heart failure with and without associated coronary artery disease. *Am J Cardiol* 2005;**96**:346–351.
9. Bryson CL, Mukamal KJ, Mittleman MA, Fried LP, Hirsch CH, Kitzman DW, Siscovick DS. The association of alcohol consumption and incident heart failure: the Cardiovascular Health Study. *J Am Coll Cardiol* 2006;**48**:305–311.
10. Mukamal KJ, Tolstrup JS, Friberg J, Jensen G, Grønbaek M. Alcohol consumption and risk of atrial fibrillation in men and women: The Copenhagen City Heart Study. *Circulation* 2005;**112**:1736–1742.
11. AHA 44th Annual Conference on Cardiovascular Disease Epidemiology and Prevention; May 2004; San Francisco, CA.
12. Dore S, et al. Society for Neuroscience Conference; October 2006; Atlanta, GA.
13. Corder R, Mullen W, Khan NQ, Marks SC, Wood EG, Carrier MJ, Crozier A. Oenology: Red wine procyanidins and vascular health. *Nature* 2006;**444**:566.

14. Volpato S, Pahor M, Ferrucci L, Simonsick EM, Guralnik JM, Kritchevsky SB, et al. Relationship of alcohol intake with inflammatory markers and plasminogen activator inhibitor-1 in well-functioning older adults: The Health, Aging, and Body Composition study. *Circulation* 2004;**109/5**:607–612.

15. Donovan E, Olsen A. Report presented at AHA Conference on Atherosclerosis, Thrombosis, and Vascular Biology; April 2007; Chicago, IL.

16. Streppel MT, Ocké MC, Boshuizen HC, Kok FJ, Kromhout D. Long-term wine consumption is related to cardiovascular mortality and life expectancy independently of moderate alcohol intake: the Zutphen Study. *J Epidemiol Community Health* 2009;**63/7**:534–540.

17. Wallerath T, Poleo D, Li H, Förstermann U. Red wine increases expression of human endothelial nitric oxide synthase. *J Am Coll Cardiol* 2003;**41**:471–478.

18. Howard AA, Arnsten JH, Gourevitch MN. Effect of alcohol consumption on diabetes mellitus: a systematic review. *Ann Intern Med* 2004;**140/3**:211–219.

19. Knoops KT, de Groot LC, Kromhout D, Perrin AE, Moreiras-Varela O, Menotti A, van Staveren WA. Mediterranean diet, lifestyle factors, and 10-year mortality in elderly European men and women: The HALE project. *J Am Med Assoc* 2004;**292**:1433–1439.

20. Mukamal KJ, Chiuve SE, Rimm EB. Alcohol consumption and risk for coronary heart disease in men with healthy lifestyles. *Arch Intern Med* 2006;**166**:2145–2150.

21. Mukamal KJ, Kuller LH, Fitzpatrick AL, Longstreth WT Jr, Mittleman MA, Siscovick DS. Prospective study of alcohol consumption and risk of dementia in older adults. *J Am Med Assoc* 2003;**289**:1405–1413.

22. Naimi TS, Brown DW, Brewer RD, Giles WH, Mensah G, Serdula MK, et al. Cardiovascular risk factors and confounders among non-drinking and moderate-drinking U.S. adults. *Am J Prev Med* 2005;28/4:369–373.

23. Klatsky A. Addiction Research and Theory (online edition). Accessed March 30, 2006.

24. Maraldi C, Volpato S, Kritchevsky SB, Cesari M, Andresen E, Leeuwenburgh C, et al. Impact of inflammation on the relationship among alcohol consumption, mortality, and cardiac events: The health, aging, and body composition study. *Arch Intern Med* 2006;**166**:1490–1497.

25. King DE, Mainous AG 3rd, Geesey ME. Adopting moderate alcohol consumption in middle age: subsequent cardiovascular events. *Am J Med* 2008;**121**:201–206.

26. Berg KM, Kunins HV, Jackson JL, Nahvi S, Chaudhry A, Harris KA Jr, et al. Association between alcohol consumption and both osteoporotic fracture and bone density. *Am J Med* 2008;121:406–418.
27. Foerster M, Marques-Vidal P, Gmel G, Daeppen JB, Cornuz J, Hayoz D, et al. Alcohol drinking and cardiovascular risk in a population with high mean alcohol consumption. *Am J Cardiol* 2009;**103**:361–368.
28. Allen NE, Beral V, Casabonne D, Kan SW, Reeves GK, Brown A, Green J. Million Women Study Collaborators. Moderate alcohol intake and cancer incidence in women. *J Natl Cancer Inst* 2009;**101**:296–305.
29. Kubo A, Levin TR, Block G, Rumore GJ, Quesenberry CP Jr, Buffler P, Corley DA. Alcohol types and sociodemographic characteristics as risk factors for Barrett's esophagus. *Gastroenterology* 2009;**136/3**:806–815.
30. Newcomb PA, Nichols HB, Beasley JM, Egan K, Titus-Ernstoff L, Hampton JM, Trentham-Dietz A. No difference between red wine or white wine consumption and breast cancer risk. *Cancer Epidemiol Biomarkers Prev* 2009;**18/3**:1007–1010.
31. Streppel MT, Ocké MC, Boshuizen HC, Kok FJ, Kromhout D. Long-term wine consumption is related to cardiovascular mortality and life expectancy independently of moderate alcohol intake: The Zutphen Study. *J Epidemiol Community Health* 2009;**63/7**:534–540.

Chapter 37
Healthy Sports

Lynda B. Ransdell
Dorothy L. Schmalz

Take a moment to picture a person who is a healthy participant in sport. Now, picture someone who is an unhealthy participant in sport. What makes these individuals different? Specifically, what about sports participation is healthy or unhealthy? People whose relationship with sport is "healthy" recognize that sports yield some important health benefits such as weight, heart disease, and cholesterol management. They also believe that sport participation reduces the risk of many chronic diseases—but their participation is not rooted solely in reaping health benefits. Rather, a person who has a healthy relationship with sport participates for the sheer enjoyment of it, whether it is physical, social, psychological, or any combination. Some may seek regular, competitive, structured participation, such as teams or leagues, while others may simply enjoy casual recreational participation at a variety of levels. To different degrees, individuals might identify as athletes in their sport or activity of choice, but their sense of self is not dependent on their participation. If they have to miss a sporting event due to family, friends, school, work, or another obligation, their day is not ruined, nor does their eating behavior or self-confidence change because of it.

On the other hand, people who have an "unhealthy" relationship with sport typically encounter a variety of challenges, many of which are varied and unpredictable. One example of an unhealthy sport participant is an obsessed sport participant. This individual defines himself or herself based on an athletic identity, perhaps body image, self-confidence, or overall sense of self. The overall sense of self, for this athlete, is dependent on an ability to participate on a regular basis. People who have an unhealthy relationship with sport might put their relationships with other people at risk because of, or build relationships with others solely on, their athletic identity. In addition, these individuals may put their physical health at risk due to overtraining, eating disorders, or other negative physical outcomes that will be discussed in this chapter.

Sports are supposed to help individuals develop healthy attitudes toward competition, discipline, respect for authority, and social relationships. The purpose of this chapter is to acknowledge potentially unhealthy practices and discuss ways to make sport participation healthy—from a lifespan perspective. Therefore, we will discuss issues related to healthy sport participation for children (4–12 yrs) and adolescents (13–17 yrs), college athletes (18–22 yrs), recreational adult athletes (18–49 yrs), and masters athletes (50 yrs and older). While the intent of the chapter is to focus on healthy aspects of participation, we would be remiss if we did not acknowledge that there are unhealthy manifestations of sport participation in addition to healthy ones.

Sports Participation Across the Lifespan

Children and Adolescents

Children. From an early age, children are encouraged to participate in sports and physical activity for a variety of reasons. Pee-wee and toddler leagues for sports of all kinds are present in various community venues such as local recreation agencies and centers, schools, and churches. Parents and guardians sign their children up for sports with a number of goals in mind including physical, social, psychological, and behavioral development. As with most children's play, sport and physical activity provide an opportunity for children to fine tune their motor skills and increase muscle and bone maturity. Sport and physical activity also provide an opportunity for children to make friends and socialize with other children while simultaneously learning the importance of sportsmanship, teamwork, competition, and leadership. Finally, sport and physical activity introduce children to a healthy and active lifestyle which combats the onset of childhood obesity, and provides an avenue for identity development. Ideally, children will reap all of these benefits from sport, however sometimes sport environments are not positive.

Although parents and guardians are the primary technical (e.g., registration), logistic (e.g., travel to and from games and practices), and emotional (e.g., cheerleading) support systems for their children, they can also detract from their child's sport-related experience. Parent over-involvement and bad sportsmanship are common occurrences on the sidelines and in coaching roles. A quick search on YouTube will yield a wealth of clips showing parent misbehavior at children's games. Parents are shown instigating fights, as well as demeaning and criticizing players, coaches, and other parents. Children learn by watching and role modeling others. Early in their sporting lives, children will pick up on these unhealthy behaviors demonstrated by their adult role models on the sidelines.

Another way parents can make the sport experience negative for their children is to apply performance pressure. In their enthusiasm, parents and guardians can become highly competitive which may lead to negative feedback and a perceived lack of emotional support. The result is perfor-mance pressure, which can negatively affect a child's interest in participa-tion, enjoyment of an activity, and perceived competence. Bad experiences with performance pressure and parent over-involvement can lead to a child quitting a sport, and can deter a child from sport for a lifetime, thus deny-ing the potential positive benefits it can yield.

Adults can also impair children's sport with the desire to structure it, and make it conform to the rules as adults understand them. While the rules do serve a purpose, and are important lessons to learn in life, adults often lose sight of the importance of unstructured play in the lives of their chil-dren. As long as safety is not an issue, children gain extraordinary benefits from unstructured, self-determined play (1). Beneficial unstructured play is characteristically freely chosen, intrinsically motivated, controlled to some degree by participants, and leaves participants feeling good and relatively competent at an activity. Too much adult involvement or structure hampers the presence of one or many of these elements.

Parent and coach education on the importance of children's sport and the benefits it can provide is imperative in order to keep their involvement within reason. Also, adults should be encouraged to facilitate a balance of structured and unstructured play in their children's lives. Both provide valuable lessons to children as they grow, and parents should be reminded of the importance of both structured and unstructured play.

In addition to adult pressures and poor role-modeling, children are also influenced by gender stereotypes in their sport participation. Children learn at early ages that girls are not supposed to wrestle, and boys are not supposed to participate in figure skating; children who don't adhere to these strict societal boundaries are at risk of being stereotyped as they pursue their favorite activities (2). Adults should be conscious of children's susceptibility to stereotypes, stigmas, and social rules. Limiting participa-tion due to societal expectations rather than pursuing personal interest inhibits self-development and identity exploration. Whether a girl is labeled a "tomboy" or a boy is labeled a "sissy," the overall outcome is negative reinforcement for pursuing something for which a child has passion. Adults should support children in whatever activity captures their interest, and they should discourage the perpetuation of stigmas regarding gender-based participation. As a means of curbing social stereotyping, children should be introduced to athletes who participate in sports that challenge gender stereotypes through guest appearances and posters. When possible, parents and guardians should provide opportunities for children to participate in activities that bust gender stereotypes (i.e., girls participate in stereotypi-cally "boys" sports such as ice hockey and baseball, and boys participate in stereotypically "girls" sports such as figure skating or gymnastics).

Adolescents. Like children, adolescents benefit from sport physically, socially, and psychologically. For many adolescents, sport participation provides an outlet for dealing with the physical and psychological frustration and confusion prompted by puberty. Moreover, being a member of a sports team provides a social network and personal identity during a time that is often filled with insecurity and self-doubt. Participation in sport and physical activity can increase self-esteem, particularly among adolescent girls (3). As a young person's body develops into its adult version, inevitable weight gain and changes in appearance fuel questions and general insecurity. However, participation in sport and physical activity, by its very nature, helps keep weight gain concerns at bay, and it provides a group of individuals who are experiencing similar issues.

Despite the well-established benefits of sport and physical activity, participation declines significantly during adolescence. Reasons for this are varied, but the physical changes brought on by puberty, uncertainty about "appropriate" masculine and feminine roles as adolescents grow into their adult bodies, and peer pressure, are among the reasons most often speculated by researchers (4). Fitting in with peers and being part of a group are among the top concerns for adolescents. The value placed on sport and athletic ability in the high school culture makes sport an extracurricular option for a select few. Some adolescents find competence and confidence in sports, and establish a niche in the high school hierarchy as an athlete. For others, out of concern that they are not good enough, their sport is not cool enough, or their sport is inappropriate for their gender, sport becomes an inaccessible activity that is "for" others. Adolescents are highly susceptible to sedentary lifestyles, increased weight gain, and lower levels of psychological well-being when they lessen their participation in sport, therefore sport leaders should be attentive to high sport dropout rates and disassociation from sport.

It is important for parents and adults to keep in mind the critical role they play in the lives of adolescents, despite the tendency for adolescents to shun or exclude them. Adults who work with adolescents can help them change their perspective on the social value of sport. First, a person does not need to be a varsity athlete in order to participate. The benefits afforded by sport can be gleaned through recreational participation, which also increases sport enjoyment. For adolescents who do not identify as athletes, the genuine *fun* of sport should be highlighted. More stress on personal task achievement as opposed to team competition and winning may be beneficial. Adults can also support valuing sports that are not typically the "popular" teams, and can stress that sports are available for everyone, regardless of gender.

It should be noted that adolescents who participate in sport are not protected from negative developmental influences. Participation in sport has been correlated with many negative behaviors, such as increased alcohol abuse, hazing, and eating disorders, which will be discussed in more detail in the section on college athletes.

Collegiate, Recreational Adult and Masters Athletes

College Athletes. When most people think of college athletes, they think of someone who is pampered—with nothing to worry about except playing sports. In reality, college athletes face a variety of challenges to healthy sport participation including, but not limited to, overtraining, alcohol abuse, hazing, homophobia, and eating disorders. These issues will be discussed one at a time, with an emphasis on prevention and, if necessary, treatment.

One of the more common challenges for today's collegiate athlete—who is often pushed beyond limits considered "normal"—is overtraining. Overtraining (the negative manifestation of too much training), in comparison to overreaching (a positive adaptation to the stress of training), occurs when athletes combine heavy training and competition schedules with busy academic demands, travel stressors, poor nutrition, and a lack of sleep. Coaches who continually push athletes and athletes who ignore their body's signals, are at risk for overtraining. Coaches, athletes, athletic trainers, and others involved with athletics should be keenly aware of the symptoms of overtraining. The most common psychological symptoms of overtraining include burnout, apathy, poor concentration, mood changes, and decreases in self-esteem. Physiological symptoms include an inability to recover from tough workouts, decreased muscular strength and coordination, increased creatine kinase (which may indicate muscle damage) and cortisol (the "stress hormone"), loss of body weight, and a decrease in quality sleep. All of these symptoms can eventually lead to an increased risk of injuries. Strategies for preventing overtraining include (a) considering the strength of an opponent, travel schedule, and days between competitions when planning in-season training sessions, (b) testing athletes' physical fitness frequently—to monitor things such as a sudden (and unexplained) decrease in performance or an increase in resting heart rate or heart rate during submaximal efforts, and (c) using periodization training strategies throughout the year, which includes tapering for "peak" competitions.

While many individuals believe that athletes are less likely to drink alcohol than their non-athletic peers, and that male athletes are more likely to drink excessively compared to their female counterparts, some researchers purport that the problem of binge drinking is worse in athletes than in non-athletes, and that female athletes are almost as likely to drink as their male counterparts (5). In addition to the potential performance decrements seen with alcohol abuse, it is associated with an increased risk of automobile accidents and unplanned sexual activity. Because this problem is so prevalent among athletes, it is imperative that those concerned with the health of athletes take steps to educate athletes about the dangers of alcohol use and abuse. Educational programs should include information about the specific stressors related to sport, positive and negative coping strategies, and the risk factors associated with alcohol abuse in athletes. For example, some athletes may cope with an injury by excessively drinking alcohol. A more positive coping strategy would be focusing on proper nutrition, attending physical therapy sessions, and training uninjured body parts. In addition, awareness of personality traits such as risk taking and social approval orientation, or sport characteristics such as participation on a team vs. individual sport or a contact vs. non-contact sport, can help prevent alcohol abuse in athletes.

Another issue that can impact the healthy sport participation of an athlete is hazing. Hazing is a ritual or task designed to cause embarrassment as a means of gaining "acceptance" onto a team or as a way to increase team camaraderie. One prominent example of hazing is the 2006 Northwestern Women's Soccer team ritual that was posted on "badjocks. com." The ritual involved players dressed in costumes or their underwear, blindfolded, with their hands bound by athletic tape. Some athletes were photographed in sexually explicit poses. As soon as the photos were discovered, the university disbanded the team and issued strong sanctions against future hazing (6).

The National Survey of Initiation Rites and Athletics stated that more than half of the athletes surveyed experienced alcohol-related hazing and that female athletes were more likely to be involved in alcohol-related hazing than in other forms of hazing. One major problem with hazing is that student-athletes feel pressured to participate in various "rituals" that team leaders demand—in the interest of "team bonding"; coaches and athletes turn their backs on many forms of hazing because they consider it a "normal" part of being on a team. To prevent hazing, coaches and other athletic personnel should provide educational programs about the risks of hazing and the potential damage that can be done to an individual and a team. Without exception, anti-hazing policies should be developed and discussed within teams.

An issue that doesn't receive as much attention as it should is the problem of homophobia (also known as homonegativism). Homophobia is an irrational fear of homosexual individuals. While examples of homophobia among gay male collegiate athletes exist, the majority of published information concerns female athletes. Individuals who experience homophobia describe a number of problems including low self-esteem and self-confidence, preoccupation with hiding one's sexuality, increased stress (some of which comes from verbal or physical harassment), and high-risk or self-abusive activities. For more information on the negative consequences of homophobia and strategies for healthy sport participation despite the presence of homophobia, see Krane, Surface, & Alexander in Ransdell and Petlichkoff (7). In addition, the Women's Sports Foundation offers a homophobia educational program with posters, "safe zone" stickers, a 15-minute DVD, and a group leader manual; many schools and organizations have used this kit successfully (8).

Finally, for male and female athletes, eating disorders can be a problem. Eating disorders typically fall along a spectrum that ranges from overeating to self-starvation. Male athletes may suffer from "muscle dysmorphia," or a fear of not having a body that is muscular enough or not enough like the typical male athlete in their sport; this can lead to the use of steroids or overtraining. Female athletes may suffer from anorexia (i.e., self-starvation) or bulimia (i.e., binging and purging) nervosa. Signs of an eating disorder include a tendency to misjudge one's body weight, preoccupation with food, depression, mood swings, social withdrawl, secretive behaviors related to eating, and gastrointestinal distress. Some of the consequences of anorexia include bradycardia (heart rate < 60 bpm), low blood pressure, electrolyte abnormalities, and a host of other significant problems. Problems that can occur with bulimia are dehydration and reflux of stomach acid from vomiting (which leads to dental enamel erosion, esophageal tears, and swollen and irritated salivary glands). Strategies for preventing eating disorders among college athletes include knowing the sports and types of athletes most at risk, providing education and resources, and involving a network of professionals to help with training, nutrition, and competition recommendations. If an athlete develops an eating disorder, forming a team of professionals responsible for referral and treatment is essential. Removing an athlete from a team may not be an optimal strategy for improvement because it will increase social isolation which can lead to additional problems. The bottom line is that health is the optimal goal for the athlete, and overall health and well-being is more important than athletic competition. For more information on eating disorders and how to prevent and/or treat them, see Reel and Beals (9) and Reel, Estes, and Soo Hoo in Ransdell and Petlichkoff (7).

One of the main ways that coaches and athletes can prevent the negative aspects of college sport participation is to emphasize not only skill and strategy development, but also individual/personal development and team building. Janssen and Dale (10) provide an excellent blueprint for developing the whole athlete and emphasizing the development of relationships and life skills—in addition to sport-related skills and strategies. Some of their recommendations include being consistent, character-based, competent, committed, caring, confidence-building, and emphasizing the importance of communicating.

Adult Recreational Athletes. When an athlete ages, unless he or she has corporate sponsorship with plans for continued high level competition, a shift occurs. That shift involves moving from practicing 5–7 days per week for at least 2 hours daily, to playing games 1–3 times per week. Or, in some cases, men or women pick up a sport as an adult because they didn't have the opportunity to compete when they were younger (for reasons related to financial status or sport availability). This type of athlete is known as a "recreational athlete" and these athletes range from 18–49 years old. Some of the issues that are relevant for healthy participation in this group include playing at an appropriate level for age and skill group, and pursuing physical fitness training beyond a "weekend warrior" mentality. Examples of "playing at the appropriate level" can be found in sports such as ice hockey where participants can play at a number of levels from A (advanced) to C (novice). Another example of offering appropriate competition is a basketball league that is divided into "competitive," "recreational," "over 50," and "under 5'9"." Clearly, sport participants will have a more positive experience if they compete with opponents who are similarly matched by age and skill level.

A second issue that is relevant to the adult recreational athlete is that he or she should participate in sport or activity more than the typical "weekend warrior." The "weekend warrior" is an individual who participates in his or her sport once a week and does very little training between competitions. This individual is more likely to get injured, and less likely to enjoy competition (because it's more like work than fun). For this reason, it is important for the adult recreational athlete to develop and follow a training program that includes not just sport competition, but also other elements of fitness such as aerobic and anaerobic components, flexibility, and muscular strength and endurance training.

Masters Athletes. Continuing along the age spectrum, the last type of athlete to consider for healthy sport participation is the masters athlete, or individual 50 years of age and older. The main issues of concern for masters athletes include "expecting" the typical age-related decline in athletic ability and performance, and allowing extra time for rest and recovery. Some of the age-related changes that masters athletes typically experience include decreased visual acuity, hearing, reaction time, muscular strength, flexibility, and aerobic capacity. Percent body fat, especially abdominal fat, typically increases. Women may experience increasing problems with urinary incontinence. As a result of the aforementioned age-related changes, performance typically declines. For example, when United States of America Track and Field (USATF) women's world record performances were compared across age groups (age 35–90+ yrs), sprint running performance declined at a rate of 0.5 to 1.5% per year until the age of 65. In endurance running events, performance declined at a much faster rate of 1.0 to 3.0% per year until the age of 65 (7).

There are always exceptions to the inevitability of aging such as Dr. Werner Hoeger, a luge athlete. He was the oldest male competitor during the 2002 Winter Olympics in Salt Lake City and the oldest actual competitor at the 2006 Winter Olympics in Turin. Dr. Hoeger not only competed in luge, but he also runs a mile in just over 5 minutes at 56 years of age. Dara Torres, the first American swimmer to compete in 5 Olympics, won three silver medals at the 2008 Olympics in Bejing at the age of 41. Neither of these individuals has experienced the typical decline in performance that occurs with aging.

To prevent problems with age-related changes, masters athletes should consider three things. First, similar to recreational adult athletes, masters athletes should maintain strength, endurance, and flexibility training in addition to their competition schedule. Second, they should allow ample time for recovery since they will likely need more time to recover than they needed when they were younger. Finally, they should make sure that they are appropriately hydrated since the thirst mechanism does not work as well in older athletes as it does in younger athletes. For more information on healthy sport participation for masters athletes, readers are referred to the chapter by Taylor in Ransdell and Petlichkoff (7).

Considerations for Professionals

Sport and physical activity are outlets for self expression and development of self esteem. Activities should also be fun and engaging so individuals will want to continue to participate for a lifetime. Ideally, everyone falls along the healthy side of participation. Unfortunately, influences that lead to unhealthy sport-related behaviors are sometimes beyond an individuals' control. A summary of potential negative consequences and strategies to prevent or cope with them are presented in Table 37.1. Unhealthy sport perspectives can be quite powerful—sometimes intense enough to override a healthier alternative. Ultimately, the power to instill healthy sport participation falls on adults and those in supervisory roles for children—and on individuals themselves as they progress through the lifespan. Knowing about some of the pitfalls related to unhealthy sport participation, as outlined across the lifespan in this chapter, can help individuals prevent the negative influences from overpowering the positive and healthy side of sport participation.

Table 37.1 Summary of potentially negative consequences of sport participation and strategies for preventing or coping with negative events

Age Group	Potentially Negative Consequences of Sport Participation	Strategies for Preventing or Coping with Negative Event
Children	Bad sportsmanship by adult role models	• Remind adults that the focus of the game is children, not elite athletes • Empower officials to eject parents and coaches from the game for misbehavior • Encourage principles of fair play among the children on the team
	Performance pressure	• Remind adults that the focus of the game is children, not elite athletes • Educate adults about the benefits of sports for children, and ways they can facilitate benefits in their emotional support on and off the field.
	Gender stereotypes	• Encourage children to participate in activities regardless of social rules of gender. • Introduce children to athletes who participate in sports that are unique for their gender through guest appearances, posters, etc.
Adolescents	Puberty	• Practice self-esteem building and body image support activities.
	High School "popularity"	• Encourage mutual respect for all sports in the curriculum. • Focus on individual task achievement goals and than team goals (e.g., teamwork vs. winning). • Encourage fun and enjoyment in sports.
College Athletes	Overtraining	• Consider strength of opponent and travel when planning in-season workouts • Test fitness frequently • Use periodization and taper for peak competition
	Alcohol Abuse	• Design educational programs that address college athlete stressors, coping strategies, and risk factors associated with alcohol abuse • Focus on positive team building activities
	Hazing	• Design anti-hazing policies • Educate athletes about the downsides to hazing • Focus on positive team building activities
	Homophobia	• Educate athletes about the negative impact of homophobia and ways to prevent it
	Eating Disorders	• Form a team of professionals to advise coaches and athletes on nutrition, training, and dealing with eating disorders • Educate athletes about the negative implications of eating disorders
Recreational Adult Athlete (18-49 yr)	Play at an appropriate level for age and skill	• Find leagues in your sport that are matched based on age and skill level
	Continue participation in physical fitness	• Work with a professional to design a training program suitable for an adult
Masters Athlete (50 yrs and older)	Expect the typical age-related decline in athletic ability	• Learn as much as possible about the typical age-related changes in physical ability • Train hard, using all components of physical fitness, to avoid the typical age-related decline in fitness
	Allow extra time for rest and recovery	• Listen to your body • Allow more time for recovery compared to a younger athlete

References

1. Larson RW. Toward a psychology of positive youth development. *Am Psychol* 2000;**55**:170–183.

2. Schmalz DL, Kerstetter DL. Girlie girls and manly men: Children's stigma consciousness of gender in sports and physical activities. *J Leisure Res* 2006;**38**:536–557.

3. Schmalz DL, Deane GD, Birch LL, Davison KK. A longitudinal assessment of the links between participation in physical activity and self-esteem among girls from age 9 through 13. *J Adolesc Health* 2007;**41**:559–565.

4. Biddle SJH, Whitehead SH, O'Donovan TM, Nevill MH. Correlates of participation in physical activity for adolescent girls: A systematic review of recent literature. *J Phys Act Health* 2003;**2**:423–434.

5. Ransdell LB, Hildebrand K, Spear C, Lucas S. Higher, faster, stronger, drunker? The need for effective strategies to prevent alcohol abuse among female athletes. *Journal of Physical Education, Recreation, and Dance* 2007;**78/3:**5–11.

6. Tao A. *Nu Team Accused of Hazing: Suggestive Photos of Women's Soccer Team Posted Online*. http://media.www.dailynorthwestern.com/media/storage/ paper853/news/2006/05/16/Sports/Nu.Team.Accused.Of.Hazing-1997261.shtml. Accessed March 23, 2009.

7. Ransdell L, Petlichkoff L. *Ensuring the Health of Active and Athletic Girls and Women*. AAHPERD Publishers: Reston, VA, 2005.

8. Women's Sports Foundation. *It Takes a Team*. http://www.womenssportsfoundation.org/Issues-And-Research/Homophobia.aspx. Accessed March 23, 2009.

9. Reel JJ, Beals KA. *The Hidden Faces of Eating Disorders and Body Image*. AAHPERD Publishers: Reston, VA, 2009.

10. Janssen J, Dale G. *The Seven Secrets of Successful Coaches: How to Unlock and Unleash Your Team's Full Potential*. Quality Books: Cary, NC, 2006.

Chapter 38

Healthy Outdoor Recreation: An Integrated Approach to Linking Physical Activity with Wellness Goals

Paul H. Gobster
David M. Buchner

The purpose of this chapter is to discuss the shared interest of the public health and leisure fields in promoting outdoor recreation. We describe how transdisciplinary integration of research efforts across these fields can lead to a better understanding of how outdoor recreation facilities and programs can help realize a full range of health and wellness benefits. Collaboration between practitioners in these fields can help a community meet its health and wellness goals. A case study of a proposed community recreational trail development is used as an example for how public health and leisure fields can collaborate to achieve shared health and wellness goals.

Outdoor Recreation and Health: Historical Precedents, Contemporary Issues

Collaboration between the public health and leisure fields may seem like a recent phenomenon. Yet more than a century and a half ago, the parks and recreation movement conceived the idea that promoting outdoor recreation could improve health. At that time, cities were growing rapidly and experiencing significant public health problems from industrial pollution, inadequate sanitary facilities, crime, and other stressors of urban life. Relying more on intuition than scientific evidence, civic leaders promoted parks and recreation as solutions to these problems. In Chicago for example, medical doctor John Rauch saw parks as the "lungs of the city" and advocated their development to provide citizens fresh air and physical health; landscape architects Swain Nelson and Frederick Law Olmsted promoted parks for aesthetic pleasure and spiritual uplift as well as a means of economic development; University of Chicago ecologist Henry Cowles and landscape architect Jens Jensen lobbied for the acquisition of nearby natural areas to protect the health of remnant native ecosystems; and social reformer Jane Addams helped establish a neighborhood parks and playground movement to address a range of social and community health issues. In their visionary 1909 *Plan of Chicago*, city planners Daniel Burnham and Edward Bennett laid out a system of parks and boulevards that would not only serve to connect the city's diverse neighborhoods to each other but would also underscore the important interconnections among the various health and wellness benefits that parks and recreation can provide: physical, psychological, economic, environmental, and social (1).

As public health science progressed, promotion of physical activity emerged as one specific reason for the collaboration between health and leisure fields. The 1996 Surgeon General's Report, *Physical Activity and Health*, found conclusive evidence that regular physical activity provides substantial health benefits. Lack of regular physical activity has major health consequences and increases risk of many chronic health conditions, including obesity, cardiovascular disease, diabetes, depression, and anxiety. The U.S. Preventive Services Task Force found strong scientific evidence that improving access to recreational opportunities resulted in higher levels of physical activity in a community. Ironically, as the evidence for the health benefits of physical activity accumulated, people were adopting less active lifestyles. As health and leisure fields began to collaborate to promote physical activity, three important issues emerged.

The first issue was how to use park and outdoor recreation opportunities to reverse the trend toward low levels of physical inactivity among adults and children. Because work and school settings are increasingly sedentary in nature, public health realized that leisure time probably represented the best chance for incorporating regular bouts of moderate-to-vigorous physical activity (2). Over the past decade a good deal of research has been conducted with the goal of identifying how park and other outdoor environments can be designed, managed, and programmed to encourage people to increase their physical activity (3).

Like many indicators of community health, levels of physical activity demonstrate disparities: generally less advantaged groups in the population have a disproportionately high burden of disease due to inactivity. A second issue, then, is how park and outdoor recreation opportunities can help reduce the substantial health and wellness disparities that exist between various segments of our population. African-American and Hispanic adults and children have higher obesity prevalence and higher rates of some chronic diseases such as asthma and diabetes than those of European-American descent (4). Similar findings prevail for those living in low-income neighborhoods, and those who are minority and/or have low incomes not only tend to have less access to opportunities for leisure time physical activity but may also live in "food deserts" that lack access to nutritious foods from local stores and restaurants (5). These physical health disparities are often compounded by substantial environmental, social, and economic disparities that afflict the communities in which they live. While park and recreation opportunities are not a panacea, attractive vegetation and open spaces can help spur economic activity and increase social capital.

A third important issue relates to how to structure the collaboration between public health and leisure fields. A consensus has emerged that the fields should move toward transdisciplinary models of collaboration, as these offer the most promise for success. This approach involves merging knowledge, concepts, frameworks, and models from public health and leisure studies, as will be discussed. Such an approach counters the tendency of public health researchers interested in the connection between health and the environment to focus narrowly on physical health issues and neglect other dimensions of health and wellness. For example, it was tempting for public health to focus only on how physical features of parks (e.g., trails, sports fields) can be used to increase active visits to parks and ignore the mental health benefits which could be obtained by either inactive or active visits. Public health can benefit from research in leisure studies, which has studied how to increase active visits as part of a broader goal of increasing quality visits to parks. At the same time, public health science can provide park and recreation practitioners more information about promoting physical activity in a manner that promotes health. For example, parks should facilitate bouts of aerobic moderate-to-vigorous physical activity of 10 minutes or more, as these bouts produce the greatest health benefits. To an increasing extent, today's program and policy decisions are based on solid research evidence. Yet disciplinary knowledge tends to be fragmented, and efforts to synthesize knowledge across disciplines are needed. While specialization is a necessary component of scientific progress, issues such health and wellness are too complex and important to be worked on in an atmosphere of disciplinary isolation.

A Framework for Transdisciplinary Collaboration

Transdisciplinary approaches to research recognize the complexity of real world problems and organize research programs around collaborative problem solving. This differs from multidisciplinary approaches, where two or more disciplines each study an issue without integrating their methods or results, and interdisciplinary approaches, where people use the models and approaches of their discipline to contribute to an integrated effort or synthesis. With a transdisciplinary approach, people move beyond discipline specific models and approaches and develop a single model or approach that meets the needs of all disciplines involved. This often entails an integration of knowledge, concepts, and models from different disciplines in a way that leads to new ways of thinking and operating, not only within a research context but in how research ideas and findings are tested and implemented through policies and programs.

Transdisciplinary approaches have become increasingly used in "active living research" that addresses how the environment and policies can be designed to incorporate greater physical activity in people's lives. In an earlier paper focusing on that issue, we discussed how models developed by public health and leisure researchers can be improved through transdisciplinary collaboration. In this section, we summarize this work in the broader context of outdoor recreation, health and wellness (6).

A Social-Ecological Model of Public Health Research and Program Delivery

Ecological models of human behavior examine the relationships between people and their environments and how interventions in these domains can affect outcomes. The public health sector has typically relied on a social-ecological model, arguing that successful solutions to complex health problems require coordinated interventions at individual, interpersonal, organizational, community, and societal levels (7). In particular, the model asserts that success in improving a health problem requires environmental and policy interventions. A social-ecological approach to promoting health and wellness through outdoor recreation might involve the following initiatives:

- *Individual:* Individual instruction to build skills and confidence in outdoor recreation activities (e.g., kayaking or rock climbing);
- *Interpersonal:* Programs for adults, children, families and other social groups that build support networks to encourage regular visits to a park;
- *Organization:* Free programs and outreach events that promote regular outdoor recreation in parks (e.g., foot races or outdoor exercise programs);
- *Community:* Community policing strategies that help ensure safe access to and in parks (e.g., community service bicycle patrols, improved lighting, and surveillance);
- *Society:* State and federal funding programs to develop park and greenway trails for outdoor recreation and health.

Socio-ecologic models are implemented using evidence-based interventions. Lacking evidence of their effectiveness, programs and policies risk failure in accomplishing desired behavioral change. Well-intentioned communities have developed parks and trails for physical activity, only to find that facilities were underutilized or are used for mainly sedentary purposes. Under such conditions, a transdisciplinary perspective can be useful. This perspective recognizes that physical access to a park is only one of many factors which affect use of the park, so that affecting only one determinant of park use may not be sufficient to influence active visits.

A Benefits Approach to Leisure Research and Management

Relying on reasoning similar to the underpinnings of the social-ecological model, leisure researchers have developed a benefits-based approach to leisure from a policy, problem-oriented perspective. The benefits approach recognizes that outdoor recreation settings and activities are situated within a larger sociopolitical context. This context could be management of wildlands, in which much of the foundational research on leisure benefits was conducted, or in urban planning situations such as the development of a trail in a low-income, minority community (8). Whatever the case, researchers and managers need to understand the potential range of benefits sought by stakeholders. Framed within a health and wellness perspective these can be described as:

- *Physical:* Outdoor recreation activities and settings can provide opportunities for people to improve their physical health through movement, active exercise, exposure to fresh air, and access to nutritional foods;
- *Psychological:* Exposure and access to outdoor recreation opportunities can help reduce psychological stress, improve attention, achieve positive mood states and emotions, and even realize valued aesthetic and spiritual experiences;
- *Economic:* Public green space and attractive landscaping can increase the value of nearby residential homes; at larger scales they can contribute to economic revitalization efforts;
- *Environmental:* A city's green infrastructure can moderate urban heat island effects, filter out air particulates, reduce runoff and flooding, and provide other important environmental services for the well-being of individuals and communities;
- *Social and community:* Attractive, well-maintained green spaces can act as crime deterrents and improve social cohesion, and participation in community greening programs can empower communities and raise social capital.

As one contemplates how this range of outdoor recreation benefits relates to health and wellness goals, it becomes clear how well such an approach marries with the social-ecological model: particular evidence-based interventions of the social-ecological approach are selected based upon their profile of benefits, with benefits occurring in a larger context than just individual physical health. Benefits are scale dependent and in providing them one must consider how they relate across the hierarchy of concerns from individual to societal levels.

In the next section of this chapter, we provide an example for how this transdisciplinary framework might be applied in a real-world setting: The proposed development of a recreational trail to address health and wellness goals within a low-income, minority community.

Case Study Example: The Englewood New ERA Community Trail Corridor

In a recent effort to identify new park and recreation opportunities in Chicago, planners discovered an abandoned rail corridor segment in the Englewood community on the city's south side. At first glance, the 2-mile, elevated rail segment did not fit the typical idea for recreational trail development. It was short and cut off from potential connections to other trails by an expressway and rail yard on either end, had few natural features of merit other than the volunteer trees and plants growing along the corridor itself, and went through one of the poorest and most crime-ridden neighborhoods in the city. But upon closer inspection community residents and advocates saw the corridor as an opportunity to connect health and outdoor recreation together in exciting new ways.

Englewood's residents are 98% African American, 43% are at or below poverty level, and since the white flight of the 1950s and 60s, the community has lost more than half its population and housing stock. Obesity prevalence and associated health problems are high, the community has been classified as a food desert, and indoor and outdoor fitness opportunities are constrained by poverty and concerns about safety. But after decades of decline, Englewood is working to address its many problems through planning and community organizing efforts that tie health and wellness issues to community revitalization. A 2005 Quality of Life Plan developed by community stakeholders and support groups set the stage by identifying strategies for revitalization through open space development, the promotion of healthy lifestyles, and the creation of recreation opportunities; these strategies link to others that aim to revitalize the community through the creation of employment, retail, and housing opportunities, as well as the improvement of neighborhood safety (Figure 38.1) (9).

The 2009 *New ERA Trail Community Vision Plan: A Path for Transformation* shows how development of the trail corridor can serve as a catalyst to help achieve the strategies put forth in the 2005 Quality of Life plan and link them through new and ongoing projects. The trail itself would provide opportunities for active outdoor recreation but would also encourage physical activity by linking parks, shopping, and other community destinations with a safe, neighborhood transportation route. One particularly

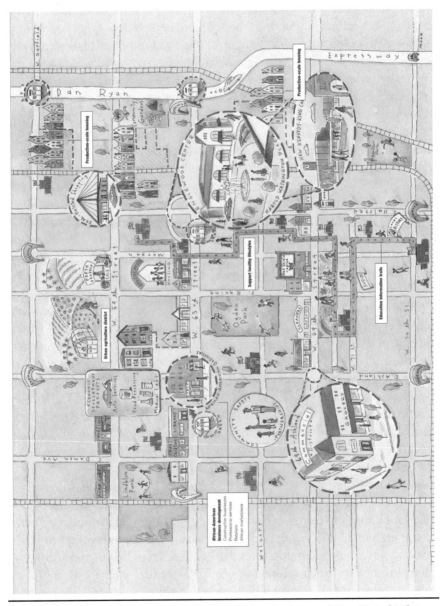

Figure 38.1 Community Vision from 2005 Englewood Quality of Life Plan (courtesy Local Initiatives Support Corporation/New Communities Program, Chicago)

important linkage is food production and delivery. Under the 2005 plan, community leaders established one of the city's first urban agriculture districts to creatively re-use a portion of Englewood's 700 acres of vacant land, and worked with the Chicago nonprofit group Growing Home to establish two urban farms. The farms train and employ homeless individuals and its greenhouses raise produce year round. An associated farmer's market run in coordination with local high school and church groups opened in 2008 to deliver the produce to residents. The foods emphasis has already been successful on many levels in improving the health and wellness of the Englewood community, and the *New ERA Trail Community Vision Plan* would more explicitly tie these goals to outdoor recreation through the development of a four-season food and festival market place, community garden plots, and orchards (Figure 38.2). Other signature features of the plan include green energy and sustainable development, and public art and signage that reflect the community's cultural heritage. The "ERA" in the proposed trail's name stands for Englewood Remaking America, and as the ambitious plan's subtitle expresses, the diverse group of stakeholders who developed the plan see the trail both literally and symbolically as "a path for transformation" for the community and beyond (10).

Discussion and Conclusion

While much work and many challenges lie ahead in realizing Englewood's vision for community revitalization, the trail project serves as a prime real-world example of a more comprehensive approach to integrating health and wellness goals through outdoor recreation. In the context of the framework we described earlier, programs and policies address many of the key levels specified in the social-ecological model of public health, and they also tap into many of the key benefits described in the benefits approach to leisure. While to our knowledge there is not yet a research component to the project, it would make an excellent "natural experiment" for transdisciplinary research collaboration to evaluate both the program and the efficacy of our framework.

It is also fitting that the Englewood trail development was selected as a model project to highlight in the 2009 centennial celebration of the Burnham Plan of Chicago. As discussed in the beginning of this chapter, it took individuals from a variety of professions to come together to advocate for parks and outdoor recreation to address health and wellness issues for the city. Such efforts are needed more than ever today, and transdisciplinary collaboration between the public health and leisure fields will be increasingly important in achieving health and wellness goals through outdoor recreation.

Figure 38.2 Englewood Trail Corridor Design Concept Incorporating an Urban Agriculture and Horticulture Component (courtesy Hitchcock Design Group)

References

1. Bachrach J. *The City in a Garden: A Photographic History of Chicago's Parks*. University of Chicago Press: Chicago, 2001.
2. U.S. Department of Health and Human Services. *Healthy People 2010: Understanding and Improving Health* (2nd ed). U.S. Government Printing Office, 2000.
3. Godbey GC, Caldwell LL, Floyd M, Payne LL. Contributions of leisure studies and recreation and park management to the active living agenda. *Am J Prev Med* 2005;**28** (Supp 2):150–158.
4. Centers for Disease Control and Prevention. Health disparities experienced by racial/ethnic minority populations. *MMWR* 2004;**53/33**:755–782.
5. Larson, NI, Story MT, Nelson MC. Neighborhood environments: disparities in access to healthy foods in the U.S. *Am J Prev Med* 2009;**36/1**:74–81.
6. Buchner D, Gobster PH. Recommendations for increasing physical activity through environmental ecologic models. *J PA Health* 2007;**4** (Supp 1):S36–S49.
7. McElroy KR, Bibeau D, Steckler A, Glanz K. An ecological perspective on health promotion programs. *Health Educ Q* 1988;**15**:351–377.
8. Driver BL, Brown PJ, Peterson GL (eds). *The Benefits of Leisure*. Venture Publishing, Inc.: State College, PA, 1991.
9. Teamwork Englewood. *Englewood: Making a Difference. Quality of Life Plan December 2005*. Local Initiatives Support Corporation/New Communities Program: Chicago, 2005.
10. Hitchcock Design Group in conjunction with Openlands. *New ERA Trail Community Vision Plan: A Path for Transformation*. Hitchcock Design Group: Chicago, 2009.

Chapter 39
Public Policy to Promote Healthy Leisure

Monica Hobbs Vinluan
Kathy J. Spangler

Introduction

Public funding for leisure, parks, and recreation services emerged in response to unhealthy living conditions spawned by industrialization and urbanization in the late 19th century. Promoting parks and recreation was viewed as a way to humanize the living environment, provide safe and healthy places for children and youth to play, and to protect natural resources in urban areas (1). The earliest pioneers of the leisure movement believed that the health of our society depended upon effective public policy to ensure that American democracy supported health in its broadest sense. In the story of these pioneers we see how citizen advocacy has historically shaped public policy and advanced the leisure movement in America. These pioneers forged a common approach to a multifaceted set of interests and issues that expanded access to public park and recreation resources throughout the 20th century.

- Frederick Law Olmsted was keenly interested in the connection between public spaces and health outcomes. He is most widely known for his abilities as a landscape architect and forefather of the public park movement, but he is also regarded as a pioneer of public health. As the first Sanitary Commissioner for New York City, Olmsted advanced public policies that resulted in planting trees along city streets to promote cleaner air in densely populated neighborhoods and to curb raging levels of scurvy.
- As the first American woman to win a Nobel Peace Prize, Jane Addams was an advocate for disadvantaged children. Among her many public policy interests, she worked tirelessly to establish Hull House, an urban oasis in Chicago that became a national model for supporting the physical, social, intellectual, and emotional well-being of disadvantaged children.
- Joseph Lee, a doctor and philanthropist, cared about the plight of children left to play in the streets of Boston while their parents toiled in the city's sweatshops. His outspoken advocacy resulted

in the birth of the public playground movement, providing safe places for children and youth to play.

- Best known for his extensive leadership role that helped bring physical education into public schools, Luther Gulick was the founder and leader of a number of organizations such as the YMCA of the USA and the Campfire Girls.

At the beginning of the 21st century, stakeholders advocating leisure- and health-focused public policy represent a broad cross-section of interests. This diversity of interests and the complexity of issues outlined in this book create a unique and daunting challenge for the leisure, health, and wellness movements: how to find common voice and influence public policy that shapes the ways leisure enhances health and wellness. For example, since the 1996 Surgeon General's Report on Physical Activity was issued, compelling evidence has accumulated to support an expanded role for leisure, parks, and recreation services to improve health outcomes (2, 3). Today, seventy-five percent of Americans live within a two-mile walk of a public park. Though these facilities are widely accessible to individuals from culturally and socioeconomically diverse populations and to those with disabilities, many do not take advantage of this free resource to promote health through leisure (4). However, research shows that people are unlikely to use community resources located more than a few miles away by car or more than a few minutes away by biking or walking (5). The public policy challenge of our time is how to leverage this extraordinary public asset for health outcomes by engaging an increasingly sedentary population in more active and restorative forms of leisure.

Policy Framework

Policy is typically defined as a deliberate plan of action to guide decisions and achieve rational outcomes. Policy can be both public in nature and private in target. By definition, public policy is an attempt by government to address a public issue. Government—whether municipal, state, or federal—develops public policy through laws, regulations, decisions, and actions (6). This type of policy can be categorized as "big P" policy. It typically involves the more formal policymaking steps (i.e., introduction of a piece of legislation, committee hearings and debate on the proposed legislation, vote by a legislative body) that characterize the work of a state legislature, the U.S. Congress, or even a local school board. "Big P" policy work also includes judicial opinions (whether issued by the U.S. Supreme Court, an administrative review judge, or a divorce court judge).

Another type of policy sometimes operates outside the formal legislative, regulatory, or judicial realm. Sometimes referred to as "little p" policy, these decisions often involve nonelected officials or individuals not officially accountable to the public. This policy arena involves actions by persons or entities that affect only their own sphere of influence. These may include social policy, economic policy, business policy, environmental policy, or even employment policy. For example, a company may engage in the "little p" to introduce or redesign an employee wellness program that allows its employees to take a physical activity break every day.

Citizens and other nonpublic actors are dynamically involved in efforts to effect change across a broad range of "little p" policy areas. In education, for example, they have urged schools to adopt policies banning the sale of sugary beverages in vending machines on school property. In the area of family policy, they have advocated for streamlined adoption procedures. In the health arena, they have promoted policies that encourage women to breastfeed. In the area of service and volunteerism, they have encouraged communities to require adolescents to contribute 25 hours of volunteer service in order to graduate from high school.

Through similar efforts, non-public actors can influence recreation and leisure policies in ways that improve public health outcomes. For example, communities might require all youth to take swimming lessons to reduce high rates of drowning and to promote lifelong physical activity. Or they can design parking areas further away from attractions, requiring more physical activity by visitors. Glendale, Arizona, employed this strategy in relocating its annual *Meet Santa* event outdoors and putting Santa at the top of a hill. As a result, children and parents had to hike to meet Santa!

One can also easily identify economic policy decisions that take place outside of the public sector. These can include a bank's policy of waiving a service fee for individuals who maintain a specific balance in their savings account, or a small business' decision to impose a $10 handling fee on all returned checks. Similarly, providing discounts or scholarships for children eligible for free and reduced lunch is a common leisure services policy.

Moving beyond an understanding that policy change should be a focus for those seeking to promote healthy leisure, it is important to understand how to achieve such change. Effective public policy (Big P) is a responsibility shared by both citizen advocates and professionals focused on establishing new standards to meet public needs. Management practices (little p) can have a lasting impact on leisure, health and wellness. These practices are interdependent and require a commitment to measure impact toward achieving goals. A leisure professional has a number of assets available to advance or reinforce both public policy and management policies including promotion, projects, programs, partnerships, and performance measures.

Public Awareness/Promotion

Public agencies should leverage all of their communication tools, such as program brochures and facility signage, to raise awareness regarding the connections between leisure and health. Building a common understanding of health benefits derived from public investments in leisure.

- For example, Gainesville, Georgia, dedicates the second page of its recreation program brochure to the connection between parks and recreation and an active, healthy lifestyle. In the brochure, a parent active in the department's activities shares a perspective on what other parents can do to help children lead a healthy life. In this way, the agency uses a promotional platform to advance public policies focused on children's health and tied to leisure services (7).

Projects/Physical Projects

Special projects bring communities together and can create a powerful force to advocate for effective policies and practices. Both leisure service and public health agencies can benefit from working together to leverage existing events and projects to advance policy. Engineering leisure and health into daily life provides all sectors of a community the opportunity to share a dialogue about how public policy can improve essential quality-of-life factors shared by community stakeholders. For example, the Las Vegas (NV) Department of Leisure Services recognized the importance of improving community access by connecting all of its parks so that citizens could walk, bike, and skate to various locations within the city. Businesses, neighborhood leaders, and government officials also saw the physical and environmental health benefits of a connected community. After extensive discussion, debate and policy enactment, the city opened the 26-mile Downtown to Redrock Bike Trail in October 2006 (8).

Programs

Programs provide an important opportunity for leisure service agencies to work toward documenting improved health outcomes. Traditional leisure service programming has given way to more integrated lifestyle programming that infuses healthy behaviors into all types of recreational activities. Recognizing that health outcomes must be documented if public policies supporting leisure services are to be realized, agencies are increasingly adopting new methodologies—such as pre- and post-testing—into their evaluation efforts. This discipline to plan, execute, and evaluate program activities against the goal of improving health outcomes is a standard of practice for any leisure agency making health claims about its services.

- For example, the Office of Parks and Recreation in Oakland, California, has worked closely with the City Council to develop a policy that mandates increased levels of physical activity in after-school programs (9).
- Nashville, Tennessee, implemented new policies to make healthy food choices more readily accessible and affordable in urban neighborhood centers (10).
- The Scottsdale, Arizona, parks and recreation department utilizes the results of an annual community health assessment to determine community needs for leisure services and targeted health goals such as reducing rates of obesity and overweight. Using available health data to inform program development, the department is able to show health improvements for program participants in areas that have been identified as key health issues (11).

Partnerships

Improving the health and livability of a community requires multiple stake-holders working together. Although individual groups may enjoy successes, the greatest impact occurs when shared community goals are addressed jointly by the public, private, and nonprofit sectors. Practitioners, researchers, and policymakers from different fields (e.g., parks and recreation and public health) and from governmental and nongovernmental agencies working together have the potential to significantly influence public policy to increase physical activity and positive health outcomes (12).

- In Longview, Washington, the parks and recreation department partnered with schools, nonprofit organizations, and health service providers to establish the Healthy Lifestyles Coalition. The coalition provides a structure for groups to share information and work together on communitywide nutrition and physical activity goals (13).

Performance Measures

Effective public policy is informed by research and performance measures that show progress toward well-defined outcomes. However, as it pertains to public health outcomes, the role of leisure service systems is not to prove that services impact individual health status. Instead, they should focus on documenting how services engage people and how many participate. For example, a leisure service agency with a goal of reducing rates of obesity should demonstrate that more people are more active more of the time that they are engaged in a program or while visiting a park setting. Correlating this information to existing health research provides the requisite data to show that, when a leisure program increases rates of activity among participants, it also promotes healthier outcomes.

Leisure and health scholars have begun to collaborate on studies that incorporate their two disciplines and strengthen the science needed to inform public policy.

- For example, the multidisciplinary team of Ariane L. Bedimo-Rung, PhD, Andrew J. Mowen, PhD, and Deborah A. Cohen, MD, studied the significance of parks to physical activity and public health. They developed a conceptual model that describes the relationships between park benefits, park use, and physical activity, and the antecedents/correlates of park use focused on park environmental characteristics that could be related to physical activity, including park features, condition, access, aesthetics, safety, and policies (14).

Multi-sector Approaches

Throughout the 20th century, a large body of knowledge developed in support of leisure and health as independent disciplines. However, collaboration between these disciplines is imperative for the creation of effective public policy that advances health promotion and disease prevention as a prevailing value of leisure, parks, and recreation. Certainly, the rehabilitative benefits of leisure have been well-documented, but the preventive value of leisure may well provide the greatest benefit to society in our technology-driven, sedentary society. The benefits of a healthy and livable community transcend the preservation of land and access to recreation resources that were primary aims during the 20th century. Increasingly, the impact of stress-related diseases has gained the attention of the business sector as employers seek to address work-life balance issues and rising health care costs.

Nonprofit organizations such as America's Promise Alliance (see Figure 39.1) offer a relevant model for creating multi-sector strategies to solve significant social issues that impact our nation's future. The Alliance encompasses nearly 300 public, private, and nonprofit partner organizations that have aligned assets and agreed to do business differently to ensure that all children have the fundamental supports they need to graduate from high school ready for college, work, and life. The Alliance believes that all children deserve healthy bodies, healthy minds, and healthful habits. It advocates for public policies that support regular checkups and needed treatment, good nutrition and exercise, healthy skills and knowledge, and good role models of physical and psychological health. With increased attention on upsurges in childhood obesity and juvenile diabetes, America's Promise Alliance has raised awareness regarding the importance of a healthy start as a critical developmental resource in a child's life. Importantly, the Alliance has aligned the need for a healthier start with larger, more systemic challenges our nation faces including the graduation crisis and its impact on the long term economic vitality of the nation.

Another example of a leading national nonprofit organization advancing health outcomes through multi-sector approaches is the YMCA of the

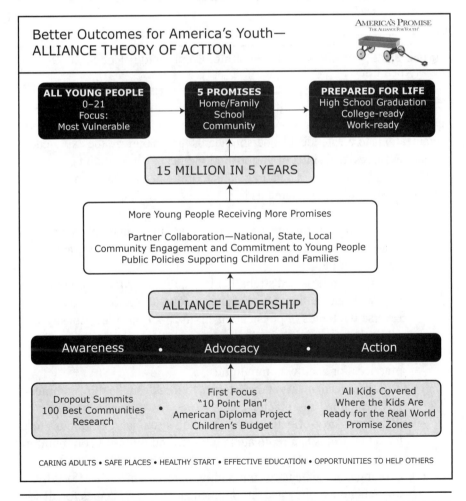

Figure 39.1 America's Promise Alliance, 2009 www.americaspromise.org

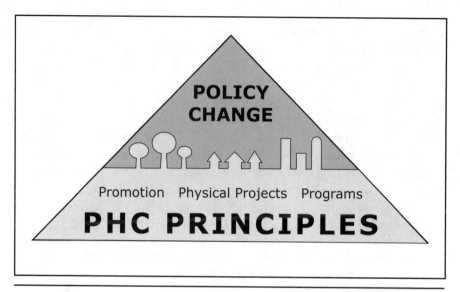

Figure 39.2 YMCA Pioneering Healthier Communities Model, 2009
www.ymca.net

USA and its Pioneering Healthier Communities initiative (see Figures 39.2 and 39.3). This model, launched in 2004, utilizes multiple sectors and diverse organizations to create local leadership teams that maximize the experience, assets, resources, and skills of various individuals in a community.

Each community team's main goal is to influence policy change to improve community environments by:

- developing community-level policy and environmental change strategies that increase opportunities for physical activity and healthy eating;
- raising awareness and strengthening the framework for community-wide and national movements among all sectors of society to reverse the trends in physical inactivity, poor nutrition, obesity, and other chronic conditions;
- strengthening community capacity to initiate and sustain promising practices for healthy communities;
- utilizing mechanisms and strategies to transform healthy community principles into practice;
- identifying cost-effective, practical, and sustainable solutions and tools that teams can replicate to educate and mobilize communities to make sustainable changes that support healthy living; and
- building complementary community, state, and national efforts by implementing policy and environmental change strategies for all sectors to increase opportunities for physical activity and healthy eating.

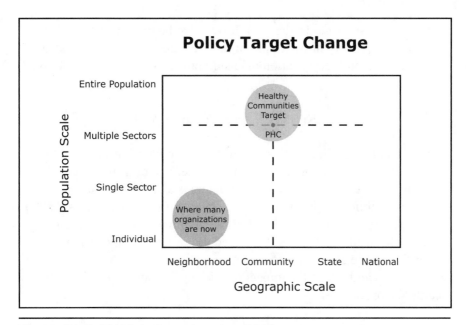

Figure 39.3 YMCA Activate America, 2009 www.ymca.net

Focusing on policy outcomes offers several advantages over investing separately in programs, physical projects, or promotion activities. A policy focus typically impacts a broader range of individuals and entities than programs, projects or promotions achieve by themselves. As a result, policy work can deliver a "bigger bang for the buck." Policy work also includes a measure of sustainability because its mechanisms are designed to be maintained and not open to continuous alteration.

Future Horizons

Environmental and public policy for leisure, parks, and recreation requires a commitment to identify, evaluate and advance health outcomes. This book identifies a number of key areas that point to reconnecting the value and benefits of parks, recreation, and leisure through a prism that focuses the field on healthy lifestyles and more livable communities. Toward that end, this book recommends a number of areas for practitioners and citizen leaders to consider as public policy priorities.

Improving Park Access and Increasing Physical Activity Levels

Increasing access to public space for health outcomes is critically important. Equally important, however, are issues related to safety, maintenance and culturally relevant design (15). It will also be important to design parks to achieve the full spectrum of leisure benefits, including rest, active recreation and rejuvenation to ensure physical, social, and emotional outcomes.

Surveillance Systems

Public Health Surveillance Systems are an effective means to track the association of access, opportunity and engagement of healthy behaviors in public spaces. Leisure service professionals at all levels should work with public health officials to advance surveillance systems that incorporate the proximity to and utilization of public park and recreation facilities for health outcomes. Increased use of technology will make it easier for leisure service practitioners and public health professionals to share data and assess the impact of utilizing community systems for health outcomes.

- Embrace parks as a venue for community connectivity.
- Parks are the key to creating a supportive community environment that reinforces health and well-being. From the design of the spaces to what they offer in their vending machines, parks need to engage in their own policy changes to embrace this role.

Support Interagency Coordination

Both the public health and leisure service systems are undergoing a transformation. On the one hand, public health agencies are adept at tracking health statistics, while leisure service systems have not been required to measure outcomes. On the other hand, public health officials benefit from public and nonprofit leisure service infrastructure that directly supports prevention and intervention efforts. At the foundation of effective public policy is a commitment to address public needs in integrated ways to establish new standards and practices that enrich society.

- Ensure that policies support public agency coordination across health, safety, transportation, parks and recreation at the local, state, or federal level.
- Ensure multi-sector collaboration on communitywide strategies that position parks and recreation as health assets. Partnering with nonprofits and businesses will strengthen the value and benefits of continued public support.

Healthy Eating

Millions of children lack consistent access to nutritious foods such as fresh fruits and vegetables. Instead, they rely on high-calorie fast foods. Low-income zip codes tend to have fewer and smaller grocery stores than higher income zip codes. Fewer supermarkets in low-income communities mean less access to healthy foods.

- Ensure that food and beverage contacts and concession contracts require balanced and nutritious choices.
- Advance system-wide approaches to promoting and providing increased availability of fruits and vegetables, particularly in disadvantaged neighborhoods.

Planning and Urban Design Elements That Encourage Walking and Physical Activity

Specific planning features that connect neighborhoods to community resources, such as parks, recreation centers and fresh-food groceries, are important ways to encourage healthy lifestyle choices.

- Participate in local coalitions that advocate connectivity and the ability of residents to reach more community resources on foot or by bicycle.
- Conduct "safety" audits of your parks and recreation centers to address real and perceived issues of safety in public park settings.

Conclusion

Our increasingly sedentary and technology-centric lifestyle has had unintended consequences that have increased rates of diabetes, heart disease, and obesity. The direct and indirect costs of chronic disease are staggering and will continue to grow until environmental policy and management practice changes occur at municipal, county, state, and federal levels to engineer more healthful living into daily life. The role of recreation and parks as public health assets will be affirmed when leisure professional and health leaders engage citizen advocates in support of public investments in parks and recreation that have an impact on health outcomes. Professional leaders must work in tandem with citizen advocates to articulate the health benefits of public recreation and parks and to establish new management practices that ensure these benefits are realized.

References

1. Cross G. *A Social History of Leisure since 1600*. Venture Publishing, Inc.: State College, PA, 1990.
2. U.S. Dept. of Health and Human Services. *Physical Activity and Health: A Report of the Surgeon General*. U.S. Dept. of Health and Human Services, Centers for Disease Control and Prevention: Atlanta, GA, 1996.
3. Crepo CJ, Keteyian SJ, Heath GW, Sempo CT. Leisure time physical activity among U.S. adults. *Arch Intern Med* 1996;**156**;93–98.
4. Godbey G, Graefe A, James S. *The Benefits of Local Recreation and Park Services: A Nationwide Study of the Perceptions of the American Public*. The Pennsylvania State University. University Park, PA, 1992.
5. U.S. Dept. of Health and Human Services. *Healthy People 2010: Physical Activity and Fitness*. Washington, DC, 2000.
6. What Is Public Policy? http://www.wisegeek.com/what-is-public-policy.htm. Accessed July 15. 2010.
7. Gainesville Parks and Recreation Agency. Program Brochure. Gainesville, GA, 2006.
8. Las Vegas Department of Leisure Services. Las Vegas, NV, 2006.
9. Oakland Parks and Recreation, Oakland, CA, 2006.
10. Nashville Parks and Recreation, Nashville, TN, 2006.
11. Scottsdale Parks and Recreation, Scottsdale, AZ, 2006
12. Godbey G, Caldwell L, Floyd M, Payne L. Contributions of leisure studies and recreation and park management research to the active living agenda. *Am J Prev Med* 2005;**28** (2S2):150–158.
13. Longview Parks and Recreation Department. Longview, WA, 2006.
13. *Am J Prev Med* 2005;**28** (2S2):159–168.
14. Yanez E, Muzzy W. *Healthy Parks, Healthy Communities: Addressing Health Disparities and Park Inequities through Public Financing of Parks, Playgrounds, and other Physical Activity Settings*. The Trust for Public Land: San Francisco, CA, 2005.

Chapter 40
Medical Profession and Healthy Leisure

Rebecca. A. Meriwether
Christine Katzenmeyer

In this chapter we will discuss opportunities for leisure time professionals to collaborate with clinicians, but we must first describe the medical context in which this collaboration will occur. We will refer to the "medical profession" primarily as the physicians and healthcare providers who work in primary care. Primary care includes family medicine, internal medicine, and pediatrics—physicians who specialize in providing a broad spectrum of preventive and curative care to individuals of all ages and often, to families as units. These providers are often in small practices of two to three providers and frequently employ nurse practitioners and physicians' assistants. They may also practice in large, multi-specialty practices, sharing administrative systems and physical facilities with specialists who care for people with selected diseases or problems. Family physicians care for people from the entire age spectrum and often care for whole families, while internists care for adults and pediatricians care for children and adolescents. All three specialties require three-year residencies following medical school for board certification.

As it relates to leisure and recreation pursuits as health options, primary care physicians are most likely to talk with patients about the benefits of leisure and recreation given their training to treat the "whole person." Other specialties that may also have a significant interest in patients' physical activity and leisure are cardiologists, endocrinologists who care for a large number of diabetic patients, and psychiatrists. Orthopedists may also have an interest in patients' physical activity and leisure pursuits since they often care for injuries sustained during leisure time. Neither leisure nor recreation are commonly points of formal study in medical school curricula or in residency training for these providers. But physicians in these specialties and those who enjoy physical activity and healthy leisure themselves are more likely to discuss the health benefits of leisure and recreation options with patients.

Physician advice is powerful but often not sufficient to elicit increased physical activity (1). Physician counseling coupled with referral to dieticians helps people with high cholesterol and diabetes adopt healthier eating (2). Yet because of a lack of time, reimbursement for lifestyle counseling, knowledge and skill in behavior change coaching, and confidence that counseling will result in behavior change, clinicians often fail to advise patients about the need for behavior change or give very brief advice that is not sufficient to elicit change. The U.S. Preventive Service Task Force (http://www.ahrq.gov/CLINIC/uspstf/uspsphys.htm) summarizes evidence-based preventive services and has concluded that evidence is not sufficient to recommend for or against clinician counseling for physical activity and recommends referral to dieticians for people with clinical conditions (e.g., high cholesterol, diabetes, obesity), but not for healthy individuals for prevention. There is growing consensus that brief clinician counseling coupled with referral for additional coaching, help and support is the strategy most likely to result in behavior change at the individual level. Built, social, and physical environments that support healthy behaviors form a third tier of intervention likely to be needed for significant increases in healthy leisure time physical activity and healthier eating. Parks and recreation and other leisure industry professionals should work with physicians, healthcare organizations, insurers, and policy makers to create a system of referral and reimbursement that supports individual level healthy leisure and adoption and maintenance of healthy behaviors in the context of policies and environments that promote and sustain healthier leisure.

Clinicians spend an average of 12–15 minutes in a typical primary care encounter of which only 1½–3 minutes is spent in education and counseling. This includes providing information about diagnosis, lab results and tests ordered, information about medications prescribed, and health behavior advice (3). Currently, clinicians are reimbursed based on the number of elements of history and physical and complexity of decision-making documented for a clinical encounter and counseling is compensated only if the content of counseling is documented along with evidence that counseling occupied over half of the time in the encounter. In this context, clinicians often urge patients to "lose weight," "walk more," or "eat healthy" but seldom provide evidence-based longitudinal, repetitive, individually tailored health behavior change interventions or discuss healthy leisure. Repetitive visits with the same provider are not available to everyone and subsequent visits are unlikely to occur at the appropriate frequency and timing to support behavior change. While some clinicians are experimenting with different approaches to clinical care that hold more promise for assisting patients with behavior change, including fewer but longer face-to-face sessions and more frequent communication via email or phone, reimbursement mechanisms are not designed to support these approaches at present. Healthcare reform could address this and create positive rather than negative incentives for clinicians to support healthy behaviors and leisure, but appears more focused at present on increasing the proportion of the population covered, use of technology to support continuity of care and reduce medical errors, and reducing short-term costs.

Another element of reforming our healthcare system is already underway, however. Nationwide, the concept of a patient-centered medical home (PCMH) is rapidly expanding and may also help to improve delivery of preventive services and counseling as well as enhance the coordination of medical care. In the PCMH, care is coordinated and the personal physician is responsible for providing or arranging for all the patient's healthcare needs, including referral to other community qualified professionals. Care is patient-centered in that the patient's personal priorities and preferences drive clinical priorities and care focuses on prevention and chronic disease self-management in addition to curing acute illnesses and healing injuries. Central to the PCMH approach is the premise that patient-centered care requires a shift in the relationship between patients and their primary care physicians. Clinicians are looking for and learning new ways to partner with community resources to support prevention and self-management, including such innovative approaches as referring to recreation centers. In the long run, the PCMH is expected to result in savings to patients, employers, and health plans. In the PCMH, primary care is no longer a single physician craft but a complex set of tasks best managed by a multidisciplinary team.

Chronic disease self management is another concept that is being incorporated as part of the evolution of clinical practice and is a large component of the PCMH. Chronic disease self-management is inherently patient-centered and requires collaboration between healthcare providers and patients with patients assuming responsibility for their own care and management, as the name implies. Chronic diseases, such as diabetes, asthma, high blood pressure, depression, chronic back pain require ongoing care rather than the cures we expect for acute illnesses like sore throats. In self-management, patients take responsibility for their own illness and healthcare professionals serve as coaches and advisors.

Group visits are another innovation in primary and chronic disease care that allows for patients with similar clinical needs to be seen in groups, receive increased health education, dietary and physical activity counseling, and peer support. Leisure time assessments and recreational therapy could also be provided. Over time it is likely that more medical care will be provided asynchronously, that is via phone, email, and Internet allowing clinicians and patients to interact more frequently, exchanging information in small increments of time while reserving longer, face-to-face encounters for more in depth assessment, coaching and planning. As these shifts in the delivery of medical care occur and as patients assume more responsibility in the relationship between patients and clinicians, the opportunity to discuss leisure time and recreational activity may increase. Chronic disease self-management and group visits provide excellent opportunities to have discussions of the benefits of healthy leisure, physical activity, and the research that supports these resources as tools for better health.

Many clinicians would happily refer patients for support of behavior change and healthy leisure, but systems are not currently in place to fill this need for most patients nor does insurance currently pay for many of these services (4). Nonetheless, some systems have been developed within the medical system to support healthier behaviors, but these systems usually follow a medical model and are focused on *patients* with specific *medical* problems or diagnoses. Examples include cardiac and pulmonary rehab, physical and occupational therapy to help individuals recover from injuries and strokes, and dietician counseling for *patients* with high cholesterol and diabetes. Each of these is considered the standard of care and objective evidence has been developed through research to define best practices, determine the effectiveness and cost-benefit of specific treatments. These services may be reimbursable through medical insurance for some, but not all patients who would benefit from them. For example, most health insurers pay for cardiac rehab for patients who have had a heart attack or heart surgery, but do not pay for extended cardiac rehab to support maintenance of behavior change for these patients nor for preventive cardiac rehab for patients at increased risk of heart attacks.

Innovative Initiatives

Innovative initiatives and research projects supporting healthier behaviors and leisure serve as models for a more comprehensive set of services. Tobacco cessation quit lines and a national STD information hotline are examples of public health responses to support healthier individual behaviors and are funded through federal, state and local public health agencies and philanthropy and could be adapted to support healthier leisure, eating and physical activity. Camps for children with diabetes or physical disabilities support initiation of healthy leisure for children with special needs. Researchers have demonstrated that telephone coaching can help people adopt and maintain increased physical activity and lose weight (5, 6) In New Zealand, the Green Prescription (7) is a proven program that links patients seen by primary care clinicians with physiotherapists to help them initiate and sustain increased physical activity. Robert Wood Johnson Foundation's Prescription for Health Program generated novel models of using internet-based resources to facilitate individual health behavior change (8) and identify and disseminate information to clinicians about resources to assist patients in adopting healthier behaviors (9). A project in New Orleans created a safe, supervised play area in a schoolyard that resulted in dramatically more children being outdoors and active over a two-year period than in a comparable neighborhood (10). A parks and recreation researcher developed an intervention in which primary care providers distributed maps of parks, trails, and other recreation venues to patients (11). Driven by evidence that proximity to affordable and accessible physical activity venues is associated with increased physical activity, one clinician obtained memberships to the Y and distributed them to low income patients in the primary care center where she works. A hypertension clinic in one southern city arranged with a nearby publicly operated recreation center for their patients to attend exercise and water aerobics classes. A small primary care center created a walking path around their building and parking lot and challenged staff and patients alike to walk for health and leisure. Some sports venues have banned smoking and tobacco ads, but often continue to offer and advertise high fat, calorie-dense, low nutrient foods. Public parks and recreation facilities are often free but vary in the availability of features and perceived safety. Some parks and most private recreation/leisure time venues charge admission and few offer reduced cost options for lower income individuals, compromising the ability of clinicians to refer patients to existing programs.

Wellness activities are a leisure option for many. The Poudre Valley Hospital in Ft. Collins, Colorado, has a wellness center for people over 50 in a beautiful "recreation center" type atmosphere. It provides medical screenings, personal training, and social programs for over 14,700 members. This type of service is becoming more common and is often financed through partnerships of local senior service programs with large hospitals. Such financing arrangements may help to keep membership costs low or even free in some cases. In such communities, physicians are able to refer patients from a clinical setting to a recreational and wellness program to help meet their social and physical leisure needs.

In Colorado, the PCMH as described above is an aggressively promoted and well-funded initiative to change healthcare delivery. As part of the PCMH initiative in Colorado, self management classes have been developed as community resource external to individual practices and available throughout the state. The Consortium for Older Adult Wellness is the gatekeeper of these classes and provides a statewide infrastructure to make sure all classes are standardized. Patients are referred by primary care practices and attend classes that are convenient to them. These classes include multiple modalities to enable participants to self manage their chronic conditions. Physical exercise and leisure activities are a big part of these discussions and participants develop individualized action plans to improve and monitor their conditions and learn how to feel better by doing things they enjoy.

Medicalized Leisure Time Activities

The medical model focuses not only on specific groups of *patients* with specific *diagnoses*, but also views health behavior interventions from a medicalized perspective. Travel clinics specialize in providing immunizations and preventive medical advice for individuals traveling to developing countries. Some physicians specialize in sports or adventure medicine. Several decades ago, Jim Fixx popularized running for health. This leisure time physical activity was embraced by the medical establishment and primary care physicians and cardiologists were soon advising patients not only that they needed to run, but that they needed to do so continuously for 20 minutes three times a day. Soon, reports began to appear in the medical and lay literature of apparently healthy individuals experiencing heart attacks or sudden cardiac deaths while or shortly following a run. Jim Fixx himself died suddenly and unexpectedly while running. Such events are rare, estimated to occur once in every 1.7 million episodes of vigorous physical activity (12). Yet physicians, concerned that they do no harm, began to search for a way to screen apparently healthy individuals prior to recommending physical activity and medical and leisure time professionals began to recommend physician clearance prior to beginning physical activity. Medical histories, physical exams, EKGs, and even cardiac stress tests were recommended prior to starting a new physical activity program. Evidence indicates that in the absence of specific cardiac symptoms, EKGs and stress tests are often falsely positive especially in women and younger men, and may lead not only to increased and needless worry but to additional, expensive, and even dangerous additional testing and interventions. The U.S. Preventive Services Task Force (http://www.ahrq.gov/CLINIC/uspstf/uspsacad.htm) currently recommends against using EKGs or stress tests to screen asymptomatic individuals for heart disease and states that there is not sufficient evidence to recommend for or against exercise stress testing prior to increasing physical activity. Professional organizations, including the American College of Sports Medicine and the American Heart Association (13) and the U.S. Centers for Disease Control and Prevention (14) now advise that such testing is not necessary for healthy young men and women to initiate a new program of vigorous physical activity nor for asymptomatic middle-aged men and women to begin a new program of moderate-intensity physical activity, but continues to recommend physician clearance for adults with chronic medical conditions, such as high blood pressure and diabetes, and those with symptoms of heart disease to see a physician prior to increasing physical activity. Because of a combination of true concern to do no harm and fear of lawsuits in a litigious society, many leisure time physical activity venues require physician clearance or signing a waiver before allowing some or all adults to participate in leisure time physical activity programs, creating an additional barrier and sending mixed messages to an increasingly overweight and sedentary population. The Canadian Society of Exercise Physiologists has taken a public health approach to this conundrum and recommends use of the PAR-Q (http://www.csep.ca/) as a means adults to determine for themselves what type of physical activity they may safely begin without medical clearance and to determine the symptoms and medical conditions for which physician advice is needed prior to increasing physical activity.

Traditional medical advice to get vigorous physical activity for 20 minutes three times a week and images of thin, well-muscled young men and women jogging in place at traffic lights or moving in time to jazzercise recordings has reinforced for many the notion that in order to be good for you, physical activity must be vigorous and continuous for at least 20 minutes. Thankfully for the majority of Americans who would not consider such vigorous activity enjoyable or even within the realm of possibility, we now know that 10-minute increments of moderate-intensity physical activity are healthful and are more likely to be initiated and maintained by previously inactive individuals. We also now know that life-style physical activity—physical activity that is incorporated into work, transportation, and home life—is more likely to be sustained than structured activity such as going to the gym or attending an exercise class (15).

Role of Leisure Time Professionals & Linkages with Healthcare Professionals

Leisure time professionals are often slim and fit and may harbor personal views and prejudices that reduce their effectiveness in assisting previously underactive children and adults to become more physically active (16). It may be hard for one who enjoys vigorous physical activity to be compassionate and nonjudgmental toward people who are overweight or who simply don't want to sweat! Effective counseling or coaching for health behavior change requires development of a therapeutic alliance a relationship predicated on trust and respect.

Opportunities exist to develop linkages of healthcare personnel and organizations with parks, recreation, and leisure time professionals and to demonstrate the effect of such linkages and the interventions they enable on initiation and maintenance of healthier leisure time and on healthcare costs and outcomes. Leisure time professionals should work locally and at the national level to create linkages with physicians, other health professionals, and healthcare organizations to alert clinicians to parks, recreation, and leisure time programs available at the local level and to develop linkages, pathways for referrals, and systems to feedback patients' participation and progress to referring clinicians. Print and web-based materials should be developed by leisure time professionals and organizations with advice and input from clinicians and be made available in healthcare settings. Parks, recreation, and other leisure time professionals can introduce themselves to healthcare providers at professional meetings by presenting scientific papers of mutual interest and by providing information through exhibits. Informal conversations in such venues can generate new ideas and inform develop-ment of materials and referral systems. Early adopters, individuals who quickly embrace a new idea or approach, can be identified in such settings or among healthcare providers who make use of parks, recreation, and leisure time facilities and programs. These individuals can form valuable partner-ships with leisure time professionals and organizations to help develop and refine referral and feedback mechanisms or can provide useful information on the content, format, and best venue for making information about local health behavior support and healthy leisure resources available to clinicians and patients. Academic detailing is a process similar to that used for many years by pharmaceutical companies, in which individuals come into medical practices and provide information and resources, often but not always over lunch. This approach could be an effective way to distribute information about a referral and feedback system once it has been developed, especially when coupled with referrals from "early adopter" clinicians.

Partnerships between parks, recreation, and leisure time professionals and health professionals and organizations should also work to develop new knowledge about how to most effectively promote and sustain healthy lifestyles and leisure through well-conceptualized and conducted research. Such partnerships can also be effective in advocating at the local, state, and national level for policies that reimburse healthcare and leisure time professionals for preventive health behavior interventions, that demedical-ize healthy leisure, and that promote healthier leisure through policies and environmental changes especially for disenfranchised populations such as the poor, racial, and ethnic minorities, and people with disabilities.

Summary

Successful examples of the roles of the medical profession in promotion of healthy leisure revolve around linkages, collaborative efforts, community resources, reducing healthcare expenditures, and increasing access to healthy leisure opportunities. We have described several examples that can and should be replicated.

In this time of healthcare delivery and financing reform, improving quality while reducing healthcare costs is central. Prevention, rather than merely treatment of disease, may at last become a core focus of the health-care system, with organization of care and reimbursement mechanisms designed to at last to support this key endeavor. As patients are called upon to assume more responsibility for their own care, new demands will be made on patients to become and stay healthy. Insurance companies have already begun to give better rates to nonsmokers and it may be only a mat-ter of time before rates are modified based on other health behaviors. New campaigns for healthy eating, physical activity, leisure, self management, and reducing stress are likely to be more prevalent components of health-care in the future.

The time is right for leisure and recreational professionals and related fields to promote the benefits of prevention and wellness. It is the perfect time for these professionals to enter into collaborations and partnerships with healthcare providers and organizations and offer concrete assistance to help *patients* adopt healthier leisure and lifestyles. Both healthcare provid-ers and leisure professional are critical to making this happen. Each group needs to continue to educate and interact with the other, no matter how that happens. There is no time like now.

References

1. Kreuter MW, Chheda SG, Bull FC. How does physician advice influence patient behavior? Evidence for a priming effect. *Arch Fam Med* 2000;**9**:426–433.

2. Thompson RL, Summerbell CD, Hooper L, Higgins JP, Little PS, Talbot D, Ebrahim S. Relative efficacy of differential methods of dietary advice: a systematic review. *Am J Clin Nutr* 2003;**77** (4 Supp): 1052S–1057S.

3. Stange KC, Woolf SH, Gjeltema K. One minute for prevention: The power of leveraging to fulfill the promise of health behavior counseling. *Am J Prev Med* 2002;**22**:320–323.

4. Tulloch H, Fortier M, Hogg W. Physical activity counseling in primary care: Who has and who should be counseling? *Patient Educ Couns* 2006;**64**:6–20.

5. Holtrop JS, Dosh SA, Torres T, Thum YM. The community health educator referral liason (CHERL): A primary care practice role for promoting healthy behaviors. *Am J Prev Med* 2008;**35** (5 Supp):S365–371.

6. Wilcox S, Dowda M, Leviton LC, Bartlett-Prescott J, Bazzarre T, Campbell-Voytal K, Carpenter RA, et al. Active for Life—Final results from the translation of two physical activity programs. *Am J Prev Med* 2008;**35/4**:340–351.

7. Elley CR, Kerse N, Arroll B, Robinson E. Effectiveness of counseling patients on physical activity in general practice: Cluster randomized controlled trial. *Br Med J* 2003;**326**:793–796.

8. Krist AH, Woolf SH, Frazier CO, Johnson RE, Rothemich SF, Wilson DB, Devers KJ, Kerns JW. An electronic linkage system for health behavior counseling effect on delivery of the 5A's. *Am J Prev Med* 2008;**35** (5Suppl):S350–358.

9. Flocke SA, Gordon LE, Pomiecko GL. Evaluation of a community health promotion resource for primary care practices. *Am J Prev Med* 2006;**30/3**:243–251.

10. Farley TA, Meriwether RA, Baker ET, Rice JC, Johnson C, Webber LS. Safe play spaces to increase physical activity in inner-city children: A pilot study of an environmental intervention. *Am J Pub Health* 2007; **97/9**:1625–1631.

11. Reed J, Malvern L, Muthukrishnan S, Hardy R, King L. An ecological approach with primary-care counseling to promote physical activity. *J Phys Act Health* 2008;**5/1**:169–183.

12. Albert CM, Mittleman MA, Chae CU, Lee IM, Hennekens CH, Manson JE. Triggering of sudden death from cardiac causes by vigorous exertion. *N Engl J Med* 2000;**343**:1355–1361.

13. Haskell WL, Lee IM, Pate RR, Powell KE, Blair SN, Franklin BA, et al. Physical activity and public health: Updated recommendation for adults from the America College of Sports Medicine and the American Heart Association. *Circulation* 2007;**116**:1081–1093. PMID: 17762377
14. Nelson ME, Rejeski WJ, Blair SN, Duncan PW, Judge JO, King AC, et al. Physical activity and public health in older adults: Recommendation from the American College of Sports Medicine and the American Heart Association. *Circulation* 2007;**116**:1094–1105. PMID: 17671236
15. USDHHS. *2008 Physical Activity Guidelines for Americans*. ODPHP Publication No. U0036. http://www.health.gov/paguidelines/. Accessed July 15, 2010.
16. Dunn AL, Marcus BH, Kampert JB, Garcia ME, Kohl HW, Blair SN. Comparison of lifestyle and structured interventions to increase physical activity and cardiorespiratory fitness: a randomized trial. *J Am Med Assoc* 1999;**281/4**:327–334.
17. Greenleaf C, Martin S, Rhea D. Fighting fat: How do fat stereotypes influence beliefs about physical education? *Obesity* 2008;**16** (Supp 2):S53–59.

Chapter 41

Public Recreation and Parks Services as a Wellness Agency

John Senior

Mardie Townsend

"Thousands of tired, nerve-shaken, over-civilized people are beginning to find out that going to the mountains is going home; that wildness is a necessity; and that mountain parks and reservations are useful not only as fountains of timber and irrigating rivers, but as fountains of life." - John Muir

Introduction

Take a moment to recall your own early childhood memories of contact with nature. We're guessing that, as you recalled those moments, you had a smile on your face and your heart gave a skip. It's probably quite a long time since you thought of those experiences, and yet they are still there in the recesses of your mind—literally cherished memories. Nature has that effect on us. Why is it so?

A famous Harvard biologist, Edward Wilson, observing the human tendency to crave contact with nature, developed an explanation for it which he called the "biophilia hypothesis." Basically, his thesis was that humans have lived in close contact with other species throughout human existence, and that it is really only in the last 250 years that we have become separated from nature. Wilson reasoned that this change has occurred too quickly for us to have adapted (in evolutionary terms) to the change. Thus, as a species we continue to crave nature contact (1).

Wilson's argument that humans continue to crave contact with nature seems to be well supported, at least in Australia. Almost two-thirds of Australian households have a pet; and figures from the Australian Garden Market Monitor show that in the 6 months to 31st December 2006, Australians spent over $3 billion on garden-related items and services. A report by Australia's Tourism and Transport Forum in 2004 (p. 8) stated: "The most common motivation reported for visiting Protected Areas is the enjoyment or experience of nature. Other common motivations include rest, relaxation or escape from everyday routine; tranquillity; sightseeing and socialising with family and friends." (2)

Over recent years, there has been a growing recognition of the fact that, in addition to the natural environment impacting on human health in detrimental ways through "environmental degradation," the lack of contact with nature may also impact on human health in detrimental ways through 'environmental deprivation.' According to the World Health Organization, more than 25% of the world's disease burden is attributable to environmental factors, but this refers solely to the human health impacts of environmental degradation. The impacts of environmental deprivation have not been quantified, but evidence is mounting that the restorative benefits of contact with nature are essential, wide-ranging, and could significantly reduce the burden of disease.

Underpinning this lack of quantification are two key factors: the generally narrow definition of "health" used in relation to data collection; and the complexity of measuring the benefits of contact with nature. The majority of health statistics measure illness or the absence of health, rather than health itself. According to the Australian Institute of Health and Welfare (AIHW) (3), holistic well-being is a crucial concept for understanding health. The seven dimensions nominated by AIHW as making up this holistic well-being are: health (physical and mental); social well-being; economic well-being; environmental well-being; life satisfaction; spiritual or existential well-being; and "other characteristics valued by humans" (p. 1). The importance of contact with nature as a determinant of holistic well-being is highlighted by Bryan Furnass (4) who notes that well-being includes satisfactory human relationships, meaningful occupation, opportunities for contact with nature, creative expression, and making a positive contribution to human society.

Accordingly, many public recreation and parks services are beginning to take account of the benefits for human health and well-being that their facilities and services offer, and are tailoring their planning, policies, and practices to optimize those benefits.

Best Practice Examples

Examples of these responses by public recreation and parks services can be divided into two categories, which we have termed "generic" and "stretching the limits."

Examples of Generic Responses

Environmental volunteering: Many public recreation and parks services provide opportunities for people to enhance their health and wellbeing through environmental volunteering. For example, the website of Parks Victoria, the body responsible for managing parks and other assets on behalf of the State of Victoria, Australia, indicates that there are more than 300 different friends groups helping Parks Victoria to maintain and protect one of the world's finest networks of parks. Friends groups vary in size, activities and structure. Groups usually meet and volunteer weekly or monthly but some volunteers are in the park every day. Some groups have weekly activities, many have a monthly activity and visitors are always welcome to attend. Friends groups, whilst being autonomous and independent, operate in partnership with Parks Victoria. This is a cooperative, mutually supportive relationship which enables friends groups to deliver some amazing and highly valuable work in parks. Recent studies by researchers from Deakin University have indicated that environmental volunteering is beneficial for physical, mental and social well-being. So, when the parks and leisure industry opens the door to becoming a friend of a park, grab it!

Economic and political recognition: Because of the inherent love of natural environments explained above, public recreation and parks services are beginning to recognize the value of their assets in terms of human well-being. As this recognition grows, there will be increasing opportunities not only to partner with governments at all levels, but also to utilize the growing body of evidence in building business case approaches to elected officials.

In the U.S., John Crompton has undertaken much research into a variety of economic returns from the existence of parks, especially in regard to their impact on raising property values and the consequent generation of municipal charges. Similarly, research in China has shown an increasing desire by apartment purchasers to have good access to green spaces and parks, and in Australia for apartment purchasers to have views of green spaces, parks or bodies of water. This research has the potential to encourage both the development and maintenance of adequate parks and green spaces, and to increase the recognition of their value for economic, political and well-being purposes.

Examples of Responses which "Stretch the Limits"

The following examples, drawn from Australia, New Zealand, Canada, England, and Japan, demonstrate some of the ways in which public recreation and parks services are interpreting their role as 'wellness agencies' in creative ways.

Healthy Parks Healthy People (Australia): Based in Melbourne, Australia, Parks Victoria manages national, state, marine and major metropolitan parks in the state of Victoria. Having initially created the expression "Healthy Parks Healthy People" as a marketing line in 1998, Parks Victoria engaged Deakin University's Faculty of Health & Behavioural Sciences to undertake what has since been acclaimed as an outstanding international literature review into the health benefits of contact with nature. Completed in 2002 and since updated in 2008, this research has encouraged and enabled Parks Victoria to make Healthy Parks Healthy People the keystone of its corporate direction. As a result, the organization has gained the reputation as one of the world's leading parks bodies. Impressed with this broader interpretation of the role of parks, the International Union for the Conservation of nature (IUCN)—the global body for conservation—auspiced Parks Victoria to lead "Healthy Environments Healthy People" which was one of three themes at the 2008 World Conservation Congress attended by 7000 delegates.

At the local level, Parks Victoria has formed alliances with the State Health department, and not-for-profit organizations like the National Heart Foundation and *BeyondBlue* (Australia's national depression body) to deliver a variety of projects and programs. One of these—the World's Greatest Pram Stroll—is an annual event to popularize mothers with young children forming walking groups to counter post-natal depression and isolation as well as for the developing of good exercise habits and habitats. As many as 5,000 people have participated, with the Stroll growing from a single event to 28 locations in only 6 years.

Healthy By Nature (Canada): Inspired by the Healthy Parks Healthy People approach pioneered by Parks Victoria in Australia, the Canadian Parks Council (a forum for Parks Canada together with 10 Provincial and 3 Territory park agencies) produced its strategy "Healthy by Nature" in 2006. This was its response to mounting evidence of obesity, type 2 diabetes, and the general Pan-Canadian Healthy Living Strategy endorsed by Canada Health Ministers in 2005. This latter document recognized the significant role that the "setting" makes to the pursuit of a healthy lifestyle.

"Healthy by Nature" carried five key messages, simply expressed as:

- Parks for your health;
- Parks for your family;
- Parks for your soul;
- Parks for your community; and
- Parks for your environment.

Since its publication, implementation has predictably varied in time, place and content. For example:

- Ontario Parks has embraced the philosophy in all its promotions.
- Manitoba Parks has built an alliance with the provincial Ministry of Health and together they are developing cooperative programs.

- Nunavut Parks use the Inuit term 'Kat ya naaw" meaning *'I am content in this beautiful special place, I have found peace, I am home'*.
- British Columbia Parks have three programs: Pick Your Trail, Project GO (for 'get outdoors')—a schools program; and "Wild At Heart"—a TV series.
- Parks Canada's Prince Edward Island National Park has a three year initiative "Healthy Parks for People" aimed at engaging interest groups and partnering organizations to develop new options for visitor experiences.

Presently the Canadian Parks Council is focused on producing an online toolkit for implementation of the Healthy by Nature strategy and placing more effort into building bridges with other sectors, especially health.

Feel Blue, Touch Green (Australia): "Feel Blue, Touch Green" was the name given to a project in which people experiencing depression, anxiety, and/or social isolation were involved in hands-on nature-based activities as a strategy to improve their well-being. It was a collaborative pilot project undertaken in Victoria (Australia) in 2006 involving Deakin University, Parks Victoria, Barwon Health, Alcoa Anglesea, Surf Coast Shire, ANGAIR (the Anglesea and Airey's Inlet Society for the Protection of Flora and Fauna) and the People and Parks Foundation. The overall project aim was to identify and promote the benefits of nature-based activities for mental health and overall well-being.

The wide range of nature-based activities, including nature walks, weeding, plant propagation, plant identification, planting, wildlife watching and wildlife counting, enabled people to choose from 3 or 4 different activities per week and accommodated various interests and abilities. The impact of the project was determined through a combination of informal and formal evaluation strategies. An Emotional State Scale (ESS) was administered at the commencement and completion of each activity to indicate changes in emotional state across 19 parameters. In addition, in-depth interviews were undertaken to capture participants' perspectives of being involved in the project and in nature-based activities. The results showed that all participants experienced positive emotional change from their participation in project activities. The in-depth interviews revealed benefits in:

- Developing capacity to be involved, taking risks, and confronting challenges;
- Improved general mental health, including confidence, and self-worth;
- Stress and anxiety management, including positive cognitive changes;

- Ability to manage depression and low mood states;
- Improved physical health;
- Building social capital: improved social networks and supports; and
- Building ecological capital: improvements in natural and urban environments.

This project shows enormous promise for the rehabilitation of people experiencing depression, anxiety and social isolation—a growing proportion of the world's population.

Green Prescriptions: The "Green Prescription" program was introduced in New Zealand in the late 1990s based on the recognition that both contact with nature and physical activity were important factors in human health. The program involves written advice by a health professional to a patient to be physically active. Because such prescriptions are predominantly designed to encourage physical activity in the form of walking or activities such as gardening, they may involve public recreation and parks services encouraging people to combine their exercise with access to green spaces (natural environments). Similar programs are now available in a number of countries including the United Kingdom, Canada, Australia, USA, and Japan.

In the New Zealand "Green Prescription" (GRx) program, Regional Sports Trusts (RSTs) "act as facilitators and a support base for patients to gain additional information on activity programs and also assist in the formation of activity groups (i.e., walking groups), which in turn provide additional avenues for interpersonal support and motivation" (5).

The program involves five steps:
1. Training and support for health professionals on implementing the GRx;
2. Issuing of the GRx to patients identified as not sufficiently active;
3. Copying the GRx to a local sports foundation (such as a RST), where an exercise specialist is assigned as a Patient Support Person (PSP) for the patient;
4. Supporting and encouragement of the patient by the PSP over a period of 3–4 months;
5. Reviewing the patient's level of exercise by the health professional, with an option for another GRx to ensure ongoing support.

Studies of the program's outcomes (6) have shown that it is both effective (in increasing energy expenditure and leisure exercise by participants) and cost-efficient (i.e., relative to other types of care, it is "better value for money"). The important role played by public recreation organizations is confirmed by participants who reported that the support from RSTs (and the extra support provided by physical activity groups organized by the RSTs) was significant in them becoming physically active.

Green Gyms: Closely related to the concept of the "Green Prescription" is the concept of the "green gym." This concept was initially developed by Dr. William Bird from the Sonning Common Health Centre, near Reading in the UK. Funded as a pilot project by the British Trust for Conservation Volunteers in 1998, the program has since spread throughout UK and beyond. Green gyms link exercise with conservation activities and the promotion of environmental awareness and, in doing so, enhance health and wellbeing by increasing levels of physical activity, by taking people into environments that are psychologically restorative, and by fostering social connections (7). Local environmental management organizations, including park management agencies and local councils, are important partners in the program, as they provide the venues in which activities are undertaken.

The national evaluation of the program, undertaken between July 2003 and August 2007, indicated that "green gyms" are beneficial for both physical and mental health and wellbeing. Other research supports this view, with one evaluation identifying improved physical fitness, flexibility and stamina as outcomes of involvement in green gyms (8), and a study of volunteers' experiences of the program (9) identifying reduced levels of stress and a heightened sense of fulfilment as major benefits. As well, there are significant benefits for social connectedness and social wellbeing. A report in the Oxford Times in March 2000 quoted participants as saying:

> "This is a lovely group of people. In three years, I've never heard a cross word here. Not many other groups or clubs could say the same thing" and "it's good to get out, have companionship, satisfaction from work well-done and physical well-being."

A more recent development has seen collaboration between Natural England (a government statutory body responsible for biodiversity conservation) and the UK National Health Service, enabling the training of 33,000 health walk leaders to guide 4,000 GP prescribed walks a week. This arrangement overcame previously poor public attitudes to such prescribed exercise, giving real meaning to "take a walk in the park." It is no coincidence that, for several years now, Dr. Bird has been engaged by Natural England as its Senior Health Advisor. There are not only physical benefits—research has shown that a walk in natural settings compared with a built up area provides twice the benefit for countering depression, tension, and improving self-esteem.

Offenders and Nature Initiatives: Over recent years, particularly in the UK and Australia, a number of programs have emerged which involve offenders (including prisoners) in conservation activities in public parks and recreation sites. Typically, these "Offenders and Nature" (O&N) schemes involve partnerships between organizations involved in the management of offenders and organizations involved in the management of the natural-environment. Underpinning these programs is the recognition that the likelihood of offenders re-offending is reduced not by imprisonment but by rehabilitation and the development of improved skills and employability.

One example of an O&N scheme is the Dartmoor Prisoner Resettlement Initiative. This program includes two stages: Stage 1, involving suitable and interested prisoners in 4–6 weeks of voluntary work with the Forestry Commission on Dartmoor; and Stage 2, involving 6 months of paid work experience and skills training, immediately prior to release. For those prisoners who have satisfactorily completed Stages 1 and 2, the Forestry Commission then offers an optional 3-month employment contract, available immediately on release.

Natural England's partnership with Phoenix Futures (a charity supporting people experiencing substance misuse and abuse) is another example, in which participants undertake "conservation therapy" by assisting with the restoration and maintenance of National Nature Reserves. Similarly, "Project Scotland" is a partnership between the Galloway District of the Forestry Commission Scotland and the Volunteer Centre South Ayrshire, which provides opportunities for conservation volunteering together with training for marginalized young people. While not all participants are offenders, the scheme is available to young offenders. Participants learn aspects of environmental management, but also have opportunities for recreational activities such as mountain-biking. A study of this group in 2007/2008 highlighted the benefits of the program, with one participant commenting that without the program he would be "probably sitting on the couch, playing on my computer all day… getting into trouble. So this is really good for getting out of trouble" (10). The report went on to highlight the benefits of the program for both skill development and social connections. One enthusiastic participant stated: "Aye, brilliant! I met hundreds of new people. It boosted my confidence well high, so it did" (p. 91).

The South Australian State Government's "Restorative Justice" program within the Department for Correctional Services includes Mobile Outback Work Camps and programs in national parks (http://www.corrections.sa.gov.au/corporate/restore.htm). Like the UK programs, this approach is aimed at providing "opportunities for prisoners and offenders to develop competencies, attitudes and behaviours, which contribute to non-offending lifestyles." Similarly, the Department of Conservation and

Land Management in Western Australia (CaLM) has a Memorandum of Understanding with the Ministry of Justice to run a program of prisoner participation in conservation and recreation projects. The Environment Minister noted the benefits in terms of "great tourist facilities," while the Justice Minister highlighted the provision of "useful and meaningful work activities for prisoners" (http://www.dec.wa.gov.au/news).

Tree-assisted therapy: A less widely recognized way in which public parks and recreation agencies can contribute to health and wellbeing is through tree climbing. In 1983, Tree Climbers International was established, along with a training facility for tree climbing in Atlanta, GA in the U.S. The organization's website highlights "the joy and wonder of seeing the world from the heights of the treetops" (http://www.treeclimbing.com/index.php). However, in other parts of the world, other benefits of tree climbing are noted. In UK, reflecting the restorative and therapeutic benefits of nature contact, recreational tree climbing is said to contribute to the "personal and social development of children and vulnerable adults, allowing them to climb out of their comfort zone and develop self-confidence" (http://www.arborteering. co.uk/output/recreational_tree_climbing.asp). In Japan, tree climbing is a popular recreational activity, with tens of thousands of people of all ages and abilities participating between 2000 and 2007 (11). However, it has now moved beyond being simply a recreational activity to being the focus of research, particularly around rehabilitation. The adaptive tree climbing techniques developed in Japan for use particularly with people experiencing physical disabilities are known as "Treehab." Climbing takes place in a range of settings, including parks and urban forests. Although the managers of the parks and forests would not generally consider themselves to be providers of health services, a small scale study in Japan comparing the effects (both physiological and psychological) of climbing trees with the effects of climbing towers indicated that tree climbing provides greater physiological and psychological benefits than tower climbing. The Japanese researchers suggest that the incorporation of tree climbing "programs into community forest planning [would] complement aesthetic, ecological, and restoration benefits and provide a new venue for recreation and conservation awareness."

Barriers to Use of Parks and Recreational Spaces for "Wellness Promotion"

The barriers fall into four self-evident headings:

- "Silo mentality" in departments and organizations, including in parks and recreation bodies;

- Safety—perceptions of "stranger danger," lack of lighting, lack of ranger or volunteer presence;
- Availability and accessibility of parks and open space—as funding is allocated to (presumed) higher priorities;
- Perceived time—parents' time to play with their children, the "convenience" and heavy marketing of electronic games.

Strategies for Overcoming the Barriers

Put simply these can be summarized as:

- More enlightened thinking assisted by increased research;
- More champions—look at the impact of the Richard Louv book and its inspiration for the Children and Nature Network in North America;
- Global leadership by the International Union for the Conservation of Nature (IUCN) and World Health Organization (WHO);
- Parks and environmentalists taking their blinkers off (i.e., opening up their thinking) and realizing that promoting the health, tourism, and ecosystem services values of nature may produce better outcomes than the narrow range of values previously used; then, developing a better understanding of those aspects so they can communicate effectively—ring the right bells rather than using traditional biodiversity and recreation terminology.

After all, this isn't new! When urban parks were first designed in 19th century Europe, there was a strong belief in the health advantages that would result. It was also believed that exposure to nature fostered psychological well-being, reduced the stresses associated with urban living, and promoted physical health. Frederick Law Olmsted believed in the restorative quality of green nature that "operates by unconscious processes to relax and relieve tensions created by the artificial surroundings of urban life." He also believed that parks improved health and vigor, and extended the life expectancy of citizens.

In Australia, the Melbourne Metropolitan Town Planning Commission's 1929 Report stated: "abundant evidence is available to substantiate the views of city planners, the medical profession and psychologists that proper outdoor recreation has a most beneficial effect on the health, morals and business efficiency of communities and consequentially on national life."

Highly relevant and timely to the publication of this book was the recent staging of the inaugural International Healthy Parks Healthy People Congress in Melbourne, Australia in April 2010. Not just a parks event, it was designed to attract delegates across disciplines and sectors not normally congregating at a single event. The Congress attracted over one thousand delegates from 36 countries and was rated an outstanding success. Proceedings, the Congress Communiqué and a summary of the outputs (which include global strategies and the progressive development of an international research agenda) are published on the Congress website: http://www.healthyparkshealthypeoplecongress.org/. The outcomes of this attempt to build understanding and collaboration also included the establishment of an ongoing web-based resource base—to which further research and case studies can be progressively added and which will also facilitate ongoing social networking opportunities: www.hphpcentral.com.

References

1. Wilson EO. Biophilia and the Conservation Ethic. In Kellert SR, Wilson EO (eds). *The Biophilia Hypothesis*. Washington, DC. Shearwater Books/Island Press, 1993, pp. 31–41

2. Tourism & Transport Forum Australia and Sustainable Tourism CRC. *A Natural Partnership: Making National Parks a Tourism Priority, Executive Summary*. TTF Australia Ltd.: Royal Exchange, NSW, 2004.

3. Australian Institute of Health and Welfare. Australia's health 1996: The fifth biennial report of the Australian Institute of Health and Welfare. AGPS, Canberra, 1996.

4. Furnass B. 1996. Introduction. In Furnass B, Whyte J, Harris J, Baker A (eds). *Survival, Health and Wellbeing into the Twenty First Century—Proceedings of a Conference Held at The Australian National University, November 30–December 1, 1995*. Nature and Society Forum, Canberra, 2005, pp. 5–6.

5. Sinclair KM, Hamlin MJ. Self-reported Health Benefits in Patients Recruited into New Zealand's 'Green Prescription' Primary Health Care Program. *Southeast Asian J Trop Med Publ Health* 2007;**38/6**:1158–1167.

6. Dalziel K, Segal L, Elley CR. 2006. Cost utility analysis of physical activity counselling in general practice. *Aust New Zeal J Publ Health* 2006;**30/1**:57–63.

7. Church C. *Changed Places, Changed Lives: The Social Impacts of Environmental Action*. BTCV: Doncaster, UK, 2007.

8. Reynolds V. *The Green Gym*. Institute for Volunteering Research, UK, 2000.

9. Birch M. Cultivating wildness: Three conservation volunteers' experiences of participation in the green gym scheme. *Br J Occup Ther* 2005;**68/6**:244–252.

10. O'Brien E, Townsend M, Ebden M. 'I like to think when I'm gone I will have left this a better place.' Environmental volunteering: motivations, barriers and benefits. Report to the Scottish Forestry Trust and Forestry Commission, July 2008.

11. Gathright J, Yamada Y, Morita M. Recreational tree-climbing programs in a rural Japanese community forest: Social impacts and "fun factors." *Urban Forestry & Urban Greening* 2007;**6**:169–179.

Subject Index

Other Books by Venture Publishing, Inc.

21st Century Leisure: Current Issues, Second Edition
>   by Valeria J. Freysinger and John R. Kelly

Active Living in Older Adulthood: Principles and Practices of Activity Programs
>   by Barbara A. Hawkins

Activity Experiences and Programming within Long-Term Care
>   by Ted Tedrick and Elaine R. Green

Adventure Programming
>   edited by John C. Miles and Simon Priest

Assessment: The Cornerstone of Activity Programs
>   by Ruth Perschbacher

Beyond Baskets and Beads: Activities for Older Adults with Functional Impairments
>   by Mary Hart, Karen Primm, and Kathy Cranisky

Boredom Busters: Themed Special Events to Dazzle and Delight Your Group
>   by Annette C. Moore

Brain Fitness
>   by Suzanne Fitzsimmons

Client Assessment in Therapeutic Recreation Services
>   by Norma J. Stumbo

Client Outcomes in Therapeutic Recreation Services
>   by Norma J. Stumbo

Conceptual Foundations for Therapeutic Recreation
>   edited by David R. Austin, John Dattilo, and Bryan P. McCormick

Constraints to Leisure
>   edited by Edgar L. Jackson

Dementia Care Programming: An Identity-Focused Approach
>   by Rosemary Dunne

Dimensions of Choice: Qualitative Approaches to Parks, Recreation, Tourism, Sport, and Leisure Research, Second Edition
>   by Karla A. Henderson

Diversity and the Recreation Profession: Organizational Perspectives (Revised Edition)
>   edited by Maria T. Allison and Ingrid E. Schneider

Effective Management in Therapeutic Recreation Service, Second Edition
>   by Marcia Jean Carter and Gerald S. O'Morrow

Everything from A to Y: The Zest Is up to You! Older Adult Activities for Every Day of the Year
>   by Nancy R. Cheshire and Martha L. Kenney

Experience Marketing: Strategies for the New Millennium
>   by Ellen L. O'Sullivan and Kathy J. Spangler

Facilitation Techniques in Therapeutic Recreation
>   by John Dattilo

File o' Fun: A Recreation Planner for Games & Activities, Third Edition
        by Jane Harris Ericson and Diane Ruth Albright
Getting People Involved in Life and Activities: Effective Motivating Techniques
        by Jeanne Adams
Health Promotion for Mind, Body, and Spirit
        by Suzanne Fitzsimmons and Linda L. Buettner
Inclusion: Including People With Disabilities in Parks and Recreation Opportunities
        by Lynn Anderson and Carla Brown Kress
Inclusive Leisure Services: Responding to the Rights of People with Disabilities, Second Edition
        by John Dattilo
Internships in Recreation and Leisure Services: A Practical Guide for Students, Fourth Edition
        by Edward E. Seagle, Jr. and Ralph W. Smith
Interpretation of Cultural and Natural Resources, Second Edition
        by Douglas M. Knudson, Ted T. Cable, and Larry Beck
Intervention Activities for At-Risk Youth
        by Norma J. Stumbo
Introduction to Outdoor Recreation: Providing and Managing Resource Based Opportunities
        by Roger L. Moore and B.L. Driver
Introduction to Recreation and Leisure Services, Eighth Edition
        by Karla A. Henderson, M. Deborah Bialeschki, John L. Hemingway, Jan S. Hodges,
        Beth D. Kivel, and H. Douglas Sessoms
Introduction to Therapeutic Recreation: U.S. and Canadian Perspectives
        by Kenneth Mobily and Lisa Ostiguy
Introduction to Writing Goals and Objectives
        by Suzanne Melcher
Leadership and Administration of Outdoor Pursuits, Third Edition
        by James Blanchard, Michael Strong, and Phyllis Ford
Leadership in Leisure Services: Making a Difference, Third Edition
        by Debra J. Jordan
Leisure and Leisure Services in the 21st Century: Toward Mid Century
        by Geoffrey Godbey
The Leisure Diagnostic Battery Computer Software (CD)
        by Peter A. Witt, Gary Ellis, and Mark A. Widmer
Leisure Education I: A Manual of Activities and Resources, Second Edition
        by Norma J. Stumbo
Leisure Education II: More Activities and Resources, Second Edition
        by Norma J. Stumbo
Leisure Education III: More Goal-Oriented Activities
        by Norma J. Stumbo
Leisure Education IV: Activities for Individuals with Substance Addictions
        by Norma J. Stumbo

Leisure Education Program Planning: A Systematic Approach, Third Edition
    by John Dattilo

Leisure for Canadians
    edited by Ron McCarville and Kelly MacKay

Leisure Studies: Prospects for the Twenty-First Century
    edited by Edgar L. Jackson and Thomas L. Burton

Leisure in Your Life: New Perspectives
    by Geoffrey Godbey

Making a Difference in Academic Life: A Handbook for Park, Recreation, and Tourism Educators
    and Graduate Students
    edited by Dan Dustin and Tom Goodale

Managing to Optimize the Beneficial Outcomes of Leisure
    edited by B. L. Driver

Marketing in Leisure and Tourism: Reaching New Heights
    by Patricia Click Janes

More Than a Game: A New Focus on Senior Activity Services
    by Brenda Corbett

The Multiple Values of Wilderness
    by H. Ken Cordell, John C. Bergstrom, and J.M. Bowker

N.E.S.T. Approach: Dementia Practice Guidelines for Disturbing Behaviors
    by Linda L. Buettner and Suzanne Fitzsimmons

The Organizational Basis of Leisure Participation: A Motivational Exploration
    by Robert A. Stebbins

Outdoor Recreation for 21st Century America
    by H. Ken Cordell

Outdoor Recreation Management: Theory and Application, Third Edition
    by Alan Jubenville and Ben Twight

Parks for Life: Moving the Goal Posts, Changing the Rules, and Expanding the Field
    by Will LaPage

The Pivotal Role of Leisure Education: Finding Personal Fulfillment in This Century
    edited by Elie Cohen-Gewerc and Robert A. Stebbins

Planning and Organizing Group Activities in Social Recreation
    by John V. Valentine

Planning Areas and Facilities for Sport and Recreation: Predesign Process, Principles, and Strategies
    by Jack A. Harper

Planning Parks for People, Second Edition
    by John Hultsman, Richard L. Cottrell, and Wendy Z. Hultsman

Programming for Parks, Recreation, and Leisure Services: A Servant Leadership Approach, Third Edition
    by Donald G. DeGraaf, Debra J. Jordan, and Kathy H. DeGraaf

Recreation and Leisure: Issues in an Era of Change, Third Edition
    edited by Thomas Goodale and Peter A. Witt

Recreation and Youth Development
    by Peter A. Witt and Linda L. Caldwell
Recreation for Older Adults: Individual and Group Activities
    by Judith A. Elliott and Jerold E. Elliott
Recreation Program Planning Manual for Older Adults
    by Karen Kindrachuk
Recreation Programming and Activities for Older Adults
    by Jerold E. Elliott and Judith A. Sorg-Elliott
Reference Manual for Writing Rehabilitation Therapy Treatment Plans
    by Penny Hogberg and Mary Johnson
Service Living: Building Community through Public Parks and Recreation
    by Doug Wellman, Dan Dustin, Karla Henderson, and Roger Moore
Simple Expressions: Creative and Therapeutic Arts for the Elderly in Long-Term Care Facilities
    by Vicki Parsons
A Social Psychology of Leisure
    by Roger C. Mannell and Douglas A. Kleiber
Special Events and Festivals: How to Organize, Plan, and Implement
    by Angie Prosser and Ashli Rutledge
Survey Research and Analysis: Applications in Parks, Recreation, and Human Dimensions
    by Jerry Vaske
Taking the Initiative: Activities to Enhance Effectiveness and Promote Fun
    by J. P. Witman
Therapeutic Recreation and the Nature of Disabilities
    by Kenneth E. Mobily and Richard D. MacNeil
Therapeutic Recreation: Cases and Exercises, Second Edition
    by Barbara C. Wilhite and M. Jean Keller
Therapeutic Recreation in Health Promotion and Rehabilitation
    by John Shank and Catherine Coyle
Therapeutic Recreation in the Nursing Home
    by Linda Buettner and Shelley L. Martin
Therapeutic Recreation Programming: Theory and Practice
    by Charles Sylvester, Judith E. Voelkl, and Gary D. Ellis
Therapeutic Recreation Protocol for Treatment of Substance Addictions
    by Rozanne W. Faulkner
The Therapeutic Recreation Stress Management Primer
    by Cynthia Mascott
The Therapeutic Value of Creative Writing
    by Paul M. Spicer
Traditions: Improving Quality of Life in Caregiving
    by Janelle Sellick
Trivia by the Dozen: Encouraging Interaction and Reminiscence in Managed Care
    by Jean Vetter